The World's Greatest Literature

THE Masterpieces of the World's Greatest Authors in *History, Biography, Philosophy, Economics, Politics; Epic and Dramatic Literature, History of English Literature, Oriental Literature (Sacred and Profane), Orations, Essays.* Sixty-one Crown Octavo Volumes :: :: ::

ILLUSTRATED WITH FRONTISPIECES, EACH A MASTER WORK OF ART IN PORTRAITURE OR HISTORIC PAINTING

Editors

Wotan's Farewell to Brunhild

Photogravure from the original painting by Konrad Dielitz

RICHARD WAGNER drew the materials of his operatic "tetralogy" from the Nibelungenlied, an epic poem which, though composed about 1200 A. D., dealt with characters and incidents of ancient Norse mythology. This illustration depicts a scene from "The Valkyr," the second of the operatic series, in which Wotan, the Scandinavian Jupiter, parts from Brunhild, the chief of those Amazons who, as our pagan ancestors believed, carried the ⸺ heroes slain in battle to Valhalla, the hall of

The Nibelungenlied

TRANSLATED BY

WILLIAM NANSON LETTSOM

WITH A SPECIAL INTRODUCTION BY

WILLIAM H. CARPENTER, Ph.D.

PROFESSOR OF GERMANIC PHILOLOGY
IN COLUMBIA UNIVERSITY

REVISED EDITION

NEW YORK
P. F. COLLIER & SON

SPECIAL INTRODUCTION

THE "Nibelungenlied," as the great national epic of Germany, is not only one of the most important literary monuments that the German mind has produced in all periods of its history, but, in reality beyond this, it is also in its matter and its manner one of the world's great classics. It is this inherently because of the universal intelligibility of its story, for the broad human sympathy which must be felt with its characters and their motives of action, and for the sustained poetic treatment of the whole in the long poem. In all these respects the "Nibelungenlied," although German in its spirit and its environment, rises inevitably above the confines of nationality, and becomes, like other works that are in a true sense great, by virtue of its universality an integral part of that cosmopolitan body that we call the literature of the world.

Like the "Iliad," or any other popular epic whatever, the "Nibelungenlied" is, however, first and foremost a picture of the national life and the national soul. Its characters in this way are, consequently, both fundamentally and of necessity a part of their own special environment into which each, according to his individuality, fits; and the manners and customs, the religion and ethics, are first of all essentially German in order to embody them and to motive their actions to the public for which the poem was originally intended. What we are given in the "Nibelungenlied" is primarily then, at least in its exterior, a picture of German life in the twelfth and thirteenth centuries. The customs are those of the courts and castles of the place and time, the men and women are the knights and ladies who inhabit them; and if the real mainsprings of motive and action sometimes go back beyond the

poet's own day and generation for reasons that shall presently
be told, the thoughts and feelings of the characters under his
hand betray on the surface no trace of it.

To an English reader there is astonishingly little in the
"Nibelungenlied" in motive that is unintelligible or hope-
lessly remote. It is not that its manners of thought are our
manners of thought, or its ethics our ethics. Its deeds, since
the real story is an ancient inheritance, are tragic with battle,
murder, and sudden death; but, in spite of all this, there is
in us an innate appreciation of it and of its spirit that it is
utterly impossible to feel in much literature that is not our
own. This of course arises from the fact that it is, in a sense,
our own, as, in part, at the beginning in very truth it was. The
difference in its whole environment from us is still, in reality,
not great, and we realize, consciously or unconsciously, that it
is in many ways our own ancient past that is chronicled in
the German poem.

For all these reasons it comes readily about that, in the
light of the poet's master touch, the characters of the "Nibelungenlied" that he has left in such actuality in his verses
are to us neither vague nor shadowy, but are real persons
who live and act before us. This is in fact truer of the "Nibelungenlied" than of almost any other great poem of the kind,
whatever its time and place of origin. Siegfried and Kriemhild,
Hagen and Rudeger are not the mere creations and imper-
sonations of a poet's imagination; they are to us real men
and women who lived their lives and died their deaths as the
poet has described them. That he has told his tale with won-
derful literary skill as a whole and at times with marvellous
appreciation of the value of the moment, is also to be stated.
Because no doubt in part from the way in which the poem
has come down to us, there is at times superfluous material
that had better been left away, but in this fact, too, the poem
differs but little from other popular epics.

As a whole, the "Nibelungenlied" is characterized by a
literary unity of treatment by no means inconsiderable, and
greater, in point of fact, than its origin would ordinarily
promise. Its unity, however, is dramatic, rather than epic in
the ordinary sense. This character it never loses throughout
the whole long action. Deed follows deed, stroke upon stroke,

until the final catastrophe is inevitably reached and the story is ended.

That this story in its origin is not narrowly German, but is Germanic property, should be borne in mind by its reader, since many of its episodes acquire thereby a broader significance, and the whole poem assumes a wider interest.

The earliest versions of the story of the Volsungs and Nibelungs, the Germanic "tale of Troy," that have come down to us are not from German territory, but from the Scandinavian North, although here, too, the scene of the principal action is on the Rhine and in the land of the Huns, which is vaguely conceived to be a part of the German country. Sigmund, the father of Sigurd, is a King in the land of the Franks; Sigurd is slain to the south of the Rhine, and in the Rhine is forever hidden the fateful hoard of the Nibelungs. The story in reality wandered out twice into the North from its original home in Germany: once apparently in the Viking age when the Northmen for the first time came into close contact with the other Germanic people on the continent and in the British Islands, a period long antecedent to the "Nibelungenlied;" and again five hundred years later, after the German poem had arisen, since it can be readily shown that this has been used as a source of a part of the material.

The very first of these Northern versions is that contained in the "Elder Edda," a collection of mythological and legendary poems in the Old Norse language, of unknown authorship, whose time and place of origin are alike matters of varying supposition. The subject was the theme of poets for centuries in the North. The oldest of the poems in the "Edda" that has to do with the story of the "Nibelungenlied," from internal evidence, was made as early as the year 900; the latest is from a time not far from 1200. These poems and fragments of poems, some of them even in prose rescript and most of them interspersed here and there with bits of prose, do not make in any sense a connected story. Their unknown collector arranged them as well as might be in connected sequence, but even then their action is not consecutive; they overlap each other, parts of the story are told and retold and not seldom with an inconsistency of detail. There is, accordingly, in the "Elder Edda" no thought of an epic

either in matter or manner. There is the material for an epic
in the rough, but without an idea in the mind of any poet of
the time of actual epical treatment.

The story as contained in the Old Norse poems is by no
means identical with the " Nibelungenlied." First and foremost, it is infinitely older in its whole conception, and much
more nearly approaches original conditions as they existed
in the mode of thought and in the manner of living of the
early Germanic people. It is a story, here, of the days when
the world was young; when the gods still walked the earth
and mixed themselves in with human affairs in which they
had an active interest; when motives were clearer and action
was more direct; when human passions burned even fiercer
than in the " Nibelungenlied," and love and hate together
knew no boundaries until they had worked themselves out
in the utter destruction of their object. Of the first of these
conditions, the " Nibelungenlied " in its character of an epic
of the Middle Ages has not kept a trace. In the Eddic poems
it is the ring cursed by the gods to all its possessors that
motives the entire action; that leads with the certainty of
fate to the death of Sigurd, the Siegfried of the " Edda," to
all the woes that follow, and to the ultimate utter destruction
of the entire race of the Nibelungs.

As most critics have pointed out, the fundamental difference in the treatment of the story consists in the fact that the
principal epic interest in the Eddic poems is the relation of
Sigurd to Brynhild, the Valkyrie, who is here a heroic fig-
ure, who rises immeasurably not only above the other women
of the tale, but above most of the other characters in impor-
tance of personality. In the " Nibelungenlied " it is Kriemhild, Gudrun in the " Edda," and Hagen who are the principal figures in the action. In the Northern version, Gudrun
does not avenge herself upon her brothers as does Kriemhild
in the " Nibelungenlied," but Atli, her husband after Sigurd,
slays them, and Gudrun then takes vengeance upon him. In
the " Edda," too, other saga cycles are brought into connection with this, viz., the Northern legend of Helgi, at the beginning, and the Gothic legend of Ermanrich, at the end.

The Eddic poems are not the only versions in Old Norse
literature. An epitome of the story based upon the poems

is contained in the " Snorra Edda," a work written by the Icelander Snorri Sturluson, who lived from 1178 to 1241, to serve as a handbook for poets and which contains in this way the myths and legends of the North.

Next to the Eddic songs the most important of the Northern versions, however, is the long " Völsunga Saga " from the second half of the thirteenth century, which, again, is based upon the Eddic poems and upon others in addition that have now been lost. Like most of the Old Norse sagas, it is prose with the occasional inclusion of verse cited to justify or to embellish its statements. It gives with extraordinary wealth of detail the whole old story in connected form and desires to be called, as it has been called, a prose epic. William Morris, in his superb translation, has deservedly characterized it as " the most complete and dramatic form of the Great Epic of the North." The story is further contained, in some of its details only, in the strange tale of " Nornagest," which has again made use of the Eddic songs and quotes one of them entire.

The Old Norse story is so important for its bearing on the intelligibility of the " Nibelungenlied " that it is absolutely necessary to take it actively into consideration in any discussion of the German poem. The epitome contained in the " Snorra Edda," since it gives the whole story from beginning to end in a form as short as may be, is here given in its entirety :

" Three gods, Odin, Hœnir, and Loki, once went out to explore the whole world. They came to a certain river, and went along the river to a waterfall, and at the waterfall there was an otter that had taken a salmon out of the fall and ate it, half asleep. Then Loki took up a stone and cast it at the otter and struck him in the head. Loki thereupon boasted of his catch that he had got at a blow both the otter and the salmon. They took the salmon and the otter and carried them along with them until they came to a farmstead, where they went in. The head of the household that dwelt there was named Hreidmar ; he was a mighty man and much skilled in magic. He invited the gods to lodge there for the night, and they told him that they had with them provisions in plenty and showed him their booty. But when Hreidmar saw the otter he called his sons Fafnir and Regin and said that Otter, their brother, had been killed, and told them who had done it. Thereupon, the father and his sons fell upon the gods and took them and bound them, saying that the otter was the son of Hreidmar. The gods offered as a ransom as much money as Hreidmar himself should determine, and that was agreed upon as a reconciliation and was bound with oaths.

" Then the otter was flayed, and Hreidmar took the otter's skin and said that they should fill it with red gold and should then cover it wholly up with gold, and that should be their atonement. Odin then sent Loki into the land of the black elves and he came to the dwarf who is called Andvari; he was a fish in the water, and Loki took him and laid upon him as a ransom all the gold that he had in his stone. And when they came into the stone where he dwelt, the dwarf brought out all the gold that he owned and that was a very great treasure. Then the dwarf slipped under his hand a little gold ring. That Loki, however, saw and bade him produce the ring. The dwarf begged him not to take the ring from him, and said that he could breed treasure out of it if he kept it. Loki told him that he should not keep back a penny, and took the ring from him and went out. The dwarf said that the ring should be the death of everyone who owned it. Loki replied that that suited him well, and that the condition should be held good, since he would bring it to the ears of them who might get possession of it. He then went away to Hreidmar's and showed Odin the gold; but when he saw the ring, it seemed to him very beautiful and he took it out of the treasure, but paid over to Hreidmar the gold.

" Then Hreidmar filled the otter's skin as full as he could and set it up on its feet when it was full; Odin then went up to cover the skin with gold and said to Hreidmar that he should see whether the skin were wholly covered. Hreidmar looked at it and considered it carefully and saw a whisker, and bade him cover that, also, or else their atonement were at an end. Then Odin brought out the ring and covered the whisker and said that they now were freed from the otter ransom. When, however, Odin had taken his spear and Loki his shoes, and they needed no longer to fear, then said Loki that what Andvari had spoken, that the ring should be the death of him who owned it, should hold good, and it did hold good thereafter.

" Hreidmar took the gold as ransom for his son, but Fafnir and Regin demanded some of it as a ransom for their brother. Hreidmar, however, would not grant them a single penny of the gold. That was the ill-advised deed of the brothers that they killed their father for the gold. Then Regin demanded that Fafnir divide the gold in halves between them. Fafnir replied that there was little chance that he would share the gold with his brother when he had killed his father for the sake of it, and bade Regin to begone or he would fare as had Hreidmar. Fafnir had then taken the helmet which Hreidmar had owned, which was called the Helmet of Awe and which all living things feared that saw it, and set it upon his head, and he took the sword which is called Hrotti. Regin had the sword that is called Refil and he fled away; but Fafnir went up upon the Glittering Heath and made him there a lair, and he took upon himself the shape of a serpent and lay upon the gold.

" Regin then went to King Hjalprek, at Thy, in Denmark, and there set up a smithy, and he took to foster Sigurd, the son of Sigmund (the son of Volsung) and of Hjordis, the daughter of Eylimi. Sigurd was the most glorious of all war kings in lineage and strength. Regin told him where Fafnir lay upon the gold, and egged him on to seek it. Then Regin made the sword that is called Gram, which was so sharp that Sigurd thrust it in the water and it cut asunder a lock of wool that drove before the current against the edge of the sword. Afterward, Sigurd clove in two Regin's anvil down to the stock with the sword. After that, Sigurd and Regin went out upon the Glittering Heath. Then Sigurd dug a pit in Fafnir's path and got into it; and when Fafnir crept to the water and came over the pit, then Sigurd thrust the sword up against him and that was his death. Regin then came up and said that Sigurd had killed his brother and offered him as a reconciliation that he should take the heart of Fafnir and roast it at the fire; but Regin himself got down and drank the blood of Fafnir and then lay down to sleep. And when Sigurd had roasted the heart and thought that it must be done, he touched it with his finger to see how hard it was.

And when the juice ran out of the heart upon his finger, he burnt himself and thrust his finger into his mouth. And when the heart's blood came upon his tongue, then he knew the speech of birds and understood what the nuthatches said that sat in the tree above him.

"Then said one:

> ' There sits Sigurd
> blood besprinkled,
> the heart of Fafnir
> at the fire roasting;
> wise methinks were
> the ring despoiler,
> if he the gleaming
> heart were eating.'

" Then said the other:

> ' There lies Regin
> with himself communing;
> he will beguile the youth
> who is trusting in him;
> in rage he brings now
> ill words together;
> the evil-worker will
> avenge his brother.'

" Then Sigurd went up to Regin and killed him, and took his horse, which was named Grani, and rode until he came to the lair of Fafnir. There he took the gold and bound it up in packs and laid it on the back of Grani, and then mounted and rode on his way. Sigurd rode until he found a house upon the fell. Within it slept a woman who had on a helmet and a coat of mail. He drew his sword and cut her coat of mail off her. Then she awoke and named herself Hild. She is called Brynhild and was a Valkyrie. Sigurd rode thence and came to the King who is named Gjuki; his wife is named Grimhild; their children were Gunnar, Högni, Gudrun, Gudny; Gotthorm was a step-son of Gjuki. There Sigurd dwelt for a long time; and he took to wife Gudrun, the daughter of Gjuki, and Gunnar and Högni swore with him oaths of brotherhood. Afterward, Sigurd and the sons of Gjuki went to Atli, the son of Budli, to ask as a wife for

Gunnar Brynhild, his sister. She dwelt upon Hind Fell, and about her hall was a flaming fire, and she had made a vow to have as a husband that man, only, who dared to ride through the flame.

"Then Sigurd and the Gjukings (who are also called Niflungs) rode up upon the fell, and Gunnar was minded to ride through the flame. He had the horse that was named Goti, but the horse did not dare to leap into the fire. Then Sigurd and Gunnar changed their shapes and also their names, since Grani would not go under any man except Sigurd. Then Sigurd leaped upon Grani and rode through the flaming fire. That night he held a wedding with Brynhild, and when they came to bed he drew the sword Gram out of its scabbard and laid it between them. And in the morning, when he awoke and dressed himself, then he gave Brynhild as a bridal gift the gold ring which he had taken on the Glittering Heath, and Loki had taken from Andvari, and he took from her another ring as a remembrance. Sigurd then leaped upon his horse and rode to his companions; Gunnar and he again changed their shapes and they went back to Gjuki with Brynhild. Sigurd had two children with Gudrun: Sigmund and Swanhild.

"It was once upon a time that Brynhild and Gudrun went to the water to bleach their hair. When they came to the river, Brynhild waded out into the water away from the land and said that she would not have on her head the water that ran out of Gudrun's hair, since she had the more noble husband. Then Gudrun went out into the river after Brynhild and said that she should wash her hair in the river above, because she had the husband who was braver than anyone else in the world, since he slew Fafnir and Regin and gained the inheritance of them both. Then Brynhild replied: ' It was of still greater renown that Gunnar rode the flaming fire and Sigurd dared not.' Then Gudrun laughed and said: ' Do you think that Gunnar rode through the flaming fire? Him I deem to have gone to bed with you, who gave me this gold ring. But the ring that you have on your hand, and that you received as a bridal gift, that is called the Ring of Andvari, and I deem that it was not Gunnar who sought it on the Glittering Heath.' Then Brynhild was silent and went home.

After that she egged on Gunnar and Högni to kill **Sigurd,** but because they had sworn oaths with him they egged on Gotthorm, their brother, to kill him. Gotthorm laid sword on him while he slept, and when he felt the wound he hurled the sword Gram after his slayer so that it cut the man asunder. Then Sigurd fell and his three-year old son, who was named Sigmund, whom they killed. After that, Brynhild turned sword upon herself and she was burned with Sigurd. And Gunnar and Högni took the treasure of Fafnir and the Ring of Andvari and ruled all the land.

" King Atli, the son of Budli, the brother of Brynhild, then took to wife Gudrun, whom Sigurd had had, and they had children together. King Atli bade Gunnar and Högni to visit him, and they went at his invitation, but before they went away from home they hid the gold, the Treasure of Andvari, in the river Rhine, and it has never since been found. And King Atli had assembled a great force and fought with Gunnar and Högni and they were taken prisoners. And Atli had the heart cut out of Högni while he lived, and that was his death. Gunnar he caused to be cast into a serpent pit, and a harp was brought to him secretly and he struck it with his toes, since his hands were bound, so that all the serpents slept except one adder, which sprang at him, and struck in through his breast so that she thrust in her head and hung upon his liver until he died. Gunnar and Högni are called Niflungs and Gjukungs, and for this reason the gold is called the Treasure of the Niflungs, or their inheritance. A little while after, Gudrun killed her two sons, and with gold and silver had beakers made out of their skulls and then was celebrated the funeral feast of the Niflungs.

" At this banquet Gudrun had King Atli served with mead from the beakers, and there was mixed with it the blood of the boys, and their hearts she caused to be roasted and brought to the King to eat. And when that was done she told him these things herself with many ugly words. There was no lack there of intoxicating mead, so that most people slept where they sat. And in the night she went to the King where he was sleeping, and with her the son of Högni, and they fell upon him, and that was his death. Then they hurled fire into the hall and the people were burned that were within. After that she went to the sea and leaped in and wished to destroy herself, but she drifted over the fjord and came to the land of King Jonakr. And when he saw her, he took her to him and wedded her. They had three sons, who were called Sörli, Hamdir, and Erp; they were all as black as ravens in the color of their hair, like Gunnar and Högni and the other Niflungs.

"There grew up Swanhild, the daughter of Sigurd; she was the most beautiful of all women. That Jörmunrek the Mighty learned and sent his son Randver to ask her hand. And when he came to Jonakr, Swanhild was given over to him that he might bring her to Jörmunrek. Then said Bikki that it had fallen out better if Randver had Swanhild, since he was young, as were they both, and Jörmunrek was old. This counsel pleased the young people well; and thereupon Bikki told it to the King. Then Jörmunrek had his son taken and brought to the gallows, but Randver took his falcon and plucked off the feathers and bade that it be sent to his father; then he was hanged. But when King Jörmunrek saw the falcon, it came into his mind that just as the falcon was incapable of flight and featherless, so was also his kingdom disabled, since he was old and without a son.

"It was once upon a time when King Jörmunrek rode out of the forest from hunting with his men that Swanhild the Queen sat bleaching her hair. Then they rode upon her and trod her to death under the horses' hoofs. And when Gudrun learned this, she egged on her sons to avenge Swanhild. And when they made ready for the journey, she got them mail, and helmets so strong that iron would not take hold upon it. She said the plan for them to follow was that when they came to King Jörmunrek they should fall upon him at night while he slept; Sörli and Hamdir should then hew off his hands and feet, and Erp his head. When, however, they came on the way, they asked Erp what assistance they might have of him if they met King Jörmunrek. He replied that he would give them such aid as the hand gave the foot. They replied that naught at all did the foot depend upon the hand. They were so angry at their mother that she had led them out with words of hatred, that they desired to do that which should be the worst thing of all to her and they killed Erp, since she loved

him most. A little while after, as Sörli walked along he slipped
with both feet, but held himself up with his hand. Then he
said: ' The hand does now help the foot; better it were that
Erp were alive!' And when they came to King Jörmunrek's
at night, and went in where he slept and hewed off his hands
and feet, he awoke and called upon his men and bade them
awaken. Then said Hamdir: ' Off were now his head, if Erp
were alive!' Then the men-at-arms arose and attacked them,
but could not overcome them with weapons. Jörmunrek then
called out that stones should be hurled at them, and this was
done. Then Sörli and Hamdir fell, and then were dead all
the race and descendants of the Gjukings."

The Eddic poems and the " Völsunga Saga " give us even
much more fully in detail than does this epitome the deeds of
Sigurd's youth of which the " Nibelungenlied " knows so little. The latter, too, has forgotten the early relationship of
Sigurd to Brynhild and her whole early history, although her
superhuman character is still remembered and obscure reference is made to their previous acquaintance. There is no
longer a reason why Siegfried and Brunhild should die together, as in the " Edda." That the ultimate catastrophe falls
out differently in the two versions of the story is due to this
very fact of the loss of original detail. In that her brothers
who had murdered Sigurd live in triumph afterward and no
true reconciliation can be possible between them, Kriemhild
must of necessity avenge herself upon them, instead of upon
Atli, as in the earlier form of the story. And, as has already
been remarked, the real significance to the action of the fateful " Ring of the Nibelungs " and the accursed hoard has
wholly vanished to give place to reasons that have much more
affinity with human motives of conduct.

The " Nibelungenlied," like the Northern poems before it,
is legendary, with only here and there a historical fact as a
nucleus about which has gathered in the course of the centuries material for many times and places. The destruction
of the Burgundians, under their King Gunther, by the Huns,
which occurred in the year 437, has undoubtedly furnished the
ultimate catastrophe. It is not known, however, that Attila,
the Atli of the " Edda " and the Etzel of the " Nibelungenlied," was the leader of the Huns on this occasion, although

the event did take place during his lifetime. Attila's brother
Bleda appears in the poem as Blœdelin. Giselher, the brother
of Gunther, is also mentioned in the old Burgundian law-code,
the *Lex Burgundionum*. Of Siegfried and Brunhild history
knows no trace, although an attempt has been made to con-
nect the one with Arminius and the other with Brünehild of
Austrasia. The appearance in the poem of Dietrich of Bern,
Theodoric the Great, the Ostrogothic conqueror of Italy, who
lived from 475 to 526, is an example of the absorption of material from another cycle into the original legend, material
which, in its turn, clusters about a historical character. The
Bishop Pilgrin, of Passau, represented in the poem as the
uncle of the Burgundian kings and of Kriemhild, has a historical prototype in an actual Pilgrin who held the see of
Passau from 971 to 991 and has, it may be, been here introduced by the poet to honor him. As for the rest, facts that
may have been ultimately historical have been freely used by
the poet of the " Nibelungenlied " and his predecessors until
it is no longer possible to tell where legend begins and history
ends.

That Siegfried and Brunhild are at the end mythical, rather
than at all historical, has been surmised, rather than proved.
It has been attempted, in point of fact, to show that the whole
story has arisen in its earliest form through a union of an
old myth of Siegfried with the historical materials that have
been indicated and others whose real significance has subsequently been obliterated and lost. The believers of this theory
have pointed to the thoroughly mythical character of the version of the story in the " Edda " and particularly of its earliest
part as plausible evidence, and they would see in the whole the
union of a Frankish myth of Siegfried, originally independent,
with a Burgundian historical narrative. Siegfried and Brunhild, in this way, have been thought to embody, at the beginning, the nature-myth of the awakening earth-goddess
from the sleep of winter at the reanimating touch of summer.
Lachmann makes the fundamental fact at the outset a myth
of the death of Balder, and Wilhelm Müller a myth of Freyr,
both light-gods of the old mythology. It is, nevertheless, impossible to follow the upholders of these theories into the
details of their interpretation, and the whole main assumption

of a mythical origin is a matter of doubt. That Siegfried and
Brunhild, however, have mythical characteristics that they
have retained after all memory of the ancient mythology as
such has been absolutely forgotten, no reader of the story can
deny, and in this respect the " Nibelungenlied " is no different
from the legendary literature of all the nations of the world.

Early German poems on the story of the Nibelungs, although it is altogether likely that they once existed, have not
been preserved. The " Nibelungenlied " itself it is not possible to follow back of the twelfth century, by the middle of
which it seems to have already had the form in which it has
come down to us. The internal evidence of metre, rhyme,
and language shows, too, beyond a doubt, that it could not
have arisen at a much earlier time.

The author of the poem is unknown. The most plausible
hypothesis as to his actual personality makes him an Austrian
knight of about 1140, possibly a member of the Kürenberg
family, who lived in the neighborhood of Linz, on the Danube.
A Kürenberg of the twelfth century is the oldest court poet
who used in his lyrics the same strophic form that is characteristic of the " Nibelungenlied," but that the two poets are
identical is by no manner of means a certainty. In the same
way, the place of origin of the poem is a matter of supposition.
In all probability, however, it arose in southeastern German
territory in Austria. Although the poet knows the region
on the Rhine about Worms, he has an infinitely wider acquaintance with Austrian localities of which he makes specific
mention. It was in Austria, too, at this time that the begin-
nings arose of the court lyric poetry, that *Minnesangs Frühling*,
as the Germans strikingly characterize the period, that presently blossomed out into one of the fullest expressions in all
its history of German life and thought.

Bartsch, in the introduction to his edition of the " Nibelungenlied," has most admirably summarized this whole matter. According to him, it was an Austrian poet who, before
the middle of the twelfth century, united songs sung at his
time and oral tradition, known to him as well as to everybody
else, into a single whole. How far folk-song and tradition
had anticipated him in this is no longer to be ascertained,
but it may be inferred from the Northern form of the legend

that it had long since taken place. It remained to him, however, to arrange the whole in its details of sequence of action, to fill out the gaps left by popular song and story, and to give it the impress of his own day, which it so unmistakably bears. That this is not in accord with other ideas of authorship and origin must nevertheless be stated. Karl Lachmann, one of the most astute, if not one of the most mistaken, critics of the poem, taking Wolf's Prolegomena to Homer for his model, set up the theory that has since played an important part in the discussion of the genesis of the " Nibelungenlied."

According to the Lachmann theory, the poem consists of no less than twenty distinct lays, each differing inherently from the rest, and each, with the exception of the Eighth and Ninth, by different authors. To arrive at this result, more than a third of the entire number of stanzas has, for one reason or another, been rejected as not genuine. As Lettsom has cleverly put it in the original preface to his translation, where this whole matter is presented with some detail: " He [Lachmann] has in fact put every stanza and every verse on its trial. Some have been condemned by him to italics, as interpolations; others to brackets, as continuations by different hands; others again, which he supposes to be the latest additions, so far from being pitied for their youth, have been visited with both kinds of punishment. He has not, however, sentenced any of the delinquents to transportation from the text; or, perhaps it would be more correct to say that he has sentenced them, but has not carried the sentence into execution. The result of the whole assize has been that out of the 2,316 stanzas 1,437 have been honorably acquitted; the rest have been italicised, bracketed, or both. . . . The twenty lays," he continues, " which had already suffered from the interpolations and corruptions incident to oral tradition, were first collected, committed to writing, and patched together into one poem about the year 1210 by some unknown compiler, whose handiwork was afterward corrected or depraved by two separate but equally unknown revisers. It is his opinion that scarcely a stanza of what we possess is older than 1190, while even the latest additions are not more recent than 1225. The whole poem, therefore, is, according to Professor Lachmann, the work of contemporary authors, whether we call their compositions spurious or genuine; and the task undertaken is neither more nor less than to distribute a mass of unowned literary property among nineteen or twenty poets and an indefinite number of poetasters, of whom nothing, not even their existence, is known except by conjecture, and of whose distinguishing characteristics we are of course completely ignorant, except as far as we may guess at them from the internal evidence, real or imagined, of the poem itself."

Lachmann's theory of separate authorship of portions of the poem has not maintained itself against the critics. That there are contradictions in its statements and different values in its parts cannot be denied, but they are not explained on the grounds here set forth. The attempted restoration of the poem by elimination and rearrangement has not left twenty or any number of lays that have actually the air of being separate poems. "It is just here," continues Lettsom, "that the failure of the hypothesis is most conspicuous. . . . Some of the lays are not ill-adapted, from the nature of their contents, to form separate poems, but they are by no means out of place as episodes in a long work, and are, besides, connected with the rest, while the latter, from the insignificance of their contents alone, from their reference to one another, from their allusions to the past and anticipations of the future, from their abrupt commencements and still more abrupt conclusions, and from their general fragmentary nature, could never have been independent lays. . . . The dream of Kriemhild forms a strange opening for a lay that just brings Siegfried to Worms, and there leaves him. Nobody, in fact, would have composed a separate poem on so insignificant a matter. The dream, however, is beyond all doubt the introduction, the fit and appropriate introduction, to a poem that must go on at least to the marriage of Kriemhild and the death of her husband.

" Professor Lachmann himself seems to be in doubt whether this First Lay be complete; he talks of 'this lay, or what has been preserved of it;' he tells us that 'it several times indi-cates a continuation, and might have deserved a better than that which follows;' but though he expresses a doubt, he gives no reasons for entertaining one. It certainly would re-quire far less ingenuity to assign cogent reasons for a doubt.

and indeed for much more than a doubt, on this point; the lay, as it stands, is a ' passage that leads to nothing,' a mountain in labor that does not produce even so much as a mouse; but it is not singular in this respect; its brethren for the most part keep it in countenance; or, if they contain matter of interest, they too often try the temper of the reader by disappointing his expectations at the most critical moment, and coming to an abrupt conclusion in the midst of an action. Thus the Eighteenth Lay ends just after the battle between Huns and Burgundians has begun; the Nineteenth stops short just at the moment when Etzel has brought up 20,000 fresh men and commenced another attack on Gunther and his followers.

" It really is a waste of words to dwell on the peculiarities of such whimsical arrangements as these. I will merely add a word or two on the Fourteenth Lay, which, inasmuch as it is an introduction to what follows, bears some resemblance to the First. The dream of Uta, the prophecy of the mermaids, and all the gloomy forebodings which give a peculiar character to this lay, are ludicrously out of place as component parts of a short poem, which merely conducts the Burgundians to Rudeger's castle, where, so far from being destroyed, they do not even run any risk whatever, except that of being killed with kindness; but in fact the whole tenor of the lay (one might almost say, every line, every word of it) proves beyond dispute that we are there in the midst of an extensive poem, which can end only with the destruction of the last Burgundian. An attentive examination of the three or four lays just noticed, would, I think, convince every unprejudiced reader that the hypothesis of twenty separate lays by different authors is utterly untenable. . . . The wisest course," he concludes, and it is easy to concur with him, " is, in such uncertainty, to take the poem as we find it, and to prefer the authority, however occasionally unsatisfactory, of manuscripts to the speculations of the most ingenious critics."

The metre of the " Nibelungenlied " needs a word of explanation. The characteristic strophe in which it is written consists of four verses, the first three of equal length, the fourth somewhat longer, rhymed in couplets on the final syllable. The rhythmical system is dependent, not upon measure, but upon accent, with considerable freedom in the addition or suppression of unaccented syllables. Every verse, with the exception of the last, is made up of two half-verses each containing three accented syllables and separated by a ringing cæsura, that is, a cæsura on an unaccented syllable. The last half-verse contains an additional accent, or four, instead of three, as in the others. A strophe in the original Middle High German, the second of the poem, will make this analysis clear:

Ez wúohs in Búregónden   ein vil édel magedín,
dáz in állen lánden   niht schǿners móhte sín,
Kríemhilt gehéizen :   diu wárt ein schǿne wíp
dar úmbe múosen dégene   víl verlíesen den líp.

The metre of the present translation follows the original, except for the lengthening of the fourth line of the stanza which the author only occasionally differentiates in this respect from the rest.

The "Nibelungenlied," like other poems of the Middle Ages that were widely read and widely copied, was subjected all along its career of transmission to additions and alterations, and has consequently come down to us not in a single form, but in a number of different versions that deviate to a greater or less extent from the original poem and from each other. Whole or in part there are no less than twenty-eight MSS. Ten of these are complete: three of them, usually cited A, B, C, are parchment MSS. of the thirteenth century, two are parchments of the fourteenth century, four are paper MSS. of the fifteenth century, and one is a parchment of the sixteenth century. Of all these manuscripts it is commonly conceded that only A, B, C have independent authenticity. It is not necessary here to go into the details of the long discussion as to the relative value of the MSS. with regard to the age and original condition of the particular text which each contains. Each one has by different critics been given the preference over the others.

Zarncke, who is one of the most rational and impartial of the critics of the poem in all its bearings, makes C, a beautifully written MS. from the dividing line between the twelfth and thirteenth centuries, preserved in the court library of Donaueschingen, the nearest in every essential way to the original form of the poem. Subsequently, the whole, according to him, was subjected to a revision which brought it more into accord with contemporary taste. The text is amplified by the introduction of new episodes into the narrative, although some of the older strophes are omitted, and, unfortunately, the old dignity and simplicity of the diction is frequently sacrificed in favor of a more pronounced effect. This stage of the poem in its full form is not represented in either of the oldest MSS. B, a manuscript from the middle of the thirteenth century, in the monastery of St. Gallen, occupied an intermediate position in length. It is made by Bartsch, who regards it " as relatively the most faithful picture of the original form of the lost poem," the basis of his edition of the " Nibelungenlied." A, a carelessly written MS. in the Munich Library, is the shortest form of the poem, but is, nevertheless, in its turn regarded by Lachmann as inherently the oldest and best version that we possess. Lettsom's translation, in that it follows the text and modern German version of Braunfels, published in 1846, is based upon A, but with the inclusion of other strophes, particularly from C.

The " Nibelungenlied " was first published at Zurich, by Bodmer, in 1757, and since then has appeared in many editions and modernized versions at home, and in numerous translations abroad, among them Low German, French, Italian, Dutch, and Hungarian.

In English, the first translations of parts of the " Nibelungenlied " are contained in the " Illustrations of Northern Antiquities," by Weber, published in 1814, in Edinburgh. The version here given consists in part only of a metrical translation, in part of prose. Lockhart, in his biography of Sir Walter Scott, states that he has no doubt but that the rhymed versions came from that poet's pen, although of this there is no more direct proof. The second attempt in this direction is not less notable. This is from 1831, when Thomas Carlyle wrote in the " Westminster Review " an essay on the " Nibelungenlied " as a review of Karl Simrock's German translation of the poem, in which are contained a number of strophes given with characteristic vigor and a genuine appreciation of the real spirit of the original. The next translation, that of Gostik, in his " Spirit of German Poetry," 1846, is metrical, but, like its predecessors, consists only of parts of the poem. The first translation to lay claim to any degree of completeness was that of Jonathan Birch, published in 1848. It is a metrical version, as its title states, of Lachmann's text, and, like it, divides the poem into twenty lays. The first complete edition of the poem in English does not, however, appear until this of Lettsom's, which has admirably retained the form of the original and much of its spirit, and which for the first time gave to English readers an adequate idea of the real work as it is.

For those who care to pursue the subject further than these pages it may be stated that the best editions of the " Nibelungenlied " in the original are those of Friedrich Zarncke, " *Das Nibelungenlied,*" originally published in 1856 and since then in several editions, and of Karl Bartsch, " *Das Nibelungenlied,*" originally published in 1866, both of which have abundant critical apparatus. The " Nibelungenlied " is not yet sufficiently well known among us, for it is, in the way that has been indicated, not alone the great epic of Germany, but in its widest sense an epic of the Germanic race.

Wm. H. Carpenter.

COLUMBIA UNIVERSITY, May 1, 1901.

CONTENTS

CONTENTS

THE NIBELUNGENLIED

FIRST ADVENTURE

KRIEMHILD'S DREAM

I

IN stories of our fathers high marvels we are told
Of champions well approved in perils manifold.
Of feasts and merry meetings, of weeping and of wail,
And deeds of gallant daring I'll tell you in my tale.

II

In Burgundy there flourish'd a maid so fair to see,
That in all the world together a fairer could not be.
This maiden's name was Kriemhild; through her in dismal
    strife
Full many a prowest warrior thereafter lost his life.

III

Many a fearless champion, as such well became,
Woo'd the lovely lady; she from none had blame.
Matchless was her person, matchless was her mind.
This one maiden's virtue grac'd all womankind.

IV

Three puissant Kings her guarded with all the care they might,
Gunther and eke Gernot, each a redoubted knight,
And Giselher the youthful, a chosen champion he;
This lady was their sister, well lov'd of all the three.

V

They were high of lineage, thereto mild of mood,
But in field and foray champions fierce and rude.
They rul'd a mighty kingdom, Burgundy by name;
They wrought in Etzel's country deeds of deathless fame.

VI

At Worms was their proud dwelling, the fair Rhine flowing by,
There had they suit and service from haughtiest chivalry,
For broad lands and lordships, and glorious was their state,
Till wretchedly they perish'd by two noble ladies' hate.

VII

Dame Uta was their mother, a queen both rich and sage;
Their father hight Dancrat, who the fair heritage
Left to his noble children when he his course had run;
He too by deeds of knighthood in youth had worship won.

VIII

Each of these three princes, as you have heard me say,
Were men of mighty puissance. They had beneath their sway
The noblest knights for liegemen that ever dwelt on ground;
For hardihood and prowess were none so high renown'd.

IX

There was Hagan of Trony of a noble line,
His brother nimble Dankwart, and the knight of Metz, Ortwine,
Eckewart and Gary, the margraves stout in fight,
Folker of Alzeia, full of manly might.

X

Rumolt the steward (a chosen knight was he),
Sindolt, and Hunolt; these serv'd the brethren three,
At their court discharging their several duties well;
Besides, knights had they many whom now I cannot tell.

XI

Dankwart was marshal to the king his lord,
Ortwine of Metz, his nephew, was carver at the board,
Sindolt, he was butler, a champion choice and true,
The chamberlain was Hunolt; they well their duties knew.

XII

The gorgeous pomp and splendor, wherein these brethren
reign'd,
How well they tended knighthood, what worship they attain'd,
How they thro' life were merry, and mock'd at woe and bale—
Who'd seek all this to tell you, would never end his tale.

XIII

A dream was dreamt by Kriemhild the virtuous and the gay,
How a wild young falcon she train'd for many a day,
Till two fierce eagles tore it; to her there could not be
In all the world such sorrow at this perforce to see.

XIV

To her mother Uta at once the dream she told,
But she the threatening future could only thus unfold;
" The falcon that thou trainedst is sure a noble mate;
God shield him in his mercy, or thou must lose him straight."

XV

" A mate for me? what say'st thou, dearest mother mine?
Ne'er to love, assure thee, my heart will I resign.
I'll live and die a maiden, and end as I began,
Nor (let what else befall me) will suffer woe for man."

XVI

" Nay," said her anxious mother, " renounce not marriage so;
Would'st thou true heartfelt pleasure taste ever here below,
Man's love alone can give it. Thou 'rt fair as eye can see,
A fitting mate God send thee, and naught will wanting be."

XVII

" No more," the maiden answer'd, " no more, dear mother,
        say;
From many a woman's fortune this truth is clear as day,
That falsely smiling Pleasure with Pain requites us ever.
I from both will keep me, and thus will sorrow never."

XVIII

So in her lofty virtues, fancy-free and gay,
Liv'd the noble maiden many a happy day,
Nor one more than another found favor in her sight;
Still at the last she wedded a far-renowned knight.

XIX

He was the self-same falcon she in her dream had seen,
Foretold by her wise mother. What vengeance took the queen
On her nearest kinsmen who him to death had done!
That single death atoning died many a mother's son.

SECOND ADVENTURE
OF SIEGFRIED

I

In Netherland then flourish'd a prince of lofty kind,
(Whose father was called Siegmund, his mother Siegelind)
In a sumptuous castle down by the Rhine's fair side;
Men did call it Xanten; 't was famous far and wide.

II

I tell you of this warrior, how fair he was to see;
From shame and from dishonor liv'd he ever free.
Forthwith fierce and famous wax'd the mighty man.
Ah! what height of worship in this world he wan!

III

Siegfried men did call him, that same champion good;
Many a kingdom sought he in his manly mood,
And through strength of body in many a land rode he.
Ah! what men of valor he found in Burgundy!

IV

Before this noble champion grew up to man's estate,
His hand had mighty wonders achiev'd in war's debate,
Whereof the voice of rumor will ever sing and say,
Though much must pass in silence in this our later day.

V

In his freshest season, in his youthful days,
One might full many a marvel tell in Siegfried's praise,
What lofty honors grac'd him, and how fair his fame,
How he charm'd to love him many a noble dame.

VI

As did well befit him, he was bred with care,
And his own lofty nature gave him virtues rare,
From him his father's country grace and honor drew,
To see him prov'd in all things so noble and so true.

VII

He now, grown up to youthhood, at court his duty paid;
The people saw him gladly; many a wife and many a maid
Wish'd he would often thither, and bide forever there;
They view'd him all with favor, whereof he well was ware.

VIII

The child by his fond parents was deck'd with weeds of pride,
And but with guards about him they seldom let him ride.
Uptrain'd was he by sages, who what was honor knew,
So might he win full lightly broad lands and liegemen too.

IX

Now had he strength and stature that weapons well he bore;
Whatever thereto needed, he had of it full store.
He began fair ladies to his love to woo,
And they inclin'd to Siegfried with faith and honor true.

X

Then bade his father Siegmund all his liegemen tell,
With his dear friends to revel it would please him well.
Where other kings were dwelling the tidings took their course.
To friends and eke to strangers he gave both weed and horse.

XI

Whosoe'er was worthy to become a knight
For his lofty lineage, did they each invite,
High-born youths and valiant to the feastful board;
With the young king Siegfried took they then the sword.

XII

Of that proud feast royal wonders one might say;
King Siegmund and Queen Siegelind well might that day
Win honor for the bounty they shower'd with lavish hand,
For which full many a stranger came flocking through their
land.

XIII

Sworded squires four hundred rich raiment had to wear
With the noble Siegfried. Full many a maiden fair
Ceaseless plied the needle to please the warrior bold;
Precious stones unnumber'd the women set in gold,

XIV

(For gold was there in plenty), and as each could best
For the love of Siegfried they work'd the jewel'd vest.
The Host rais'd seats unnumber'd for many a martial wight
On the fair midsummer when his heir was dubb'd a knight.

XV

Forthwith to the high minster flock'd many a squire along,
And many a knight of worship.   To fitly train the young
The old should lend that service which once to them was lent.
They pass'd the hours in pastime and gentle merriment.

XVI

But first to God's due honor a holy mass they sung,
And then a press and struggle arose the crowd among,
And then with pomp befitting each youth was dubb'd a knight.
In sooth, before was never seen so fair a sight.

XVII

All ran at once, where saddled many a war-horse stood.
In the court of Siegmund the tourney was so rude,
That both hall and palace echoed far around,
As those high-mettled champions shock'd with thundering
    sound.

XVIII

Old and young together fiercely hurtling flew,
That the shiver'd lances swept the welkin through;
Splinters e'en to the palace went whizzing many a one
From hands of mighty champions; all there was deftly done.

XIX

The Host bade cease the tourney; the steeds were led away;
Then might you see, all shatter'd how many a shield there lay,
And store of stones full precious from bucklers beaming sheen
In those fierce shocks were scatter'd upon the trampled green.

XX

Thence went the guests in order, and sat around the board;
Many dainty dishes their wearied strength restor'd,
And wine, of all the richest, their burning thirst allay'd:
To friends alike and strangers was fitting honor pay'd.

XXI

Albeit in ceaseless pastime they sent the livelong day,
The mummers and the minstrels never ceas'd their play.
They flock'd to golden largess, a roving frolic band,
And pour'd a flood of praises on Siegmund's fertile land.

XXII

The king, too, as his father to him before had done,
Enfeoff'd with lands and castles Siegfried his youthful son;
Gifts to his sword-companions he gave with liberal hand,
So glad was he, it pleased them to come into his land.

XXIII

The gorgeous feast it lasted till the seventh day was o'er;
Siegelind the wealthy did as they did of yore;
She won for valiant Siegfried the hearts of young and old,
When for his sake among them she shower'd the ruddy gold.

XXIV

You scarce could find one needy in all the minstrel band;
Horses and robes were scatter'd with ever open hand.
They gave as though they had not another day to live,
None were to take so ready, as they inclin'd to give.

XXV

So was dissolv'd with honor the mighty festival:
The high-descended Barons assembled there in hall,
That youth were well contented as lord to serve and sue,
But that desir'd not Siegfried, the champion stout and true.

XXVI

While Siegelind and Siegmund yet liv'd and flourished there,
Full little reck'd their offspring the royal crown to wear.
He only would be master and exercise command,
'Gainst those whose pride o'erweening disturb'd the peaceful
    land.

XXVII

None ventur'd to defy him; since weapons first he took,
The bed of sloth but seldom the noble knight could brook.
He only sought for battles; his prowess-gifted hand
Won him renown eternal in every foreign strand.

THIRD ADVENTURE

HOW SIEGFRIED WENT TO WORMS

I

'Twas seldom teen or sorrow the warrior's heart assay'd;
At length he heard the rumor, how a lovely maid
In Burgundy was dwelling, the fairest of the fair.
From her he won much pleasure, but dash'd with toil and care.

II

By fame her peerless beauty was bruited far and wide,
Nor less her lofty virtue, and her pure virgin pride
Was day by day reported among the martial band.
This drew guests every flocking to good King Gunther's land.

III

For all the host of suitors that sought to bend her will,
True to her own coy promise remain'd fair Kriemhild still,
That she, for all their wooing, would love vouchsafe to none.
He was a distant stranger, who at last her favor won.

IV

Then sought the son of Siegelind to gain the haughty fair;
The vows of other suitors to his were light as air.
Such knight deserv'd to vanquish the coyest maiden's pride;
Ere long the noble Kriemhild became bold Siegfried's bride.

V

His kinsmen and his liegemen then gave him counsel true,
That now, if he in honor were inclin'd to woo,
He should be bound in wedlock to no unequal make:
Then said the noble Siegfried, " Sure will I fair Kriemhild take,

VI

" The bright Burgundian maiden, best gem of Gunther's
    throne,
Whose far-renown'd beauty stands unapproach'd, alone;
On earth nor king nor kaiser lives there so proud, I ween,
But he might deem him happy to win so fair a queen."

VII

Forthwith were the tidings to Siegmund's ear preferr'd;
His anxious liegemen told him; from them his father heard
The high design of Siegfried; it much to heart he laid,
That he aspir'd so boldly to win so fair a maid.

VIII

The news came eke to Siegelind, the noble monarch's wife;
Full sore the mother trembled for her darling's life,
For well she knew fierce Gunther and his vassals stern;
So strove they both the champion from his high emprise to
    turn.

IX

Then spake the valiant Siegfried, " Dearest father mine,
The love of high-born women forever I'll resign,
Rather than play the wooer but where my heart is set."
Howe'er they sought to move him, but small success they met.

X

" Since naught can then dissuade thee," outspake his royal sire,
" Glad am I, blood of Siegmund should to such height aspire,
And so thy hopes to forward I'll do the best I can;
Yet in his court has Gunther many a proud o'erweening man.

XI

" E'en were there none but Hagan, that redoubted knight
In pride can match the proudest, the mightiest in might;
So that, my son, I fear me, this hour we both may rue,
If our minds are settled the stately maid to woo."

XII

" What can ill befall us? " Siegfried made reply;
" If that misproud Burgundian my friendly suit deny,
Be sure, as much and more, too, I'll seize by strength of hand;
In this I trust to strip him of liegemen and of land."

XIII

" Little thy words content me," the hoary prince replied,
" In the land of King Gunther thou sure durst never ride,
If, on the Rhine, young Siegfried, this tale were only told.
Gunther and eke Gernot I know them both of old.

XIV

" By force, fair son, assure thee, can none the maiden woo,"
Resum'd the princely Siegmund, " this I have heard for true;
But if with knights to back thee, thou'lt ride to Gunther's land,
We've friends enough, and forthwith I'll summon all the band."

XV

" 'Tis not to me well pleasing," the fiery youth replied,
" That I the Rhine should visit with warriors by my side,
As in array of battle, and 'twould my honor stain,
If I should need assistance the peerless maid to gain.

XVI

" I little care to win her save by my own good hand;
With comrades but eleven I'll hence to Gunther's land.
Thus far, father Siegmund, of you help I pray."
Then his friends, to trim their garments, receiv'd striped furs
    and gray.

XVII

To his mother Siegelind the heavy news they bore;
The queen straight for her Siegfried began to sorrow sore.
She shudder'd lest the lov'd one should all untimely die
By the fierce knights of Gunther, and wept full bitterly.

XVIII

Then in haste went Siegfried where she her moan did make,
And thus his sobbing mother tenderly bespake,
" Weep not for me, dear mother, in better hope repose,
Count me forever scathless e'en 'midst a thousand foes.

XIX

" So give me all that's needful through Burgundy to ride,
That I and mine may journey with such fair weeds supplied
As best becomes companions of high degree to wear,
And from my heart I'll thank thee for all thy love and care."

XX

" Since naught avails to stay thee," so spake his mother mild,
" I'll equip thee for the journey, my dear, my only child,
Thee and thy bold companions, and send thee richly dight
With weeds the best and fairest that e'er were worn by knight."

XXI

Then to the queen young Siegfried in duty bent him low,
And said, " Upon this journey I would not that we go
More than twelve together, so these with robes provide.
Full fain am I to witness how stands it with my bride."

XXII

Fair women at the needle were sitting night and day;
Scarcely could a seamstress her head on pillow lay,
Till robes were work'd for Siegfried and all his company.
The youth was ever yearning to start for Burgundy.

XXIII

His sire prepar'd his armor, and nothing left undone,
That he might leave his country as fitted Siegmund's son;
Well temper'd were their breast-plates that flash'd against the
    light,
Of proof were their morions, their bucklers broad and bright.

XXIV

Their way they now were ready to Burgundy to take;
Then man and wife were heavy with sorrow for their sake,
Lest evil should befall them, and bar their homeward road,
With weapons and apparel the heroes bad the sumpters load.

XXV

High-mettled were their chargers, gold-bright their riding
    weed,
None ever rode more proudly (little were there need)
Than then did noble Siegfried, and that fair company
That with him leave were taking, all bound for Burgundy.

XXVI

The king and queen, each weeping, gave him leave to part,
And he to both gave comfort all with a loving heart.
" Weep not," said he, " dear parents, of better courage be,
I'm safe where'er I travel, so take no thought for me."

XXVII

Ah! woe were then the warriors, and wept, too, many a maid,
Their hearts, I ween, the future in deepest gloom array'd,
And told them from that journey many a dear friend would
    bleed.
Full cause had they for sorrow, it brought them woe indeed.

XXVIII

On the seventh fair morning by Worms along the strand
In knightly guise were pricking the death-defying band.
The ruddy gold fair glitter'd on every riding vest;
Their steeds they meetly govern'd, all pacing soft abreast.

XXIX

Their shields were new and massy and like flame they glow'd,
As bright too shone their helmets, while bold Siegfried rode
Straight to the court of Gunther to woo the stately maid;
Eye never look'd on champions so gorgeously array'd.

XXX

Down to their spurs loud clanging reach'd the swords they
    wore;
Sharp and well temper'd lances the chosen champions bore.
One, two spans broad or better, did Siegfried sternly shake,
With keen and cutting edges grim and ghastly wounds to
    make.

XXXI

Their golden-color'd bridles firm they held in hand;
Silken were their pöitrels; so rode they through the land.
On all sides the people to gaze on them began;
Then many of Gunther's liegemen swift to meet them ran.

XXXII

Many a haughty warrior, stout squire, and hardy knight,
Went to receive the strangers as fitting was and right,
And, as to guests high honor'd, did courteous service yield,
Their steeds held as they lighted, and took from each his shield.

XXXIII

They were in act the chargers to lead away to stall,
When the redoubted Siegfried quick to them did call,
"Nay, leave us here the horses, we look not long to stay,
Anon with my companions I shall wend upon my way.

XXXIV

"Affairs of high concernment this squadron hither bring,
So, whoso knows, straight tell me where I may find your king,
The wide-renowned Gunther, who reigns in Burgundy."
Then one who near was standing thus answer'd courteously,

XXXV

"If you would find the monarch, you need not long to wait;
In yonder hall at leisure myself I left him late
Begirt with all his warriors; there you may feast your sight:
In sooth you'll find about him full many a stately knight."

XXXVI

Now to great King Gunther were the tidings told,
That there had journey'd thither hardy knights and bold,
Yclad in flashing armor and glittering vesture gay,
But who and whence the strangers, could no Burgundian say.

XXXVII

Much wonder'd the monarch, whence came the gallant band,
That with so fair equipment had reach'd Burgundian land,
And with so massy bucklers; that none could tidings bring
Of those heroic strangers, but little pleas'd the king.

XXXVIII

To Gunther then made answer the knight of Metz, Ortwine,
A warrior bold and mighty, and of the loftiest line,
"Since none of us can tell you who these same knights may be,
Send for my uncle Hagan; let him strangers see.

XXXIX

He knows the proud and puissant of every foreign land;
So we, what now we guess not, from him shall understand."
Him and his warlike vassals the impatient king bade call,
And soon redoubted Hagan strode tow'ring through the hall.

XL

"What would the king with Hagan?" the warrior made
    demand.
"Here in my house are wand'rers from some far-distant land,
Unknown to all around me; observe the strangers well,
And if thou e'er hast seen them, the truth, good Hagan, tell."

XLI

"That will I straight," said Hagan; to a window then he went,
And his eyes attentive on the strangers bent.
Well pleas'd him their fair vesture, and well their armor sheen,
Yet sure the like he never in Burgundy had seen.

XLII

"Whencever come these champions whom chance to
    Rhineland brings,
Kings might they be," said Hagan, " or messengers of kings.
How highly bred their chargers! how gorgeous their array!
Wherever lies their country, high-mettled lords are they."

XLIII

And thereto added Hagan, " This too I'll vouch for yet;
Albeit on noble Siegfried I never eyes have set;
Still to aver I'll venture, that (let whate'er befall)
'Tis he that's stalking yonder, so stately and so tall.

XLIV

"He brings some new adventure to our Burgundian land;
The valiant Nibelungers he slew by strength of hand,
Nibelung and Shilbung the princes stern in fight,
And since has many a wonder achiev'd with all-surpassing
    might.

XLV

"As all alone and aidless he was riding once at will,
As I have heard reported, he found beside a hill
With Nibelung's hoarded treasure full many a man of might;
Strange seem'd they to the champion, till he came to know
    them right.

XLVI

" They had brought the treasure, as just then befell,
Forth from a yawning cavern; now hear a wonder tell,
How those fierce Nibelungers the treasure would divide;
The noble Siegfried eyed them, and wonder'd as he eyed.

XLVII

" He nearer came and nearer, close watching still the clan,
Till they got sight of him too, when one of them began,
' Here comes the stalwart Siegfried, the chief of Netherland.'
A strange adventure met he with that Nibelungers' band.

XLVIII

" Him well receiv'd the brethren Shilbung and Nibelung.
With one accord they begg'd him, those noble princes young,
To part the hoard betwixt them, and ever pressing bent
The hero's wavering purpose till he yielded full consent.

XLIX

" He saw of gems such plenty, drawn from that dark abode,
That not a hundred wagons could bear the costly load,
Still more of gold so ruddy from the Nibelungers' land.
All this was to be parted by noble Siegfried's hand.

L

" So Nibelung's sword they gave him to recompense his pain,
But ill was done the service, which they had sought so fain,
And he so hard had granted; Siegfried, the hero good,
Fail'd the long task to finish; this stirr'd their angry mood.

LI

" The treasure undivided he needs must let remain,
When the two kings indignant set on him with their train,
But Siegfried gripp'd sharp Balmung (so hight their father's
     sword),
And took from them their country and the beaming precious
     hoard.

LII

" For friends had they twelve champions, each, as avers my tale,
A strong and sturdy giant, but what could all avail?
All twelve to death successive smote Siegfried's mastering
    hand,
And vanquish'd chiefs seven hundred of the Nibelungers' land.

LIII

" With that good weapon Balmung; by sudden fear dismay'd
Both of the forceful swordsman and of the sword he sway'd,
Unnumber'd youthful heroes to Siegfried bent that hour,
Themselves, their lands, their castles, submitting to his power.

LIV

" Those two fierce kings together he there depriv'd of life,
Then wag'd with puissant Albric a stern and dubious strife,
Who thought to take full vengeance for both his masters slain,
But found his might and manhood with Siegfried's match'd
    in vain.

LV

" The mighty dwarf successless strove with the mightier man;
Like to wild mountain lions to th' hollow hill they ran;
He ravish'd there the cloud-cloak from struggling Albric's
    hold,
And then became the master of th' hoarded gems and gold.

LVI

" Whoever dar'd resist him, all by his sword lay slain,
Then bade he bring the treasure back to the cave again,
Whence the men of Nibelung the same before had stirr'd;
On Albric last the office of keeper he conferr'd.

LVII

" He took an oath to serve him, as his liegeman true,
In all that to a master from his man is due.
Such deeds," said he of Trony, " has conqu'ring Siegfried done;
Be sure, such mighty puissance, knight has never won.

LVIII

" Yet more I know of Siegfried, that well your ear may hold;
A poison-spitting dragon he slew with courage bold,
And in the blood then bath'd him; this turn'd to horn his skin.
And now no weapons harm him, as often proved has been.

LIX

" Receive then this young hero with all becoming state;
'Twere ill advis'd to merit so fierce a champion's hate.
So lovely is his presence, at once all hearts are won,
And then his strength and courage such wondrous deeds have
    done."

LX

Then spake the mighty monarch, " Thou counsellest aright.
See how stands full knightly, prepar'd for fiercest fight,
He and his hardy comrades, the death-defying man!
Straight we'll descend to meet him as courteous as we can."

LXI

" That be assur'd," said Hagan, " with honor may be done;
Of lofty kin is Siegfried, a mighty monarch's son.
Me seemeth, if to purpose his bearing I have eyed,
By heaven, 'tis no light matter hath bidd'n him thither ride."

LXII

Then spake the country's ruler, " He shall be welcome here,
Bold is the knight and noble, that I discover clear,
And much shall it avail him on our Burgundian ground."
Then thither went King Gunther where he Siegfried found.

LXIII

The host and his companions so well receiv'd the guest,
That nothing there was wanting that courtesy express'd;
And low inclin'd the warrior to all in presence there,
Since they had giv'n him greeting so friendly and so fair.

LXIV

" I wonder much," said Gunther, " and fain would understand,
Whence comes the noble Siegfried to this Burgundian land,
And what he here is seeking at Worms upon the Rhine."
The guest to the king made answer, " Concealment is no art
    of mine.

LXV

" Afar I heard the tidings, e'en in my father's land,
That here with you were dwelling (fain would I know the band)
The best and prowest champions so voic'd by all and some,
That ever king surrounded; I'm therefore hither come.

LXVI

" Your own renown I've heard, too, through all this country
        ring,
That never eye of mortal has seen so bold a king.
Your prowess and your knighthood are vouch'd by high and
        low,
Now ne'er will I turn homeward till this by proof I know.

LXVII

" I too am a warrior, and shall a sceptre sway,
And I would fain bring all men perforce of me to say,
That I both land and liegemen have nobly merited.
This to maintain I'll freely pledge, my honor and my head.

LXVIII

" Now since you are so famous for manhood and for skill,
Naught reck I, if my purpose be taken well or ill,
But all that's own'd by Gunther I'll win by strength of hand,
And force to my obedience his castles and his land."

LXIX

The king was lost in wonder, and with him all the rest,
At such a strange pretension from that o'erweening guest,
Who claim'd his whole possessions that stretch'd so wide
        around.
His vassals heard the challenge, and for anger sternly frown'd.

LXX

" How," cried the valiant Gunther, " have I deserv'd this
        wrong,
That what my noble father with honor rul'd so long,
I now should yield to anv. o'ermaster'd by his might?
Ill should I show, that I too can bear me like a knight! "

LXXI

"I'll ne'er renounce my purpose," the fiery youth replied;
"If through thy might thy country cannot in peace abide,
I'll take on me to rule it, and what I hold in fee,
If thou by strength canst take it, shall alike submit to thee.

LXXII

Let thy broad lands and mine too be laid in equal scale,
And whichsoe'er in battle o'er th' other shall prevail,
To him let all be subject, the liegemen and the land."
But Hagan sought, and Gernot, such purpose to withstand.

LXXIII

"To us 'tis little pleasing," Gernot made reply,
"That we should lands be seizing, whose lords should
    slaughter'd lie
That we may win unjustly; our lands are fair and wide;
We are their rightful masters, and none they need beside."

LXXIV

Grim glar'd King Gunther's warriors (of gathering wrath the
    sign!)
Among them lower'd the darkest the knight of Metz, Ortwine.
"It irks me much," exclaim'd he, "to hear these words of
    pride.
Sir King! by haughty Siegfried thou'rt wrongfully defied.

LXXV

"Were thou and thy brave brethren stript of those arms you
    boast,
While he to back his quarrel should bring a royal host,
E'en then I'd trust to teach him a humbler pitch to fly,
And cower as low before us, as now he mounteth high."

LXXVI

Wroth was at this defiance the chief of Netherland.
He cried, "Thou durst not venture 'gainst me to lift thy hand.
I am a mighty monarch, a monarch's man art thou;
Should twelve like thee resist me, twelve such to one should
    bow."

LXXVII

Then 'gan for swords call loudly the knight of Metz, Ortwine,
The sister's son of Hagan, pride of his lofty line.
It irk'd him that his uncle so long had silent stood.
Bold Gernot interposing thus cool'd his fiery mood.

LXXVIII

" Ortwine ! " said he, " be calmer ; why thus to weapons run ?
To us the valiant stranger no such offence has done.
We yet may part in kindness ; I rede thee, wrath give o'er,
And make a friend of Siegfried ; this still were to our credit
      more."

LXXIX

" It well may irk," said Hagan, " all us good knights of thine,
That this imperious wanderer e'er rode unto the Rhine.
Such strife-producing journey were better ne'er begun.
Ne'er had the kings my masters by him so evil done."

LXXX

Thereto straight answer'd Siegfried, fiercely frowning still,
" If these my words, Sir Hagan, have chanc'd to please you ill,
Be sure, high deeds of valor, you at these hands shall see,
Deeds, that e'en less may please you here in Burgundy."

LXXXI

" This I alone," said Gernot, " can turn from evil end ; "
So all his warriors bade he the stranger not offend
With words that breath'd defiance, and thus the turmoil stay'd ;
And Siegfried too was thinking upon the stately maid.

LXXXII

" How suits this strife with either ? " the prudent warrior said,
" How many chiefs soever should in this broil lie dead,
By us would little honor, by you small gain be won."
Thereto gave answer Siegfried, King Siegmund's haughty son :

LXXXIII

" But wherefore lingereth Hagan, and wherefore proud
    Ortwine,
That, with their friends thus swarming upon the banks of
    Rhine,
Nor one, nor other ventures a stranger's arm to brave? "
Both kept unwilling silence, such counsel Gernot gave.

LXXXIV

" You shall to us be welcome," resum'd Queen Uta's son,
" You and your faithful comrades, all and every one.
We shall be proud to serve you, I and all kin of mine."
Then for the guests 'twas order'd to pour King Gunther's wine.

LXXXV

Then spoke the sov'reign ruler, " Whatever ours we call,
Should you in honor claim it, is at your service all—
Our persons—our possessions—if so it seems you good."
Thereat became Sir Siegfried of somewhat milder mood.

LXXXVI

Forthwith their whole equipment down from their beasts was
    brought;
For Siegfried and his fellows with fitting zeal were sought
Of all convenient chambers the choicest and the best.
At length the bold Burgundians look'd friendly on their guest.

LXXXVII

Thenceforth were fitting honors paid him many a day,
A thousand-fold, be certain more than I can say.
This earn'd his strength and valor; so gracious was his state,
'Twas rare that any mortal could look on him with hate.

LXXXVIII

Their hours they spent in pastime — the kings and all the
    rest—
Whate'er the sport that pleas'd them, 'twas Siegfried play'd
    it best.
Such was his skill and puissance, that none could come him
    near
To hurl the stone tempestuous or dart the whizzing spear.

LXXXIX

Whene'er before the ladies, all in courtly guise,
Plied the contending champions their knightly exercise,
Then all look'd on delighted as noble Siegfried strove;
But he his thoughts kept ever fix'd on his lofty love.

XC

At court the lovely ladies were asking evermore,
Who was the stately stranger that so rich vesture wore,
At once so fair of presence and so strong of hand.
Then many a one gave answer, " 'Tis the King of Netherland."

XCI

He ever was the foremost, whate'er the game they play'd.
Still in his inmost bosom he bore one lovely maid,
Whom he beheld had never, and yet to all preferr'd;
She too of him in secret spoke many a kindly word.

XCII

When in the court contending fierce squire and hardy knight,
As fits the young and noble, wag'd the mimic fight,
Oft Kriemhild through her window would look, herself
    unseen:
Then no other pleasure needed the gentle queen.

XCIII

What then had been his rapture, could he have only guess'd,
That on him she was looking, who reign'd within his breast!
Could he but once have seen her, I ween, not all the bliss,
That all the world can lavish, would he have ta'en for this.

XCIV

Whene'er, as is the custom at intervals of sport,
He midst the crowd of heroes was standing in the court,
So graceful was the bearing of Siegelind's matchless son,
That the heart of every lady that look'd on him he won.

XCV

Oft too would he be thinking, "How now can it be,
That I the noble maiden with mine eyes may see,
Whom I in heart love dearly, and so long have done?
And she's an utter stranger! Ah! Woe is me, unhappy one!"

XCVI

Whene'er the kings it needed through their land to ride,
Then kept their faithful liegemen attendance by their side,
And with them forth must Siegfried; this irk'd his lady sore;
He through her love was pining the while as much or more.

XCVII

So with those kings, high honor'd Siegmund's noble son
In Gunther's land was dwelling till full a year was run,
Nor, all that weary season, a single glimpse could gain
Of her, who after brought him such pleasure and such pain.

FOURTH ADVENTURE

HOW SIEGFRIED FOUGHT WITH THE SAXONS

I

Now strange and stirring tidings were brought to Gunther's
throne
By messengers commission'd from foreign chiefs unknown,
Who bore the brethren malice, and whom they well might fear.
When they receiv'd the message, right heavy was their cheer.

II

The same I now will tell you; King Ludeger the bold,
From the land of the Saxons (a mightier ne'er was told)
Was leagued with him of Denmark, King Ludegast the strong,
And many a famous warrior both brought with them along.

III

Their messengers, hard riding, came to King Gunther's land,
As his far-distant foemen had given them in command;
Then ask'd the crowd, what tidings the unknown guests might
bring.
To court they straight were hurried, and set before the king.

IV

Them well the monarch greeted: "You're welcome; never
      fear;
From whom you come, I know not, but willingly would hear,
And it is yours to tell me." So spake the monarch good.
Then 'gan they sore to tremble at Gunther's angry mood.

V

" Since you, O king! permit us to utter plain and true
This our high commission, naught will we hide from you.
Our masters we will tell you, who gave us this command.
King Ludegast and King Ludeger will visit you in this land.

VI

" You have deserved their anger; for truth can I relate,
That both our puissant masters bear you deadly hate.
They'll lead a host unnumber'd to Worms unto the Rhine.
Of this be warn'd for certain; fix'd is their proud design.

VII

" Within twelve weeks at farthest their camp will onward go;
If you've good friends to aid you, 'twill soon be time to show.
Their best will sure be needed to guard both fort and field,
Soon shall we here be shiv'ring many a helm and many a shield.

VIII

" Or would you seek a treaty, let it at once be said,
Ere their prevailing myriads, one wasteful ruin spread
Through all your wide dominions with their consuming might,
And Death unsated feast him on many a gallant knight."

IX

" Now wait awhile, ye strangers," thus spake the noble king,
" I must think, ere I answer the message that you bring.
I've friends and faithful liegemen, whose sage advice I use,
And with them I must counsel take on this heavy news."

X

The nigh approaching danger irk'd King Gunther sore,
And the proud defiance deep in heart he bore;
He sent for valiant Hagan and many another knight,
And Gernot, too, bade hasten with all the speed he might.

XI

At once they flock'd around him, a stern and stately band;
Then spake the king, " Proud strangers, here, in our own good
    land,
Have sent to bid us battle; weigh well such tidings told."
Thereto straight answer'd Gernot, a hardy knight and bold.

XII

" Then with our swords we'll meet them; defiance we'll defy;
None but the death-doom'd perish, so bravely let them die;
I'll ne'er forget my honor for all they choose to send.
So fierce a foe to Gernot is welcome as a friend."

XIII

" Rash hold I such hot counsel," said Hagan, Trony's knight,
" Both Ludegast and Ludeger are men of mickle might:
In so few days our vassals we scarce can muster well."
He paused a space, then added, " The news to Siegfried tell."

XIV

Meanwhile they lodg'd the strangers within the city fair;
Though all were foes around them, King Gunther bade them
    share
All courteous entertainment; so fitly dealt the king,
Till he had learn'd, what forces he might together bring.

XV

Right ill at ease was Gunther; his brow was clouded o'er;
A gallant knight, who mark'd him what heavy cheer he bore,
Who had not heard the tidings, nor thus the truth could guess,
With friendly will thus mov'd him his sorrow to confess.

XVI

" I wonder much," said Siegfried, " why I of late have seen
With care so overshadow'd that frank and merry mien,
That gave a zest to pleasure, and heighten'd each delight."
Whereto gave answer Gunther the far-renowned knight;

XVII

"To all the world I cannot my bitter bale impart;
Bear it I must, and wrap it close in my inmost heart.
Bosom woes can only to bosom friends be said."
Thereat the hue of Siegfried wax'd both white and red.

XVIII

He thus bespake the monarch, "I ne'er denied you aught,
And now will serve you truly, whate'er be in your thought.
Need you friends, King Gunther? no firmer friend than I.
Is it a deed of danger? I'll do it, or I'll die."

XIX

"Now God reward you, Siegfried; your words they please me
    well;
E'en should your strength avail not this danger to repel,
There's comfort in such friendship as you have shown to-day.
Let me live a little longer, well will I all repay.

XX

"And now my source of sorrow, Sir Siegfried, you shall know;
It comes of two proud princes, each my deadly foe,
Who me with war would visit, and all my lands o'errun,
A deed that here by warrior before was never done."

XXI

"Take little thought," said Siegfried, "of them and their
    emprise;
Calm but your anxious spirit, and do as I advise.
Let me for you advantage as well as honor win,
And bid at once to aid you your warriors hasten in.

XXII

"If your o'erweening foemen can together call
Thirty thousand champions, I'll stand against them all
With but a single thousand; for that rely on me."
"For this," replied King Gunther, "I'm ever bound to thee."

XXIII

" So from your army give me a thousand men at most,
Since I, who well could muster at home a gallant host,
Have here twelve comrades only; thus will I guard your land.
Count on true service ever from Siegfried's faithful hand.

XXIV

" And Hagan too shall help us, and with him stout Ortwine,
Dankwart and Sindolt those loving lords of thine,
And fear-defying Folker shall our companion be;
He shall bear our banner; better none than he.

XXV

And forthwith did the envoys back to their lords return:
" Tell them they soon shall see us, and to their cost shall learn
How we devise protection for castle and for town."
Straight call'd the king his kinsmen and the suitors of his
    crown.

XXVI

The messengers of Ludeger before th' assembly went;
They heard with joy and gladness that home they would be
    sent.
With costly presents Gunther their parting steps pursued,
And with them sent an escort; this rais'd full high their mood.

XXVII

" Ye messengers," said Gunther, " thus to your masters say,
They'd best be pricking homeward as quickly as they may;
Or, should they please to seek us among our liegemen true,
Let but our friends be faithful, we'll find them work to do."

XXVIII

Then forth the costly presents to the messengers they bore;
Enough, be sure, and more, too, King Gunther had in store.
King Ludeger's men to take them in sooth were nothing coy;
Then leave they took of Gunther, and parted thence with joy.

XXIX

Now when back to Denmark were come the envoys bold,
And to the stout King Ludegast had the tidings told,
How they of Rhine were coming, fierce war themselves to
        bring,
To hear of their high courage troubled sore the king.

XXX

Said they, " Yon proud Burgundian has many a man of might,
But for the first and foremost we mark'd a matchless knight,
One that men call Siegfried, a chief of Netherland."
Ill foreboded Ludegast from such a foe at hand.

XXXI

When to them of Denmark were these tidings told,
The more their friends they summon'd to muster manifold,
Nor press nor hasty message did stout Sir Ludegast slack,
Till twenty thousand champions were marching at his back.

XXXII

Alike to brave Sir Ludeger did his Saxons throng,
Till they in arms had gather'd full forty thousand strong,
Ready at his bidding through Burgundy to ride,
Nor less at home did Gunther his men at arms provide.

XXXIII

His kinsmen and his brethren he begg'd at once to speed,
And to the war that dar'd them their muster'd vassals lead,
And death-defying Hagan; they gather'd far and nigh.
Full many a chief thereafter that journey brought to die.

XXXIV

They one and all were stirring; no loiterer was there;
The danger-daring Folker the standard was to bear.
To cross the Rhine they purpos'd and leave their native land.
Hagan the knight of Trony was marshal of the band.

XXXV

With them, too, rode Sindolt, and with them Hunolt bold,
Both resolv'd by service to earn King Gunther's gold,
And Dankwart, Hagan's brother, and the brave Ortwine,
Alike would seek for honor in the march beyond the Rhine.

XXXVI

" Sir King," said noble Siegfried, " here sit at home and play,
While I and your vassals are fighting far away;
Here frolic with the ladies and many a merry mate,
And trust to me for guarding your honor and estate.

XXXVII

Those foes of yours, that threaten'd as far as Worms to roam,
I will be their surety, that they shall bide at home.
So deep within their country we are resolv'd to ride,
To wail shall turn their vaunting, to penitence their pride."

XXXVIII

From Rhine through Hesse advancing they rode upon their
way,
Toward the Saxon country, where after happ'd the fray.
Far and wide they ravag'd, and fiery brands they toss'd,
Till both the princes heard it and felt it to their cost.

XXXIX

They now were on the borders; then hasten'd every man,
When the stalwart Siegfried thus to ask began:
" Who shall be appointed to guard our company?
Sure ne'er was raid that threaten'd such ill to Saxony."

XL

They answered, " Let to Dankwart the charge committed be
To guard the young and heedless; more nimble none than he.
We thus the less shall suffer from aught our foes design.
To him commit the rearward, and with him too Ortwine."

XLI

" Myself alone," said Siegfried, " will ever forward ride,
Till I have found our foemen and all their strength espied.
Keep watch and ward unceasing till I this task have done."
Then donn'd at once his armor fair Siegelind's martial son.

XLII

At parting he his people in charge to Hagan gave,
And with him eke to Gernot the prudent and the brave;
Then all alone went riding through the wide Saxon realm;
And soon that day he shatter'd the band of many a helm.

XLIII

That mighty host next spied he, as wide encamp'd it lay.
It might his single puissance a hundred-fold outweigh.
Better than forty thousand were muster'd there for fight,
Sir Siegfried mark'd their numbers, and gladden'd at the sight.

XLIV

Before the camp he noted a knight, that on his ground
Strong watch and ward kept heedful, and peer'd on all around.
At once of him was Siegfried, and he of Siegfried ware,
And each began on the other angrily to glare.

XLV

Who was this watchful warder, now you shall be told.
At hand by him lay ready a flashing shield of gold.
'Twas e'en the stout King Ludegast, that watch'd his gather'd
      might.
Fiercely upon the monarch sprung the stranger knight.

XLVI

As fiercely too against him the fiery monarch sped;
In the flank of the war-horse each dash'd the rowels red:
The lance with all his puissance each level'd at the shield.
Ill chance befell King Ludegast in that disastrous field.

XLVII

Beneath the spur blood-dripping the steeds together flew;
Champion clos'd with champion as though a tempest blew.
Then wheel'd they round full knightly; each well the bridle
      sway'd
Again they met unsated, and with blade encounter'd blade.

XLVIII

Such strokes there struck Sir Siegfried, that all the field it
      rang;
At each, as e'en from torches, the fire-red sparkles sprang
From Ludegast's batter'd helmet. So strive they all they can
And either stormy champion in th' other finds his man.

XLIX

At Siegfried too Sir Ludegast struck many a sturdy stroke;
Each on his foeman's buckler his gather'd fury broke.
Full thirty men of Ludegast's meanwhile had spied the fray,
But, ere they up could hasten, Siegfried had won the day.

L

Thrice smote he the bright breast-plate, and pierc'd it through
    and through;
Thrice the blood in torrents from the king he drew,
Those three strokes have ended that encounter keen.
Down sunk woful Ludegast grovelling on the green.

LI

He straight for life sued humbly, and yielded up his claim
To all his lands, and told him that Ludegast was his name.
On this up came his warriors, who from afar had seen
The fight, that at the ward-post so fiercely fought had been.

LII

Thence Siegfried thought to bring him, when sudden all the
    band
Of thirty set upon him; well then the hero's hand
Maintain'd his royal captive with many a mighty blow.
The peerless champion wrought them yet heavier loss and woe.

LIII

He fought with all the thirty till all but one were slain;
To him his life he granted; he trembling rode amain,
And told the truth disastrous to all the gaping crew;
On his bloody helmet they might see it written, too.

LIV

Woe were the men of Denmark to hear the deadly tale;
Their king too was a captive; this added bale to bale.
They told it to his brother; he straight to storm began.
Wroth was he to have suffer'd such loss by arm of man.

LV

So by the might of Siegfried was Ludegast led away
To where the men of Gunther in watchful leaguer lay,
And given in charge to Hagan; when they came to hear
The prisoner was King Ludegast, they scarcely shed a tear.

LVI

Now rear they bade the banner the bold Burgundian crew.
" Up! " cried the son of Siegelind, " more will be yet to do,
If there be life in Siegfried, and that ere day be done.
Woe to the Saxon mothers! they'll weep for many a son.

LVII

" Ye hardy knights of Rhineland, take of me good heed.
Right through the ranks of Ludeger your valor will I lead.
You'll see by hands of heroes helmets cleft amain.
Shame shall they learn and sorrow ere we ride home again."

LVIII

At once to horse good Gernot and all his meiny sprung,
At once the glittering banner to the breeze was flung
By the bold minstrel Folker riding in the van;
So moved they on to battle, war-breathing every man.

LIX

No more than e'en a thousand went on the hard emprise;
With them twelve stranger champions.   Now 'gan the dust
     arise
Along the paths they trampled; they rode by copse and field
And startled all the country with the flash of many a shield.

LX

Against them with their myriads came on the Saxons bold.
Their swords they well were sharpen'd, as I have since been
     told.
Keen cut the temper'd weapons in their well-practised hands,
To guard from those fierce strangers their castles and their
     lands.

LXI

The war-directing marshal led on the troop amain,
And thither too fierce Siegfried brought up the scanty train,
That had his fortunes follow'd from distant Netherland.
Busied that day in battle was many a bloody hand.

LXII

Sindolt and Hunolt and noble Gernot too
In the fierce encounter many a champion slew,
Who, ere they felt their puissance, little thought to quail;
Many a noble lady then had cause to wail.

LXIII

Folker and Hagan, and eke the fierce Ortwine,
Death-defying champions, dimm'd many a helmet's shine
With bloody streaming torrents that down began to run;
There too were by Dankwart mighty marvels done.

LXIV

Every man of Denmark frankly tried his hand;
You might have heard a clatter ring throughout the land
Of shiver'd shields and sword-blades; 'sooth the work was
        rough,
And the hurtling Saxons damage did enough.

LXV

Where the stern Burgundians plung'd into the strife,
Many a wound was given, and let out many a life.
The blood from that red slaughter above the saddles stood;
Woo'd as a bride was honor by heroes bold and good.

LXVI

But louder still and louder in every hero's hand
Clash'd the keen-ground weapons, when those of Netherland
Behind their charging master rush'd into the fight.
On they came with Siegfried; each bore him as a knight.

LXVII

Not a lord of Rhineland could follow where he flew.
You might see red spouting the riven helmets through
Sudden streams of slaughter where Siegfried smote around,
Till he at last King Ludeger before his comrades found.

LXVIII

Thrice pierc'd he through the Saxons, and thrice return'd
    again,
From van to utmost rear-guard still trampling down the slain;
Nor was it long, ere Hagan came up his part to bear.
Down then must proudest champions before th' unconquer'd
    pair.

LXIX

When the stalwart Ludeger saw noble Siegfried nigh,
Who in his hand wide-wasting ever heav'd on high
The storm-descending Balmung, and slew him many a slain,
Grimly frown'd the monarch, and burn'd with wrath amain.

LXX

Dire was the storm and struggle, and loud the sword-blades
    clash'd,
When both the thick battalions each on the other dash'd,
Each angry leader panting to meet in stern debate.
The crowd began to scatter; then fiercer rose their hate.

LXXI

Well the Saxon ruler that day perform'd his part;
To know his brother taken cut him to the heart.
He heard it first reported, Gernot the deed had done,
But now he knew for certain, 'twas Siegelind's conqu'ring son.

LXXII

So burly were the buffets which Ludeger dealt in field,
That Siegfried's panting charger under the saddle reel'd.
Soon as the steed recover'd, a fiercer passion stirr'd
His angry lord, and hotter through the red press he spurr'd.

*

LXXIII

Then up to help him Hagan, and up good Gernot sped,
Dankwart and Folker; round lay in heaps the dead;
And Sindolt came, and Hunolt, and the good knight Ortwine.
Down sunk the Saxons trampled by the warriors of the Rhine.

LXXIV

Close fought the chiefs, unsever'd 'spite of the hurtling bands
Then might you see the lances from mightiest heroes' hands
Fly o'er the nodding helmets, and pierce the bucklers through;
Many a glittering armor was dyed a bloody hue.

LXXV

In the fierce encounter many a mighty man
Tumbled from the saddle; each on th' other ran
Ludeger and Siegfried, each the other's peer;
Many a shaft was flying, whizzing many a spear.

LXXVI

Off flew Ludeger's shield-plate by dint of Siegfried's hand.
Then look'd at last for conquest the knight of Netherland
Over the struggling Saxons, such force was in that stroke.
Then too how many a breast-plate the strong-arm'd Dankwart
  broke!

LXXVII

Just then it chanc'd King Ludeger had a crown espied
Painted upon the buckler that guarded Siegfried's side.
Straight knew the astonish'd Saxon, 'twas he, the mighty man,
And to his friends the hero to call aloud began.

LXXVIII

"Stop! stop! enough of fighting, my merry men each one!
Here in this bloody battle I've met with Siegmund's son.
The chief-destroying Siegfried for certain seen have I.
The devil has sent him hither to harry Saxony."

LXXIX

He bade them lower the banners; forthwith they lower'd them
    all;
And peace he then demanded; 'twas granted at his call;
But go he must a pris'ner to good King Gunther's land;
This was from him extorted by Siegfried's conqu'ring hand.

LXXX

With one accord agreeing the bloody strife they left;
The shining shields all shiver'd, the helmets hack'd and cleft
They laid aside o'er-wearied; whatever down they threw
Bore from Burgundian falchions a stain of bloody hue.

LXXXI

They took whome'er it pleas'd them, none could their will
    gainsay.
Gernot and valiant Hagan at once bade bear away
The faint and feeble wounded, and with them carried then
Off to the Rhine as captives five hundred chosen men.

LXXXII

With wailing back to Denmark the bootless warriors came;
The late o'erweening Saxons bore off but loss and shame
From that disastrous struggle; each hung his pensive head.
They last their friends remember'd, and sorrow'd for the dead.

LXXXIII

Anon they bade the sumpters be loaded for the Rhine;
And thus victorious Siegfried his perilous design
Had brought to full performance; well had he done in fight;
This every man of Gunther allow'd him as of right.

LXXXIV

To Worms straight did a message from good Sir Gernot come,
To tell throughout the country to all his friends at home
Whate'er in that encounter to him and his befell,
And how they all their duty had knightly done and well.

LXXXV

The youths they ran their swiftest, and nois'd abroad the
  whole.
Then laugh'd who late lamented; delight succeeded dole.
All bosoms straight were beating to learn the news they bore,
And every noble lady would ask them o'er and o'er,

LXXXVI

How the knights of Gunther in Saxony had sped.
Then too the lovelorn Kriemhild had one in secret led
(For publicly she durst not) to a distant bower apart,
For she would learn how far'd it with the chosen of her heart.

LXXXVII

Soon as to the chamber the melancholy maid
Saw the youth approaching, sweetly thus she said,
" Now tell me happy tidings, and I'll give thee gold in store,
And if 'tis truth thou tell'st me, I'll befriend thee evermore.

LXXXVIII

" Tell me how in battle my brother Gernot sped,
And all our friends around him; is any of them dead?
Who prov'd the best and bravest? this thou must tell me true."
" No coward," the youth made answer, "had we in all the crew;

LXXXIX

" But sure to fight or foray (the simple truth to tell)
Fair and noble princess! rode never knight so well
As the noble stranger from distant Netherland.
Wonders that mock believing were wrought by Siegfried's
  hand.

XC

" However well the others have borne them in the fight,
Dankwart and Hagan, and all our men of might,
Howe'er deserv'd the honor, that other swords have won,
'Tis a puff of wind to Siegfried, King Siegmund's glorious son.

XCI

" Well plied the rest the falchion, and wielded well the spear,
But ne'er from tongue of mortal expect at full to hear
What feats were done by Siegfried, when he broke the
    squadrons through;
Those feats the weeping sisters of slaughter'd brethren rue.

XCII

" There lay the heart's-beloved of many a mourning bride;
Beneath his sounding sword-strokes cleft morions, gaping
    wide,
Let out the ruddy life-blood gushing fearfully.
Sir Siegfried is in all things the flower of chivalry.

XCIII

" There too won no small worship the knight of Metz, Ortwine;
Whomever reach'd the warrior with keen-edg'd falchion fine,
Down went they from the war-horse, some wounded, others
    dead.
There too your valiant brother as wide the slaughter spread,

XCIV

" As e'er was done, believe me, since armies met in fight;
So much must all men witness of that redoubted knight.
There too the proud Burgundians so nobly strove for fame,
That well they have assur'd them from every taint of blame.

XCV

" Before their level'd lances was many a saddle void;
Around the field re-echoed when they the sword employ'd.
The noble knights of Rhineland fought so well that day,
Their foes had sure done wiser at once to flee away.

XCVI

" The gallant men of Trony did deeds they well may boast
When with united squadrons to battle rode the host.
What numbers fell by Hagan and Hagan's chivalry!
Long shall their glory flourish here in broad Burgundy.

XCVII

" Sindolt and Hunolt, each Gernot's liegemen true,
And never-daunted Rumolt so rush'd the foemen through,
That ever will King Ludeger repent his vain design
To meet your royal brethren on the banks of Rhine.

XCVIII

" But of all feats, the fairest, that in that field befell,
From first to last most glorious, as all who saw can tell,
Were those achiev'd full knightly by Siegfried's deadly hand.
Now many a wealthy captive brings he to Gunther's land.

XCIX

" Beneath his arm, submission the brother kings have learn'd;
Proud Dane and haughty Saxon alike defeat have earn'd;
Dead lie their loving vassals wide o'er the bloody green.
Now to my tale yet listen, high and noble queen!

C

" Now both are hither wending, the thralls of Siegfried's hand;
Chief ne'er such countless captives brought to Burgundian
     land,
As now to Rhine are coming, o'ermastered by his might."
Ne'er heard the royal maiden a tale of such delight.

CI

" More than five hundred prisoners, for truth, high lady! know,
Unhurt, are hither coming; full eighty biers, I trow,
Trail on the deadly wounded : you soon will see them here;
The most bear bloody witness of Siegfried's sword and spear.

CII

"Those kings, who late so haughty would dare us on the Rhine,
Must now to Gunther's pleasure their lives, their all resign.
Our shouts salute their coming, our joy is on the gale."
She brighten'd into blushes to hear the happy tale.

CIII

Her cheek, late pale as lily, now glow'd with rosy red,
To hear how youthful Siegfried so gloriously had sped,
Rais'd from the depth of peril to loftiest height of fame.
She joy'd too for her kinsmen as maiden well became.

CIV

Then spake she midst her blushes, " Well hast thou earn'd thy
 meed,
Well hast thou told thy story, so take thee costliest weed,
Now straight I'll bid be brought thee ten marks of ruddy gold."
No wonder, to rich ladies glad news are gladly told.

CV

Straightforth was brought the vesture, and down the gold was
 paid;
Then hurried to the windows full many a lovely maid,
And look'd out on the highway, nor long delay'd to spy
The high-descended victors return'd to Burgundy.

CVI

The safe and sound came forward; the wounded did the same;
Merry was the meeting; none fear'd reproach or blame.
Forth rode the host to meet them; his mirth had no alloy;
The woe, that long had worn him, was now shut up in joy.

CVII

His own full well receiv'd he, and well the strangers too;
Sure nothing so befitting could wealthy monarch do,
Than kindly greet such victors as now his court had sought
With gain of such clear honor from field so sternly fought.

CVIII

Then ask'd the noble Gunther of the conquering train,
How many of his warriors had in the strife been slain.
There had been lost but sixty in the fight they won.
They were mourn'd and forgotten, as with many has since
 been done.

CIX

Th' unwounded bore exulting, grim trophies of the field,
Full many a batter'd morion, full many a shiver'd shield.
Before the hall of Gunther from horse the champions sprung;
Around from joyful thousands one shout of welcome rung.

CX

The warriors in the city were lodg'd as might be best;
The king with courteous service bade wait on every guest.
He found the hurt fit chambers for tendance and repose,
And prov'd his noble nature in the treatment of his foes.

CXI

Thus he said to Ludegast, " King Ludegast, welcome here.
Much at your hands I've suffer'd, and more had cause to fear
But all's at full repaid me, if smooth my fortune run.
God requite my warriors! they well for me have done."

CXII

" Ay, you may gladly thank them," said Ludeger, " 'tis their
    due;
King ne'er had such high captives as they have won for you.
Meanwhile, for courteous treatment, good store of gold we'll
    bring,
And look for such reception as king may claim from king."

CXIII

" Take what you ask," said Gunther, " both set I gladly free.
Still must I have assurance that here awhile with me
My foes consent to tarry, and do not leave my land
Till peace be made between us."   To that King Ludeger gave
    his hand.

CXIV

So now the kings to rest them were to their chambers led.
With tender care the wounded were softly laid a-bed,
While for the whole and hearty were pour'd the mead and wine.
Never were men so merry as these beside the Rhine.

CXV

Attendants to safe keeping the batter'd bucklers bore,
The blood-bespatter'd saddles, whereof was plenteous store,
They hid, lest sight so sorry should make the women weep.
Many a good knight o'erwearied home was glad to creep.

CXVI

The guests from good King Gunther all noble treatment found.
With friends as well as strangers his country swarm'd around.
He bade for the sore wounded all needful aid be sought.
Where was their haughty courage? how low it now was
    brought!

CXVII

Whoe'er had skill in leechcraft was offer'd coin untold,
Silver without measure as well as glittering gold,
To cure the fainting champions by wounds of war oppress'd.
The bounteous monarch sent, too, rich gifts to every guest.

CXVIII

Those who, of feasting weary, homeward sought to wend,
Were press'd to tarry longer, as friend will deal with friend.
King Gunther call'd a council; he would his men requite,
Who for his sake so nobly had won that gallant fight.

CXIX

Then spake the good Sir Gernot, " At present bid them go.
When full six weeks are over, we'll let the warriors know,
We here shall need their presence at feasting rich and high;
Then will restor'd be many, who yet sore wounded lie."

CXX

And now would noble Siegfried to Gunther bid adieu;
Soon as the friendly monarch the warrior's purpose knew
He lovingly besought him a longer stay to make.
He ne'er had so consented but for his sister's sake.

CXXI

Besides, he was too wealthy to stoop to soldier's pay,
Albeit he well deserv'd it; him lov'd the more each day,
The king and all his kinsmen, who on the battle plain,
Had seen him deal destruction on Saxon and on Dane,

CXXII

For the sake of that fair lady he yet would linger there,
If he perchance might see her; and soon was eas'd his care.
He came to know the maiden to his utmost heart's desire,
Then home he rode rejoicing to the kingdom of his sire.

CXXIII

The king bade practise knighthood and joust from day to day,
Well did his youthful warriors and willingly obey.
Seats too before the city he rais'd along the strand
For those who were to visit the fam'd Burgundian land.

CXXIV

So bade the royal Gunther, and now the time was near,
Ere came the joyful tidings to his fair sister's ear,
That he with his dear comrades high festival would hold.
Then were fair women stirring; their toil was manifold.

CXXV

With kirtles, and with head-gear, and all that each should wear,
Uta, the rich and noble, amidst her maidens fair
Heard of coming warriors, a bold and haughty train;
Straight was from out the wrappers store of rich vesture ta'en.

CXXVI

For the sake of her dear children the garments forth were laid,
Wherewith array'd were richly many a wife and many a maid,
And many a youthful champion of warlike Burgundy;
She bade, too, many a stranger be rob'd as gorgeously.

FIFTH ADVENTURE
HOW SIEGFRIED FIRST SAW KRIEMHILD

I

Now might you ever daily see riding toward the Rhine
Troops of good knights ambitious at that proud feast to shine.
Whoe'er for love of Gunther to Gunther's court would speed,
Was at his hands provided with vesture and with steed.

II

Assign'd were seats befitting to every high-born guest.
Thither, as has been told us, the noblest and the best
Came two and thirty princes to that high festal tide.
In gawds and gems the women each with her neighbor vied.

III

Now here, now there was busy the youthful Giselher;
He and his brother Gernot each with his meiny there
Right hospitable welcome to friend and stranger made,
And every fitting honor to every warrior paid.

IV

Full many a gold-red saddle, full many a sparkling shield,
With store of sumptuous vesture for that high festal field,
Were then convey'd to Rhineland; many an ailing wight
Grew merry again and gladsome to see so fair a sight.

V

Each, who in bed lay wounded, though like to yield his breath,
Could now no more remember the bitterness of death.
By the sick the healthy could now no longer stay;
Comrade laugh'd with comrade against the festal day

VI

On the good entertainment prepar'd for young and old;
Measureless contentment, enjoyment manifold
Enliven'd all the people, and spread from band to band.
The note of pleasure echoed through all King Gunther's land

VII

'Twas on a Whitsun' morning the warriors you might see,
Five thousand men or better, fair pricking o'er the lea,
Yclad in courtly raiment, to that high festival,
In jollity and pastime were vying one and all.

VIII

Right well had mark'd King Gunther, who love could under-
     stand,
What heartfelt love impassion'd the knight of Netherland,
E'en though he ne'er had seen her, his peerless sister bare,
The maid proclaim'd by all men the fairest of the fair.

IX

Said he, " Now all advise me, kinsmen and men of mine,
How best of this high tourney to perfect the design,
So that our earnest efforts henceforth none may blame.
'Tis but on deeds deserving that rests enduring fame."

X

He scarce had thus address'd them, when answer'd bold
     Ortwine,
" Would you, O King! full honor to this high feast assign,
Bring forth our choicest treasures to this proud chivalry,
The matrons and the maidens of our fair Burgundy.

XI

" What more the heart enraptures, or courage more inflames
Than to look on lovely damsels, on high and stately dames?
Bid too come forth your sister to feast each stranger's sight."
Well was approv'd the counsel by each surrounding knight.

XII

" 'Tis well advis'd," said Gunther, " I straight will do my part."
Whoever heard his answer was inly glad at heart.
Then bade he Lady Uta and her fair daughter call
To grace the court and tourney, them and their maidens all.

XIII

In haste through all the presses for rich attire they sought,
What lay in wrappers folded alike to light was brought,
Bracelets and clasps and brooches all ready forth were laid.
Soon deck'd in all her choicest was every noble maid.

XIV

Many a young knight that morning, within his flutt'ring breast,
Long'd, that on him, contented, bright beauty's glance might
    rest;
Such glance he would not barter for all a king can own.
Each look'd on each full gladly, albeit before unknown.

XV

Then bade the wealthy monarch with royal pomp and state
Of his men a hundred on his sister wait,
His and the maiden's kinsmen; each carried sword in hand.
These were the chosen courtiers of Burgundy's fair land.

XVI

With her the wealthy Uta there coming too was seen;
She had with her in waiting of fair and stately mien,
A hundred dames or better, all gorgeously array'd.
Her daughter, too, was followed by many a noble maid.

XVII

On from bower advancing they came in fair array;
Much press was there of heroes along the crowded way
Through anxious glad expectance to see that beauty rare,
The fairest and the noblest of the noble and the fair.

XVIII

Now went she forth, the loveliest, as forth the morning goes
From misty clouds out-beaming; then all his weary woes
Left him, in heart who bore her, and so, long time, had done.
He saw there stately standing the fair, the peerless one.

XIX

Many a stone full precious flash'd from her vesture bright;
Her rosy blushes darted a softer, milder light.
Whate'er might be his wishes, each could not but confess,
He ne'er on earth had witness'd such perfect loveliness.

XX

As the moon arising outglitters every star
That through the clouds so purely glimmers from afar,
E'en so love-breathing Kriemhild dimm'd every beauty nigh.
Well might at such a vision many a bold heart beat high.

XXI

Rich chamberlains before them march'd on in order due;
Around th' high-mettled champions close and closer drew,
Each pressing each, and struggling to see the matchless maid.
Then inly was Sir Siegfried both well and ill apaid.

XXII

Within himself thus thought he: "How could I thus misdeem
That I should dare to woo thee? sure 'twas an idle dream!
Yet, rather than forsake thee, far better were I dead."
Thus thinking, thus impassion'd, wax'd he ever white and red.

XXIII

So stood the son of Siegelind in matchless grace array'd,
As though upon a parchment in glowing hues portray'd
By some good master's cunning; all own'd, and could no less,
Eye had not seen a pattern of such fair manliness.

XXIV

Those, who the dames attended, bade all around make way;
Straight did the gentle warriors, as such became, obey.
There many a knight, enraptur'd, saw many a dame in place
Shine forth in bright perfection of courtliness and grace.

XXV

Then the bold Burgundian, Sir Gernot, spoke his thought,
"Him, who in hour of peril his aid so frankly brought,
Requite, dear brother Gunther, as fits both him and you,
Before this fair assembly; th' advice I give, I ne'er shall rue.

XXVI

"Bid Siegfried come to Kriemhild; let each the other meet;
'Twill sure be to our profit, if she the warrior greet.
'Twill make him ours forever, this man of matchless might,
If she but give him greeting, who never greeted knight."

XXVII

Then went King Gunther's kinsmen, a high-born haughty band,
And found, and fair saluted the knight of Netherland.
"The king to court invites you; such favor have you won;
His sister there will greet you; this to honor you is done."

XXVIII

Glad man was then Sir Siegfried at this unlook'd-for gain;
His heart was full of pleasure without alloy of pain,
To see and meet so friendly fair Uta's fairer child.
Then greeted she the warrior maidenly and mild.

XXIX

There stood he, the high-minded, beneath her star-bright eye,
His cheek as fire all glowing; then said she modestly,
"Sir Siegfried, you are welcome, noble knight and good!"
Yet loftier at that greeting rose his lofty mood.

XXX

He bow'd with soft emotion, and thank'd the blushing fair;
Love's strong constraint together impell'd th' enamour'd pair;
Their longing eyes encounter'd, their glances, every one,
Bound knight and maid for ever, yet all by stealth was done.

XXXI

That in the warmth of passion he press'd her lily hand,
I do not know for certain, but well can understand.
'Twere surely past believing they ventur'd not on this;
Two loving hearts, so meeting, else had done amiss.

XXXII

No more in pride of summer nor in bloom of May
Knew he such heart-felt pleasure as on this happy day,
When she, than May more blooming, more bright than sum-
    mer's pride,
His own, a dream no longer, was standing by his side.

XXXIII

Then thought full many a champion, "Would this had happ'd
    to me
To be with lovely Kriemhild as Siegfried now I see,
Or closer e'en than Siegfried; well were I then, I ween."
Never yet was champion who so deserv'd a queen.

XXXIV

Whate'er the king or country of the guests assembled there,
All could look on nothing save on that gentle pair.
Now 'twas allow'd that Kriemhild the peerless knight should
    kiss.
Ne'er in the world had drain'd he so full a draught of bliss.

XXXV

Then spake the King of Denmark the gather'd crowd before,
" Because of this high greeting lie many wounded sore,
As I know to my sorrow, by Siegfried's might and main.
God grant, he ne'er to Denmark may find his way again."

XXXVI

Then 'twas proclaim'd on all sides to make for Kriemhild way;
Straight went to church the maiden in royal rich array
With a bold train of warriors, a fair and courtly sight.
There soon from her was parted the lofty-minded knight.

XXXVII

She now the minster enter'd; her follow'd many a dame;
There so her stately beauty her rich attire became,
That droop'd each high aspiring, born but at once to die.
Sure was that maid created to ravish every eye.

XXXVIII

Scarce could wait Sir Siegfried till the mass was sung.
Well might he thank his fortune, that, all those knights among,
To him inclin'd the maiden whom still in heart he bore,
While he to her, as fitted, return'd as much or more.

XXXIX

When now before the minster after the mass she stood,
Again to come beside her was call'd the champion good.
Then first by that sweet maiden thanks to the knight were given,
That he before his comrades so warrior-like had striven.

XL

" God you reward, Sir Siegfried!" said the noble child,
" For all your high deservings in honor's beadroll fil'd,
The which I know from all men have won you fame and grace."
Sir Siegfried, love-bewilder'd, look'd Kriemhild in the face.

XLI

"Ever," said he, "your brethren I'll serve as best I may,
Nor once, while I have being, will head on pillow lay,
Till I have done to please them whate'er they bid me do,
And this, my lady Kriemhild, is all for love of you."

XLII

For twelve days the maiden each successive day
With the knight beside her took to court her way,
While, as they pass'd together, their friends were looking on.
Out of love to Siegfried was this fair service done.

XLIII

From morn was there to evening and day by day withal
Shouting and merry-making about King Gunther's hall,
Within, without, from joyance of many a mighty man.
Ortwine and valiant Hagan high wonders there began.

XLIV

Whatever sports they wish'd for were ready at their will;
Of each, as each had liking, each might take his fill.
Thus proved were Gunther's warriors by stranger chivalry,
Whence fame accrued and honor to all broad Burgundy.

XLV

They too, who lay sore wounded, crept forth to the free air;
They long'd with loving comrades the gentle sports to share,
To skirmish with the buckler, and hurl the spear amain;
And most through such fair pastime came to full strength again.

XLVI

The host of that high festal all and some had cheer
With meats and drinks the choicest; he kept him ever clear
From blame or ought unkingly in action or intent;
And now with friendly purpose to his guests he went.

XLVII

Said he, "Good knights and noble, ere you hence retire,
Receive the gifts I offer, as proofs of my desire
In all I can to serve you, this I'm resolv'd to do;
Disdain not now the riches I'd gladly share with you."

XLVIII

Straight the men of Denmark to the king replied,
" Ere hence we part and homeward to our own country ride,
A lasting peace assure us; such peace must captives need,
Who have seen their dearest comrades beneath your champions
    bleed."

XLIX

Now whole again was Ludegast and all his gashes heal'd,
The Saxon too recover'd after that luckless field.
Some dead they left behind them entomb'd in Rhenish ground
Then thither went King Gunther where he Sir Siegfried found.

L

To the good knight thus said he, " Now tell me what to do;
Early to-morrow morning ride home the Danish crew;
With me and mine from henceforth they seek to be at one;
Therefore advise me, Siegfried, what best is to be done.

LI

" What these two monarchs offer, I'll to you declare;
As much as steeds five hundred of shining gold can bear,
That will they gladly give me to set them free at will."
Then answer'd noble Siegfried, " You then would do but ill.

LII

" Better hence unfetter'd let both together go,
And that neither warrior henceforth as a foe
Venture to make entry on Burgundian land,
For this in full assurance let either give his hand."

LIII

" Your counsel I will follow, thus let them home return."
His captive foes his message were not slow to learn,
No one their gold demanded which they had offer'd late.
Meanwhile their friends in Denmark mourn'd for their lost
    estate.

LIV

Many a shield heap'd with treasure was brought at Gunther's
    call;
Among the friends around him unweigh'd he shar'd it all;
Five hundred marks or better each warrior home might bring;
This frank and liberal counsel bold Gernot gave the king.

LV

Leave soon the guests were taking; their minds were homeward
    bent;
Then might you see how each one before fair Kriemhild went,
And eke where Lady Uta sat like a queen in place.
Never yet were warriors dismiss'd with so much grace.

LVI

Empty was left each chamber as thence the strangers rode,
Yet still in royal splendor the king at home abode
With many a noble warrior and vassal of his court,
Whom you might see to Kriemhild day by day resort.

LVII

And now the noble Siegfried leave to take was fain.
What he so deeply yearn'd for he little hop'd to gain.
It was told King Gunther that he would hence away.
'Twas Giselher the youthful that won the chief to stay.

LVIII

" Why would you leave us, Siegfried, noble friend and true?
Tarry here among us (what I entreat you, do)
With Gunther and his liegemen, warriors frank and free.
Here are store of lovely ladies, whom you may gladly see."

LIX

Then spake the valiant Siegfried, " Lead in the steeds again;
Forthwith to ride I purpos'd, but now will here remain;
And back, too, bear the bucklers; indeed I homeward yearn'd,
But Giselher with honor my fix'd intent has turn'd."

LX

So stay'd the bold Sir Siegfried for love and friendship's sake;
Nor surely could he elsewhere so gladly tarriance make
As at the court of Gunther, for there throughout his stay
The love-devoted warrior saw Kriemhild every day.

LXI

Through her unmeasur'd beauty Sir Siegfried linger'd there;
His friends with many a pastime charm'd from him every care,
Save longing love for Kriemhild; this mov'd him oft to sigh,
This too thereafter brought him most miserably to die.

SIXTH ADVENTURE

HOW GUNTHER WENT TO WOO BRUNHILD

I

BEYOND the Rhine high tidings again were nois'd around.
There many a maid was dwelling for beauty wide renown'd,
And one of these King Gunther, 'twas said, design'd to woo:
Well pleas'd the monarch's purpose his knights and liegemen
    true.

II

There was a queen high seated afar beyond the sea;
Never wielded sceptre a mightier than she;
For beauty she was matchless, for strength without a peer;
Her love to him she offer'd who could pass her at the spear.

III

She threw the stone, and bounded behind it to the mark;
At three games each suitor with sinews stiff and stark
Must conquer the fierce maiden whom he sought to wed,
Or, if in one successless, straight must lose his head.

IV

E'en thus for the stern virgin had many a suitor died.
This heard a noble warrior who dwelt the Rhine beside,
And forthwith resolv'd he to win her for his wife.
Thereby full many a hero thereafter lost his life.

V

Once on a day together sat with his men the king,
Talking each with the other, and deeply pondering,
What maiden 'twas most fitting for their lord to woo,
One who him might comfort, and grace the country too.

VI

Then spake the lord of Rhineland: "Straight will I hence to
    sea,
And seek the fiery Brunhild howe'er it go with me.
For love of the stern maiden I'll frankly risk my life;
Ready am I to lose it, if I win her not to wife."

VII

" That would I fain dissuade you," Sir Siegfried made reply,
" Whoe'er would woo fair Brunhild, plays a stake too high;
So cruel is her custom, and she so fierce a foe.
Take good advice, King Gunther, nor on such a journey go."

VIII

Then answer'd thus King Gunther: " Ne'er yet was woman
  born
So bold and eke so stalwart, but I should think it scorn
Were not this hand sufficient to force a female foe."
" Be still," replied Sir Siegfried, " her strength you little know.

IX

" E'en were you four together, nought could all four devise
'Gainst her remorseless fury; hear then what I advise
From true and steadfast friendship, and, as you value life,
Tempt not for love of Brunhild a vain, a hopeless strife."

X

" How strong she be soever, the journey will I take,
Whatever chance befall me, for lovely Brunhild's sake;
For her unmeasur'd beauty I'll hazard all that's mine.
Who knows, but God may bring her to follow me to the Rhine? "

XI

" Since you're resolv'd," said Hagan, " this would I chief advise;
Request of noble Siegfried in this dread enterprise
To take his part among us; thus 'twould be best, I ween,
For none so well as Siegfried knows this redoubted queen."

XII

Said Gunther, " Wilt thou help me, Siegfried tried and true,
To win the lovely maiden? What I entreat thee, do,
And if I only gain her to my wedded wife,
For thee I'll gladly venture honor, limb and life."

XIII

Thereto answer'd Siegfried, Siegmund's matchless son,
" Give me but thy sister, and the thing is done.
The stately queen fair Kriemhild let me only gain,
I ask no other guerdon for whatever toil and pain."

XIV

" I promise it," said Gunther, " and take in pledge thy hand,
And soon as lovely Brunhild shall come into this land,
To thee to wife my sister surely will I give,
And may you both together long time and happy live."

XV

Then each they swore to th' other, the high-born champions bold,
Which wrought them toil and trouble thereafter manifold,
Ere to full completion they brought their high design,
And led at last the lady to the banks of Rhine.

XVI

I have heard strange stories of wild dwarfs, how they fare;
They dwell in hollow mountains, and for protection wear
A vesture that high cloud-cloak, marvellous to tell;
Whoever has it on him may keep him safe and well.

XVII

From cuts and stabs of foemen; him none can hear or see
As soon as he is in it, but see and hear can he
Whate'er he will around him, and thus must needs prevail;
He grows besides far stronger; so goes the wond'rous tale.

XVIII

And now with him the cloud-cloak took fair Sieglind's son;
The same th' unconquer'd warrior with labor hard had won
From the stout dwarf Albric in successful fray.
The bold and wealthy champions made ready for the way.

XIX

So, as I said, bold Siegfried the cloud-cloak bore along.
When he but put it on him, he felt him wond'rous strong.
Twelve men's strength then had he in his single body laid.
By trains and close devices he woo'd the haughty maid.

XX

Besides, in that strange cloud-cloak was such deep virtue found,
That whosoever wore it, though thousands stood around,
Might do whatever pleas'd him unseen of friend or foe.
Thus Siegfried won fair Brunhild, which brought him bitterest
    woe.

XXI

" Before we start, bold Siegfried, tell me what best would be;
Shall we lead an army across the sounding sea,
And travel thus to Brunhild as fits a royal king?
Straight could we together thirty thousand warriors bring."

XXII

" Whate'er our band," said Siegfried, " the same would still
    ensue;
So savage and so cruel is the queen you woo,
All would together perish by her o'ermastering might;
But I'll advise you better, high and noble knight.

XXIII

" As simple knights we'll travel a-down the Rhine's fair tide,
Two to us two added, and followers none beside.
We four will make the voyage, true comrades one and all,
And thus shall win the lady, whatever thence befall.

XXIV

" I will be one companion, thou shalt the second be,
The third shall be Sir Hagan, in sooth a goodly three!
The fourth shall be Sir Dankwart that redoubted knight.
Trust me, no thousand champions will dare us four to fight."

XXV

" Fain would I learn," said Gunther, " ere we hence depart
On the hard adventure, that so inflames my heart,
Before the royal Brunhild what vesture we should wear,
That may best become us; this, Siegfried, thou declare."

XXVI

" Garments the best and richest that ever warriors wore
Robe in the land of Brunhild her lieges evermore;
And we should meet the lady array'd at least as well;
So shame will ne'er await us, when men our tale shall tell."

XXVII

Then answer'd good King Gunther, " I'll to my mother dear,
That she and her fair maidens ere we for Issland steer,
May furnish us with raiment in full and copious store,
Which we may wear with honor the stately queen before."

XXVIII

Hagan, the Knight of Trony, then spake in courtly wise,
" Why would you ask your mother such service to devise?
If only your fair sister our purpose understood,
She's in all arts so skilful, the clothes would needs be good."

XXIX

Then sent he to his sister, that he'd to her repair,
And with him only Siegfried; ere they could thither fare,
Kriemhild in choicest vesture her beauty had array'd;
Little did their coming displease the gentle maid.

XXX

And deck'd too were her women as them best became.
Now were at hand the princess; straight the queenly dame,
As she beheld them coming, rose stately from her seat,
And went the noble stranger and her brother, too, to greet.

XXXI

" Welcome to my brother and to his comrade dear,"
Said the graceful maiden, " your news I fain would hear.
Tell me what brings you hither, what deeds are now to do;
Let me know how fares it, noble knights, with you."

XXXII

Then spake the royal Gunther, " Dame, I will tell my care.
We must with lofty courage a proud adventure dare.
We would hence a-wooing far over seas away;
For such a journey need we apparel rich and gay."

XXXIII

" Now sit thee down, dear brother, and tell me frank and free,"
Said the royal maiden, " who these dames may be,
Whom you would go a-courting in a distant land."
Both the chosen warriors then took she by the hand.

XXXIV

'Anon she both led thither where before she sat
On rich embroider'd cushions (I can vouch for that),
O'erwrought with goodly figures well rais'd in glitt'ring gold.
There they with the fair lady might gentle converse hold.

XXXV

Many a glance of rapture, many a longing look,
As there talk'd the lovers, either gave and took.
He in his heart enshrin'd her; she was to him as life.
Thereafter lovely Kriemhild became bold Siegfried's wife.

XXXVI

Then said to her King Gunther, " Right noble sister mine,
What I wish can never be but with help of thine.
We'll to the land of Brunhild to take our pastime there,
And must before the lady princely apparel wear."

XXXVII

Then spake the queen in answer, " Right loving brother mine,
If ought I can will profit whatever end of thine,
Depend on me to do it; thou'lt find me ready still.
If any aught denied thee, 'twould please thy Kriemhild ill.

XXXVIII

" Noble knight, thou should'st not, as doubting, ask and pray,
But, as my lord and master, command, and I'll obey.
Thou'lt find me, whatsoever thou hast in heart to do,
Not more a loving sister than a servant true."

XXXIX

" Dearest sister Kriemhild, we must wear costly weed,
And therewith to equip us thy snowy hand we need,
And let thy maids their utmost upon the same bestow,
For sure my purpos'd journey never will I forego."

XL

Then spoke the noble virgin, " Mark now what I say;
I've silk myself in plenty; on shields, as best you may,
Precious stones bid bring us to work the clothes withal.
Gunther and eke Siegfried bade bring them at her call.

XLI

" And who are the companions," ask'd the royal maid,
" Who you to court will follow thus gorgeously array'd?"
" We're four in all," he answer'd; " two of my men beside,
Dankwart and Hagan, with us to court will ride.

XLII

" And, dame, mark well, I pray thee, what I have yet to say.
Let each be well provided three changes every day,
And for four days successive, and all be of the best;
So back shall I wend homeward no scorn'd, dishonor'd guest."

XLIII

So with kind dismissal away the warriors strode.
Then quick the fair queen summon'd from bowers where they
    abode
Thirty maids, her brother's purpose to fulfil,
Who in works of the needle were the chief for craft and skill.

XLIV

Silks from far Arabia, white as driven snow,
And others from Zazamanc, green as grass doth grow,
They deck'd with stones full precious; Kriemhild the garments
    plann'd,
And cut them to just measure with her own lily hand.

XLV

Of the hides of foreign fishes were linings finely wrought;
Such then were seen but rarely, and choice and precious thought;
Fine silk was sewn above them to suit the wearers well.
Now of the rich apparel hear me fresh marvels tell.

XLVI

From the land of Morocco and from the Libyan coast
The best silk and the finest e'er worn and valued most
By kin of mightiest princes, of such had they good store.
Well Kriemhild show'd the favor that she the wearers bore.

XLVII

E'er since the chiefs were purpos'd the martial queen to win,
In their sight was precious the goodly ermelin
With coal-black spots besprinkled on whiter ground than snow,
E'en now the pride of warriors at every festal show.

XLVIII

Many a stone full precious gleam'd from Arabian gold;
That the women were not idle, scarcely need be told.
Within seven weeks, now ready was the vesture bright,
Ready too the weapons of each death-daring knight.

XLIX

Now when all was ready, by the Rhine you might mark
Built with skill and labor a stout though little bark,
Wherein a-down the river to sea they were to go.
To the noble maidens their toil brought mickle woe.

L

When now 'twas told the champions, that the vesture gay,
Which they should carry with them, was ready for the way,
And that nought impeded their firmly-fixed design,
No longer would they tarry by the banks of Rhine.

LI

So to their loving comrades a messenger was sent,
That they the goodly vesture might see before they went,
If it for the warriors too short were or too long.
Much thanks they gave the women when found was nothing
          wrong.

LII

Whomever met the warriors, all could not but admire;
In all the world not any had seen such fair attire;
At Brunhild's court 'twould surely become the wearers well.
Of better knightly garments not a tongue could tell.

LIII

Much thank'd was each fair seamstress for her successful toil.
Meanwhile, on point of parting for a far and dangerous soil,
The warriors would of Kriemhild take leave in knightly wise,
Whereat moist clouds of sorrow bedimm'd her sunbright eyes.

LIV

Said she, " Why thus, dear brother, to foreign regions run?
Stay here and woo another; that were far better done,
Than on so dire a venture to set your fame and life.
You'll find among our neighbors a fairer, nobler wife."

LV

Their hearts, I ween, foreboded what thence was to befall.
How spake they ever boldly, sore wept they one and all.
Their tears the gold o'ermoisten'd that on their breasts they
    wore;
So thick they from their eyelids stream'd down upon the floor.

LVI

" To you," said she, " Sir Siegfried, at least may I resign,
To your faith, to your honor, this brother dear of mine,
That no mischance beset him in Brunhild's fatal land."
Straight promis'd he the maiden, and clasp'd her clay-cold hand.

LVII

Then spake the loving champion, " Long as I have life,
Dismiss the cares, fair lady, that in your breast are rife.
I'll bring you back your brother safe and well a-pay'd;
Take that for sure and certain."   Low bow'd the thankful maid.

LVIII

Their golden-color'd bucklers were borne down to the strand,
With all their costly vesture, and softly led in hand
Were their high-mettled chargers; they now would straight
    depart.
Then many an eye was weeping, and throbbing many a heart.

LIX

Fair maids stood at the windows as they hoisted sail;
The bark rock'd, and the canvas flapp'd with the fresh'ning gale.
So on the Rhine were seated the comrades frank and free;
Then said good King Gunther, " Who shall our steersman
    be? "

LX

" I will," said noble Siegfried; " well all our course I know,
Well the tides and currents how they shift and flow.
Trust me, good knight, to pilot you and your company."
So from Worms and Rhineland they parted joyously.

LXI

With that straight seiz'd Sir Siegfried a pole that lay at hand,
And with strong effort straining 'gan push off from the strand;
Gunther himself as ready took in hand an oar;
So fell off the vessel and parted from the shore.

LXII

They had on board rich viands, thereto good store of wine,
The best that could be met with e'en on the banks of Rhine.
Their steeds in easy quarters stood tractable and still;
The level bark ran smoothly; nothing with them went ill.

LXIII

Their sail swell'd to the breezes, the ropes were stretch'd and
    tight;
Miles they ran full twenty ere the fall of night.
With a fair wind to seaward down dropp'd the gallant crew.
Their dames had cause long after their high emprise to rue.

LXIV

By the twelfth bright morning, as we have heard it told,
The winds the bark had wafted with the warriors bold
Towards Isenstein, a fortress in the martial maiden's land;
'Twas only known to Siegfried of all th' adventurous band.

LXV

Soon as saw King Gunther, wondering as well he might,
The far-stretch'd coast, and castles frowning from every height,
"Look! friend," said he, "Sir Siegfried, if thou know'st,
    declare,
Whose are all these fair castles, and all this land as fair.

LXVI

"In all my life, assure thee, the simple truth to tell,
I never met with castles plann'd and built so well,
Anywhere soever, as here before us stand.
He must needs be mighty who took such work in hand."

LXVII

Thereto made answer Siegfried: " Well what you ask I know.
Brunhild's are all these castles, this land, so fair a show,
And Isenstein this fortress; 'tis true what now I say.
Here will you meet, Sir Gunther, many a fair dame to-day.

LXVIII

" I'll give you counsel, heroes! e'en as it seems me good;
Keep in one tale together; be this well understood.
To-day we must, as fits us, at Brunhild's court be seen;
We must be wise and wary when we stand before the queen.

LXIX

" When we behold the fair one and all her train around,
Let but this single story in all your mouths be found.
That Gunther is my master, and I am but his man;
To give him all his longing you'll find no surer plan.

LXX

" 'Tis not so much for thy sake, I own, such part I bear,
As for thy sister Kriemhild's, the fairest of the fair.
She to me is ever as my own soul and life.
Fain do I such low service to win her for my wife."

LXXI

With one accord they promis'd to do as he desir'd;
None through pride or envy to thwart his wish aspir'd.
So all took Siegfried's counsel, and sure it brought them good
Soon after, when King Gunther before Queen Brunhild stood.

SEVENTH ADVENTURE

HOW GUNTHER WON BRUNHILD

I

MEANWHILE the bark had drifted unto the shore so high
Beneath the high-tower'd castle, that the king could spy
Many a maiden standing at every window there;
That all to him were strangers, was what he ill could bear.

II

Forthwith he ask'd of Siegfried, his valiant friend and true,
" Know you ought of these maidens, whom here we have in view
Down upon us looking, though not, methinks, in scorn?
Whoe'er their lord they're surely high-minded and high-born."

III

Him answer'd Siegfried smiling, " Now you may closely spy,
And tell me of these damsels which pleases best your eye,
And which, if you could win her, you for your own would hold."
" So will I," answer'd Gunther the hardy knight and bold.

IV

" One see I at a window stand in a snow-white vest;
Around her all are lovely, but she's far loveliest.
Her have mine eyes selected; Sir Siegfried, on my life,
If I can only gain her, that maid shall be my wife."

V

"In all this world of beauty thine eyes have chosen well;
That maid's the noble Brunhild, at once so fair and fell,
She, who thy heart bewilders, she, who enchants thy sight."
Her every act and gesture to Gunther was delight.

VI

Then bade the queen her maidens from the windows go;
Them it ill befitted to stand a sight and show
For the rude eyes of strangers; they bow'd to her behest,
But what next did the ladies, we since have heard confest.

VII

They rob'd them in their richest to meet the strangers' gaze;
Such, ever since were women, were ever women's ways.
Through every chink and loophole was levelled many an eye
At the unweeting champions, through love to peep and pry.

VIII

There were but four together who came into the land.
The far-renowned Siegfried led a horse in hand.
This Brunhild at a window mark'd with heedful eye.
As lord of such a liegeman was Gunther valued high.

IX

Then humbly by the bridle he held the monarch's steed,
Huge of limb and puissant and of the purest breed,
Till in the royal saddle King Gunther proudly sat;
So serv'd him noble Siegfried, which he too soon forgat.

X

Then his own the warrior led from ship to shore;
He of a truth such service hath seldom done before,
As to stand at the stirrup, when another mounted steed.
Of all, close at the windows, the women took good heed.

XI

To look upon these champions was sure a glorious sight;
Their horses and their garments were both of snowy white,
And both match'd well together; each bore a polished shield,
Which, still as it was shaken, flash'd around the field.

XII

So forward rode they lordly to Brunhild's gorgeous hall:
Rich stones beset their saddles, their pöitrals, light and small,
Had golden bells down-hanging that tinkled as they went.
On mov'd the proud companions led by their bold intent.

XIII

Their spears were newly sharpen'd as if to meet a foe;
Their swords of choicest temper down to the spur hung low;
Keen of edge was each one, and thereto broad of blade.
All this was mark'd by Brunhild, the chief-defying maid.

XIV

With them together Dankwart and Hagan came ashore
'Tis told us in old stories that these two warriors wore
Apparel of the richest, but raven-black of hue;
Ponderous were their bucklers, broad and bright and new.

XV

Stones from the land of India display'd each gorgeous guest,
That ever gleam'd and glitter'd in the flutt'ring vest.
They left their bark unguarded beside the dashing wave,
And straight on to the fortress rode the champions brave.

XVI

Six and eighty turrets saw they there in all,
Three palaces wide-stretching, and the fairest hall
Of the purest marble (never was grass so green),
Where with her fair damsels sat the fairer queen.

XVII

Unlock'd was straight the castle, the gates flew open wide;
Up in haste to meet them Brunhild's liegemen hied,
And bade the strangers welcome to their lady's land,
And took his horse from each one and the shield from every
		hand.

XVIII

A chamberlain then bespoke them: " Be pleas'd to give us now
Your swords and glitt'ring breastplates." " That can we ne'er
		allow,"
Hagan of Trony answer'd, " our arms ourselves will bear."
The custom of the castle then Siegfried 'gan declare.

XIX

" 'Tis the use of this castle, as I can well attest,
That never warlike weapons should there be borne by guest.
'Twere best to keep the custom; let th' arms aside be laid."
Hagan, Gunther's liegeman, unwillingly obey'd.

XX

Wine to the guests they offer'd, and goodly welcome gave;
Then might you see apparel'd in princely raiment brave
Many a stately warrior, on to court that pass'd,
And many a glance of wonder upon the strangers cast.

XXI

Meanwhile to fair Queen Brunhild one came and made report,
That certain foreign warriors had come unto her court
In sumptuous apparel, wafted upon the flood.
Then thus began to question the maiden fair and good:

XXII

" Now tell me," said the princess, " and let the truth be shown,
Who are these haughty champions from foreign shores
    unknown,
Whom there I see so stately standing in rich array,
And on what hard adventure have they hither found their way?"

XXIII

One of her court then answer'd, " I can aver, fair queen,
Of this stout troop of warriors none have I ever seen,
Save one, who's much like Siegfried, if I may trust my eyes.
Him well receive and welcome; this is what I advise.

XXIV

" The next of the companions, he of the lofty mien,
If his power match his person, is some great king, I ween,
And rules with mighty sceptre broad and princely lands.
See, how among his comrades so lordly there he stands!

XXV

" The third of the companions—a low'ring brow has he,
And yet, fair queen, you rarely a manlier form may see.
Note but his fiery glances, how quick around they dart!
Firm is, I ween, his courage, and pitiless his heart.

XXVI

" The fourth knight is the youngest, he with the downy cheek,
So maidenly in manner, so modest and so meek.
How gentle all his bearing! how soft his lovely cheer!
Yet we all should rue it, should wrong be done him here.

XXVII

" How mild soe'er his manner, how fair soe'er his frame,
Cause would he give for weeping to many a high-born dame,
Were he once stirr'd to anger; sure he's a warrior grim,
Train'd in all knightly practice, bold of heart and strong of
    limb."

XXVIII

Then spake the royal Brunhild, "Bring me my vesture straight,
If far-renowned Siegfried aspire to be my mate,
And is hither come to woo me, on the cast is set his life;
I fear him not so deeply, as to yield me for his wife."

XXIX

Soon was the lovely Brunhild in her robes array'd.
With their lovely mistress went many a lovely maid,
Better than a hundred, and all were richly dight;
For the noble strangers, I trow, a goodly sight.

XXX

With them of Brunhild's warriors advanc'd a chosen band,
Better than five hundred, each bearing sword in hand,
The very flower of Issland; 'twas a fair yet fearful scene.
The strangers rose undaunted as near them came the queen.

XXXI

Soon as the noble Siegfried met the fair Brunhild's sight,
In her modest manner she thus bespoke the knight.
"You're welcome, good Sir Siegfried; now, if it please you, show
What cause has brought you hither; that I would gladly know."

XXXII

"A thousand thanks, Dame Brunhild," the warrior made reply,
"That thou hast deign'd to greet me before my better nigh,
Before this noble hero, to whom I must give place.
He is my lord and master; his rather be the grace.

XXXIII

"On the Rhine is his kingdom; what should I further say?
Through love of thee, fair lady, we've sail'd this weary way.
He is resolv'd to woo thee whatever thence betide;
So now betimes bethink thee; he'll ne'er renounce his bride.

XXXIV

"The monarch's name is Gunther, a rich and mighty king;
This will alone content him, thee to the Rhine to bring.
For thee above the billows with him I've hither run;
Had he not been my master, this would I ne'er have done."

XXXV

Said she, " If he's thy master, and thou, it seems, his man,
Let him my games encounter, and win me if he can.
If he in all be victor, his wedded wife am I.
If I in one surpass him, he and you all shall die."

XXXVI

Then spake the Knight of Trony, " Come, lady, let us see
The games that you propose us ; ere you the conqueress be,
Of my good lord King Gunther, hard must you toil, I ween.
He trusts with full assurance to win so fair a queen."

XXXVII

" He must cast the stone beyond me, and after it must leap,
Then with me shoot the javelin ; too quick a pace you keep ;
Stop, and awhile consider, and reckon well the cost,"
The warrioress made answer, " ere life and fame be lost."

XXXVIII

Siegfried in a moment to the monarch went ;
To the queen he bade him tell his whole intent.
" Never fear the future, cast all cares away ;
My trains shall keep you harmless, do Brunhild what she may."

XXXIX

Then spake the royal Gunther, " Fair queen, all queens before,
Now say what you command us, and, were it yet e'en more,
For the sake of your beauty, be sure, I'd all abide.
My head I'll lose, and willing, if you be not my bride."

XL

These words of good King Gunther when heard the royal
    dame,
She bade bring on the contest as her well became.
Straight call'd she for her harness, wherewith she fought in
    field,
And her golden breastplate, and her mighty shield.

XLI

Then a silken surcoat on the stern maiden drew,
Which in all her battles steel had cut never through,
Of stuff from furthest Lybia; fair on her limbs it lay;
With richest lace 'twas border'd, that cast a gleaming ray.

XLII

Meanwhile upon the strangers her threatening eyes were bent;
Hagan there stood with Dankwart in anxious discontent,
How it might fall their master in silence pondering still.
Thought they, " This fatal journey will bring us all to ill."

XLIII

The while, ere yet observer his absence could remark,
Sudden the nimble Siegfried stepp'd to the little bark,
Where from a secret corner his cloud-cloak forth he took.
And slipp'd into it deftly while none was there to look.

XLIV

Back in haste return'd he; there many a knight he saw,
Where for the sports Queen Brunhild was laying down the law.
So went he on in secret, and mov'd among the crowd,
Himself unseen, all-seeing, such power was in his shroud!

XLV

The ring was mark'd out ready for the deadly fray,
And many a chief selected as umpires of the day,
Seven hundred all in harness with order'd weapons fair,
To judge with truth the contest which they should note with
        care.

XLVI

There too was come fair Brunhild; arm'd might you see her
        stand,
As though resolv'd to champion all kings for all their land.
She bore on her silk surcoat gold spangles light and thin,
That quivering gave sweet glimpses of her fair snowy skin.

XLVII

Then came on her followers, and forward to the field
Of ruddy gold far-sparkling bore a mighty shield,
Thick, and broad, and weighty, with studs of steel o'erlaid,
The which was wont in battle to wield the martial maid.

XLVIII

As thong to that huge buckler a gorgeous band there lay;
Precious stones beset it as green as grass in May;
With varying hues it glitter'd against the glittering gold.
Who would woo its wielder must be boldest of the bold.

XLIX

Beneath its folds enormous three spans thick was the shield,
If all be true they tell us, that Brunhild bore in field.
Of steel and gold compacted all gorgeously it glow'd.
Four chamberlains, that bore it, stagger'd beneath the load.

L

Grimly smil'd Sir Hagan, Trony's champion strong,
And mutter'd as he mark'd it trail'd heavily along,
" How now, my lord King Gunther? who thinks to 'scape
    with life?
This love of yours and lady—'faith she's the devil's wife."

LI

Hear yet more of the vesture worn by the haughty dame;
From Azagouc resplendent her silken surcoat came
Of all-surpassing richness, that from about her shone
The eye-bedimming lustre of many a precious stone.

LII

Then to the maid was carried heavily and slow
A strong well-sharpen'd jav'lin, which she ever us'd to throw,
Huge and of weight enormous, fit for so strong a queen,
Cutting deep and deadly with its edges keen.

LIII

To form the mighty spear-head a wondrous work was done;
Three weights of iron and better were welded into one;
The same three men of Brunhild's scarcely along could bring;
Whereat deeply ponder'd the stout Burgundian king.

LIV

To himself thus thought he, " What have I not to fear?
The devil himself could scarcely 'scape from such danger clear.
In sooth, if I were only in safety by the Rhine,
Long might remain this maiden free from all suit of mine."

LV

So thinking luckless Gunther his love repented sore;
Forthwith to him only his weapons pages bore,
And now stood clad the monarch in arms of mighty cost.
Hagan through sheer vexation, his wits had nearly lost.

LVI

On this Hagan's brother undaunted Dankwart spake,
"Would we had ne'er sail'd hither for this fell maiden's sake!
Once we pass'd for warriors; sure we have cause to rue,
Ingloriously thus dying, and by a woman too;

LVII

"Full bitterly it irks me to have come into this land.
Had but my brother Hagan his weapons in his hand,
And I with mine were by him, proud Brunhild's chivalry,
For all their overweening, would hold their heads less high.

LVIII

"Ay, by my faith, no longer should their pride be borne;
Had I oaths a thousand to peace and friendship sworn,
Ere I'd see thus before me my dearest master die,
Fair as she is, this maiden a dreary corse should lie."

LIX

"Ay," said his brother Hagan, "we well could quit this land
As free as we came hither, were but our arms at hand.
Each with his breast in harness, his good sword by his side,
Sure we should lower a little this gentle lady's pride."

LX

Well heard the noble maiden the warrior's words the while,
And looking o'er her shoulder said with a scornful smile,
"As he thinks himself so mighty, I'll not deny a guest;
Take they their arms and armor, and do as seems them best.

LXI

"Be they naked and defenceless, or sheath'd in armor sheen,
To me it nothing matters," said the haughty queen.
"Fear'd yet I never mortal, and, spite of yon stern brow
And all the strength of Gunther, I fear as little now."

LXII

Soon as their swords were giv'n them, and arm'd was either
    knight,
The cheek of dauntless Dankwart redden'd with delight.
" Now let them sport as likes them, nothing," said he, " care I;
Safe is noble Gunther with us in armor by."

LXIII

Then was the strength of Brunhild to each beholder shown.
Into the ring by th' effort of panting knights a stone
Was borne of weight enormous, massy and large and round.
It strain'd twelve brawny champions to heave it to the ground.

LXIV

This would she cast at all times when she had hurl'd the spear;
The sight of bold Burgundians fill'd with care and fear.
Quoth Hagan, " She's a darling to lie by Gunther's side.
Better the foul fiend take her to serve him as a bride."

LXV

Her sleeve back turn'd the maiden, and bar'd her arm of snow,
Her heavy shield she handled, and brandished to and fro
High o'er her head the jav'lin; thus began the strife.
Bold as they were, the strangers each trembled for his life;

LXVI

And had not then to help him come Siegfried to his side,
At once by that grim maiden had good King Gunther died.
Unseen up went he to him, unseen he touch'd his hand.
His trains bewilder'd Gunther was slow to understand.

LXVII

" Who was it just now touch'd me?" thought he and star'd
    around
To see who could be near him; not a soul he found.
Said th' other, " I am Siegfried, thy trusty friend and true;
Be not in fear a moment for all the queen can do."

LXVIII

Said he, " Off with the buckler and give it me to bear;
Now, what I shall advise thee, mark with thy closest care.
Be it thine to make the gestures, and mine the work to do."
Glad man was then King Gunther, when he his helpmate knew.

LXIX

" But all my trains keep secret; thus for us both 'twere best;
Else this o'erweening maiden, be sure, will never rest,
Till her grudge against thee to full effect she bring.
See where she stands to face thee so sternly in the ring! "

LXX

With all her strength the jav'lin the forceful maiden threw.
It came upon the buckler massy, broad and new,
That in his hand unshaken, the son of Sieglind bore.
Sparks from the steel came streaming, as if the breeze before.

LXXI

Right through the groaning buckler the spear tempestuous
    broke;
Fire from the mail-links sparkled beneath the thund'ring
    stroke.
Those two mighty champions stagger'd from side to side;
But for the wondrous cloud-cloak both on the spot had died.

LXXII

From the mouth of Siegfried burst the gushing blood;
Soon he again sprung forward; straight snatch'd the hero good
The spear that through his buckler she just had hurl'd amain,
And sent it at its mistress in thunder back again.

LXXIII

Thought he " 'Twere sure a pity so fair a maid to slay; "
So he revers'd the jav'lin, and turn'd the point away;
Yet, with the butt-end foremost, so forceful was the throw,
That the sore-smitten damsel totter'd to and fro.

LXXIV

From her mail fire sparkled as driven before the blast;
With such huge strength the jav'lin by Sieglind's son was cast,
That 'gainst the furious impulse she could no longer stand.
A stroke so sturdy never could come from Gunther's hand.

LXXV

Up in a trice she started, and straight her silence broke,
" Noble knight, Sir Gunther, thank thee for the stroke."
She thought 'twas Gunther's manhood had laid her on the lea;
No! 'twas not he had fell'd her, but a mightier far than he.

LXXVI

Then turn'd aside the maiden; angry was her mood;
On high the stone she lifted rugged and round and rude,
And brandish'd it with fury, and far before her flung,
Then bounded quick behind it, that loud her armor rung.

LXXVII

Twelve fathoms' length or better the mighty mass was thrown,
But the maiden bounded further than the stone.
To where the stone was lying Siegfried fleetly flew;
Gunther did but lift it, th' Unseen it was, who threw.

LXXVIII

Bold, tall and strong was Siegfried, the first all knights among;
He threw the stone far further, behind it further sprung.
His wondrous arts had made him so more than mortal strong,
That with him as he bounded, he bore the king along.

LXXIX

The leap was seen of all men, there lay as plain the stone,
But seen was no one near it, save Gunther all alone.
Brunhild was red with anger, quick came her panting breath
Siegfried had rescued Gunther that day from certain death.

LXXX

Then all aloud fair Brunhild bespake her courtier band,
Seeing in the ring at distance unharm'd her wooer stand,
" Hither, my men and kinsmen: low to my better bow;
I am no more your mistress; you're Gunther's liegemen now."

LXXXI

Down cast the noble warriors their weapons hastily,
And lowly kneel'd to Gunther the King of Burgundy.
To him as to their sovran was kingly homage done,
Whose manhood, as they fancied, the mighty match had won.

LXXXII

He fair the chiefs saluted bending with gracious look;
Then by the hand the maiden her conquering suitor took,
And granted him to govern the land with sovran sway;
Whereat the warlike nobles were joyous all and gay.

LXXXIII

Forthwith the noble Gunther she begg'd with her to go
Into her royal palace; soon as 'twas order'd so,
To his knights her servants such friendly court 'gan make,
That Hagan e'en and Dankwart could it but kindly take.

LXXXIV

Wise was the nimble Siegfried; he left them there a space,
And slily took the cloud-cloak back to its hiding-place,
Return'd then in an instant, where sat the ladies fair,
And straight, his fraud to cover, bespoke King Gunther there.

LXXXV

"Why dally, gracious master? why not the games begin,
Which by the queen, to prove you, have here appointed been?
Come, let us see the contest, and mark each knightly stroke."
As though he had seen nothing, the crafty warrior spoke.

LXXXVI

"Why how can this have happen'd," said the o'ermaster'd
    queen,
"That, as it seems, Sir Siegfried, the games you have not seen,
Which 'gainst me good King Gunther has gain'd with won-
    drous might?"
The word then up took Hagan, the stern Burgundian knight;

LXXXVII

" Our minds indeed you troubled, our hopes o'er-clouded dark;
Meanwhile the good Knight Siegfried was busy at the bark,
While the Lord of Rhineland the game against you won;
Thus," said King Gunther's liegeman, " he knows not what
    was done."

LXXXVIII

" Well pleas'd am I," said Siegfried, " that one so proud and
    bold
At length has found a master in one of mortal mold,
And has been taught submission by this good lord of mine.
Now must you, noble maiden, hence follow us to the Rhine."

LXXXIX

Thereto replied the damsel, " It cannot yet be so;
First must my men and kinsmen th' intended journey know;
To bring my friends together, besides, 't were surely fit.
T' were wrong, methinks, so lightly my lands and all to quit."

XC

So messengers in hurry through all the country went;
To liegemen, and to kinsmen, and all her friends she sent.
To Isenstein she begg'd them to come without delay.
And bade give all in plenty rich gifts and garments gay.

XCI

Daily to Brunhild's castle early they rode and late,
In troops from all sides flocking, and all in martial state.
" Ay! ay!" said frowning Hagan, " ill have we done, I fear;
Surely 't will be our ruin to wait this gathering here.

XCII

" Let her strength be only here together brought
(And of the queen's intentions we little know or naught),
If so her passion wills it, we're lost at once, I trow.
In sooth this dainty damsel was born to work us woe."

XCIII

Then spoke the valiant Siegfried, " I'll undertake for all;
Trust me, what now you look for, that shall ne'er befall.
Safe and sound to keep you, I'll hither bring a crew
Of fierce, selected champions, of whom ye never knew.

XCIV

" Inquire not of my journey; I hence must instant fare;
The little while I'm absent God have you in his care.
Again here will I quickly with a thousand men be found,
The bravest and the boldest that ever moved on ground,"

XCV

" Be sure then not to linger," the anxious Gunther said,
" For we meanwhile shall ever be longing for your aid."
" In a few days you'll see me at hand for your defence,
And tell," said he, " fair Brunhild, that you have sent me
    hence."

EIGHTH ADVENTURE

HOW SIEGFRIED CAME TO THE NIBELUNGERS.

I

THENCE in his cloud-cloak Siegfried descended to the strand;
There he found a shallop, that close lay to the land;
Unseen the bark he boarded, that from the harbor pass'd
Moved by the son of Siegmund, as though before the blast.

II

The steersman could see no man; yet the vessel flew
Beneath the strokes of Siegfried the yielding water through.
'T was a tempest thought they, that drove it furious on.
No! 't was the strength of Siegfried, fair Sieglind's peerless
    son.

III

All that day they were running, and all the night the same,
Then to a famous country of mighty power they came,
Days' journey full a hundred stretching far away,
The Nibelungers' country, where his hard-won treasure lay.

IV

Alone the champion landed in a meadow wide;
Straight to the shore securely the little bark he tied,
And then went to a castle seated upon a hill,
To ask for food and shelter as weary travellers will.

V

All found he barr'd and bolted as near the walls he drew;
Men both life and honor kept then as now they do.
The stranger all impatient began a thundering din
At the well fasten'd portal. There found he close within

VI

A huge earth-shaking giant, the castle set to guard,
Who with his weapons by him kept ever watch and ward.
" Who beats the gate so stoutly? " the yawning monster ask'd;
His voice, as he gave answer, the crafty hero mask'd,

VII

And said, " I am a warrior; open me the gate;
I'm wroth with lazy losels who make their betters wait,
While they on down are snoring as if they'd never wake."
It irk'd the burly porter that thus the stranger spake.

VIII

Now had the fearless giant all his weapons donn'd,
Bound on his head his helmet, and in his monstrous hond
A shield unmeasur'd taken; open the gate he threw,
And his teeth grimly gnashing at Siegfried fiercely flew.

IX

" How could he dare to call up men of mettle so? "
With that he let fly at him many a wind-swift blow,
That the noble stranger put back with wary fence.
At last upheav'd the giant an iron bar immense,

X

And his firm shield-band shatter'd; scarce could the warrior
        stand,
He fear'd, though for a moment, grim death was close at hand,
With his enormous weapon the porter smote so sore,
Yet for his dauntless bearing he lov'd him all the more.

XI

With the mighty conflict the castle rung around;
To th' hall of the Nibelungers reach'd the stunning sound.
At length the vanquish'd porter he bound with conquering
        hand.
Far and wide flew the tidings through the Nibelungers' land.

XII

While in the dubious combat they both were struggling still,
Albric the wild dwarf heard it far through the hollow hill.
Straight he donn'd his armor, and thither running found
The noble guest victorious, and the panting giant bound.

XIII

A stout dwarf was Albric, and bold as well as stout;
With helm and mail securely he was arm'd throughout;
A golden scourge full heavy in his hand he swung.
Straight ran he to the rescue, and fierce on Siegfried sprung.

XIV

Seven ponderous knobs from th' handle hung, each one by its
        thong;
With these the dwarf kept pounding so sturdy and so strong,
That he split the shield of Siegfried to the centre from the rim,
And put the dauntless champion in care for life or limb.

XV

Away he threw his buckler broken all and smash'd;
His long well-temper'd weapon into its sheath he dash'd,
To spare his own dependents his virtue mov'd him still,
And to his heart sore went it his chamberlain to kill.

XVI

With mighty hands undaunted in on the dwarf he ran;
By the beard he caught him, that age-hoary man,
He dragg'd him, and he shook him, his rage on him he wreak'd,
And handled him so roughly, that loud for pain he shriek'd.

XVII

Loud cries the dwarf o'ermaster'd, "Spare me and leave me
    free,
And could I ever servant save to one hero be,
To whom I've sworn allegiance as long as I have breath,"
Said the crafty Albric, "you would I serve to death."

XVIII

Then bound was writhing Albric as the giant just before;
The nervous grasp of Siegfried pinch'd him and pain'd him
    sore.
Then thus the dwarf address'd him; "Be pleas'd your name to
    tell."
Said he, "My name is Siegfried; I thought you knew me well."

XIX

"Well's me for these good tidings," Albric the dwarf replied.
"Now know I all your merit, which I by proof have tried.
High rule o'er all this country well you deserve to bear;
I'll do whate'er you bid me; the vanquish'd only spare."

XX

Then said the noble Siegfried: "You must hence with speed,
And bring me, of the warriors that best we have at need,
A thousand Nibelungers; them I here must view;
No evil shall befall you, if this you truly do."

XXI

The dwarf and eke the giant the champion straight unbound;
Then ran at once swift Albric where he the warriors found.
The slumbering Nibelungers he wak'd with eager care,
Saying, "Up, up, ye heroes! ye must to Siegfried fare."

XXII

Up from their beds they started, and instant ready made,
Nimble knights a thousand richly all array'd.
So flock'd they quick, where waiting they saw Sir Siegfried
    stand;
Then was there goodly greeting with word of mouth and clasp
    of hand.

XXIII

Straight lit was many a taper; then the spiced draught he
    drank;
His friends, who came so quickly, he did not spare to thank.
He said, " You hence must instant far o'er the wave with me."
He found them for th' adventure as ready as could be.

XXIV

Full thirty hundred warriors were come at his request;
From these he chose a thousand the bravest and the best.
Helmets and other armor were brought for all the band,
For he resolv'd to lead them e'en to Queen Brunhild's land.

XXV

He said, " Good knights adventurous, to my words give heed.
At the proud court of Brunhild our richest robes will need.
There many a lovely lady will look on every guest,
So we must all array us in our choicest and our best."

XXVI

" How? " said a beardless novice, " that sure can never be.
How can be lodg'd together so many knights as we?
Where could they find them victual? where could they find them
    vests?
Never could thirty kingdoms keep such a crowd of guests."

XXVII

You've heard of Siegfried's riches; well could he all afford
With a kingdom to supply him, and Niblung's endless hoard.
Rich gifts were in profusion to all his knights assign'd.
Much as he drain'd the treasure, as much remain'd behind.

XXVIII

Early upon a morning in haste they parted thence.
What prowest warriors Siegfried brought to his friend's
    defence!
Their armor darted radiance, their horses toss'd the foam.
Well equipp'd and knightly came they to Brunhild's home.

XXIX

At the windows standing look'd out the maidens gay.
Then cried their royal mistress, " Can any of you say,
What strangers there far-floating over the billows go?
Their canvas they are spreading whiter far than snow."

XXX

Then spake the king of Rhineland, " They're men of mine,
    fair dame,
Whom I left not distant, when late I hither came;
Since, I have bid them join me, and now you see them here."
The noble guests receiv'd them with good and friendly cheer.

XXXI

Then might they see bold Siegfried, array'd in robes of pride,
Aboard a bark high standing, and many a chief beside.
Then said the queen to Gunther, " Sir king, what now shall I?
Greet the guests advancing, or that grace deny? "

XXXII

Said he, " To meet them, lady, forth from your palace go,
That, if you're glad to see them, the same they well may know."
Then did the queen, as Gunther had said him seem'd the best,
And Siegfried in her greeting distinguish'd from the rest.

XXXIII

They found them fitting quarters, and took their arms in
    charge;
The guests were now so many, that they were ill at large,
Such troops of friends and strangers flock'd in on every side.
So the bold Burgundians now would homeward ride.

XXXIV

Then said the fair Queen Brunhild, " Him for my friend I'd
    hold,
Who'd help me to distribute my silver and my gold
Among my guests and Gunther's; no little store have I."
Bold Giselher's bold liegeman Dankwart straight made reply:

XXXV

" Right noble queen and gracious, trust but your keys with me;
Your wealth I'll so distribute, all shall contented be,
And as to blame or damage, let that be mine alone."
That he was free and liberal, that made he clearly shown.

XXXVI

Soon as Hagan's brother had the keys in hand,
Gold began and silver to run away like sand.
If one a mark requested, gifts had he shower'd so rife,
That home might go the poorest merry and rich for life.

XXXVII

By th' hundred pounds together he gave uncounted out.
Crowds in gorgeous vesture were stalking all about,
Who ne'er had worn such splendor, and scarce so much as
    seen.
They told the tale to Brunhild; it fretted sore the queen.

XXXVIII

Straight she spoke to Gunther, " Sir king, I've cause to grieve.
Your treasurer, I fear me, scarce a rag will leave
Of all my choice apparel, my last gold piece he'll spend.
Would somebody would stop it! I'd ever be his friend.

XXXIX

" He wastes so, he must fancy in his wayward will
I've sent for death to fetch me, but wealth I can use still,
And what my father left me can waste myself, I ween."
Treasurer so free-handed never yet had queen.

XL

Then spake the knight of Trony, " Lady, you must be told,
The king of Rhine has plenty of raiment and of gold,
And can of both so lavish, that we may well dispense
With all fair Brunhild's vesture, nor need bring any hence."

XLI

" Nay, for my love," said Brunhild, " with gold and silken vests
Let me from all my treasure fill twenty travelling chests,
That when we come together in Burgundy to live,
This hand may still have something royally to give."

XLII

Forthwith her chests were loaded with many a precious stone.
She o'er the work appointed a treasurer of her own.
She would not trust to Dankwart, Giselher's thriftless man.
Gunther thereat and Hagan both to laugh began.

XLIII

Then spake the martial maiden, " Whom shall I leave my
    lands?
This first must here be settled by our united hands."
The noble monarch answer'd, " Who most is in your grace,
Him will we leave behind us to govern in our place."

XLIV

One of her near relations was standing by the maid;
He was her mother's brother; to him she turn'd and said,
" Take to your charge my castles, and with them all my land,
Till I or else King Gunther give otherwise command."

XLV

She chose a thousand heroes from all her chivalry
To the Rhine's distant borders to bear her company,
With the thousand champions from the Nibelungers' land.
They bown'd them for their journey, and hasten'd to the strand.

XLVI

Six-and-eighty women, a hundred maidens too
She took with her from Issland; fair were they all to view.
They now no longer tarried; they ready were to go.
From those they left behind them what tears began to flow!

XLVII

In manner as became her she left her native ground;
She kiss'd her nearest kindred who weeping stood around.
So with fair dismissal they came down to the shore.
To her father's country the maid return'd no more.

XLVIII

With sound of all sweet music they floated on their way;
From morn to eve was nothing but change of sport and play;
The soft sea-breeze they wish'd for was fluttering in their sail;
Yet for that voyage how many were yet to weep and wail!

XLIX

But still her lord deferring with maidenly delay
Brunhild reserv'd one pleasure to the fair wedding-day,
When home to Worms together the king and queenly dame,
Full flown with mirth and rapture, with all their heroes came.

NINTH ADVENTURE

HOW SIEGFRIED WAS SENT TO WORMS

I

NINE days had now the travellers been faring on their way,
When spake the knight of Trony, " Give ear to what I say.
We're slow to send the tidings of our adventure home;
Your messengers already should to Burgundy have come."

II

To him replied King Gunther, " What you have said, is true,
And none should be so ready this very task to do,
As e'en yourself, friend Hagan; so ride unto my land;
None, I am sure, can better proclaim that we're at hand."

III

Thereto gave answer Hagan, " Such duty suits not me;
Let me tend the chambers, and linger still at sea;
Or I'll stay with the women, and their wardrobe keep,
Till to the Rhine we bring them safe from the blustering deep.

IV

From Siegfried ask a journey of such a weary length,
For he can well perform it with his surpassing strength,
And, should he e'en refuse it, him to consent you'll move,
If you but beseech him for your sister's love."

V

Straight sent he for the warrior; he came as soon as found;
Said Gunther, " Now we're coming home to my native ground,
Fain would I give quick notice by some sure friend of mine
To my sister and my mother that we approach the Rhine.

VI

" This I entreat you, Siegfried; now do what I desire,
And I'll in full requite you, whatever you require."
But ne'er consented Siegfried, the never-conquer'd man,
Till in another fashion the king to ask began.

VII

Said he, " Nay, gentle Siegfried, do but this journey take,
Not for my sake only, but for my sister's sake.
You'll oblige fair Kriemhild in this as well as me."
When so implor'd was Siegfried, ready at once was he.

VIII

" Whate'er you will, command me; let naught be left unsaid;
I will gladly do it for the lovely maid.
How can I refuse her who my heart has won?
For her, whate'er your pleasure, tell it, and it is done."

IX

" Tell then my mother Uta, the rich and mighty queen,
We in our dangerous journey right fortunate have been.
Inform my loving brothers, we have succeeded well;
And to my court and kindred the same glad tidings tell.

X

" From my gentle sister nothing conceal'd must be;
Bear her the kindest greeting from Brunhild and from me.
Proclaim to every liegeman and every anxious friend,
That my heart's lingering longing I've brought to happy end.

XI

" And tell my loving nephew, the knight of Metz, Ortwine,
That seats he bid in order be rais'd along the Rhine.
And do my other kinsmen to wit, both most and least,
That I will hold with Brunhild a gorgeous marriage-feast.

XII

" Fail not to tell my sister, that soon as she shall hear
That I, returning homeward, with all my guests are near,
She well receive so kindly the lady of my heart,
And love and service ever shall be her's on Gunther's part."

XIII

Leave then took Sir Siegfried of Gunther's haughty dame,
And of her fair attendants, as him well became,
And for the Rhine departed; never could there be
In all this world a better messenger than he.

XIV

With four-and-twenty warriors to Worms he hotly sped;
King Gunther came not with him, when this abroad was spread,
The hearts of all his servants were wrung with mortal pain;
They fear'd, the might of Brunhild their noble king had slain.

XV

Down sprang all from their horses; their thoughts were proud
     and high;
Straight the good young King Giselher ran to them hastily,
And Gernot his bold brother, soon spoke he, having eyed
The troop, and miss'd King Gunther from noble Siegfried's
     side,

XVI

" Welcome to Worms, Sir Siegfried; tell us what news you
     bring,
What have you done with Gunther, our brother and our king?
I fear me, we have lost him, fierce Brunhild was too strong;
So has his lofty passion brought us but loss and wrong."

XVII

" Away with fear and sorrow! to you and all his kin
My comrade sends his greeting; a conqu'ror he has been,
And safe and sound I left him; from him despatch'd I come
To bring the gladsome tidings to all his friends at home.

XVIII

" You also must contrive it, for your's the task should be,
How I may straight your mother and your fair sister see,
To carry them the message that I receiv'd so late
From Gunther and from Brunhild; both are in best estate."

XIX

Young Giselher then answer'd; " Go straight to them and tell
The tale you're charg'd to carry; 'twill please my sister well.
Fear for the fate of Gunther is heavy on her breast.
I'll vouch, that with the maiden you'll prove a welcome guest."

XX

Then spake the noble Siegfried, " Whatever I can do
To serve her, she shall find me a willing friend and true.
Who now will tell the ladies, that I an audience crave?"
Giselher took the message, the high-born youth and brave.

XXI

To the lovely maiden and the stately dame
Spoke the youthful warrior, when to their sight he came,
" Siegfried is come with tidings for our hearing meant;
Him my brother Gunther hither to the Rhine has sent.

XXII

" By him he's charged to tell us, how stands it with the king;
Permit him then his message hither to court to bring;
Whate'er befell in Issland from him you'll truly know."
E'en thus the noble ladies still harbor'd fear and woe.

XXIII

Up for their robes they started, and each herself array'd,
Then bade Sir Siegfried enter; he willingly obey'd,
For much he long'd to see them; then, ere the warrior spoke,
Silence the blushing Kriemhild with friendly accents broke.

XXIV

" Welcome, Sir Siegfried, hither, boldest of the bold!
Where is my brother Gunther? straight be your tidings told.
I fear me, we have lost him, and here are left forlorn.
Woe's me unhappy maiden, that ever I was born!"

XXV

Then spake the warrior, " Give me the guerdon of good news;
You weep for sake of weeping; so you fair ladies use.
I left him safe and hearty; of this assure you well.
He to you both has sent me the joyful tale to tell.

XXVI

" To you, as best beseems him, with gracious kind intent
He and his bride their service, right noble queen, have sent.
And soon will both come hither, so dry your idle tears."
For many a day such gladness had never bless'd her ears.

XXVII

Straight with her snow-white apron she wip'd her tears away,
And dried her eyes from weeping; then, once more fresh and
     gay
Began to thank the envoy for his happy tale,
That ended her deep sorrow and heart-consuming wail.

XXVIII

She bade the knight be seated; nothing loth was he;
Then spake the lovely maiden; " 'Twere no small joy for me,
Could I with gold reward you for what you just have said;
But you're for that too wealthy; take my good will instead."

XXIX

" Were I," replied the champion, " the lord of thirty lands
Still would I take with pleasure a gift from your fair hands."
Straight said the modest damsel, " Then you shall be content."
So for the costly guerdon her treasurer she sent.

XXX

Four and twenty bracelets she gave him for his fee,
Each set with stones full precious; yet so proud was he,
That he would not keep them, but gave the jewels rare
To her lovely maidens, whom he found in waiting there.

XXXI

And then her mother greeted the noble warrior well.
" To both of you," replied he, " I yet have more to tell,
Whereof the king entreats you, and, if you but attend
To what he asks so dearly, he'll ever be your friend.

XXXII

" His noble guests, he begs you, and his beauteous bride
Receive with kindly welcome, and forth to meet them ride
On the strand before the city.   To you has sent the king
This true and gracious message, which I as truly bring."

XXXIII

" I'm ready at his bidding," the lovely maid replied,
" Whate'er I can to serve him shall never be denied,
So heartily and truly his pleasure will I do."
Then her love-kindled blushes glow'd a deeper hue.

XXXIV

Never prince's envoy a heartier welcome won;
Had she dar'd to kiss him, fain would she so have done.
In loving wise he parted from th' unwilling maid.
Forthwith the bold Burgundians did as the warrior bade.

XXXV

Sindolt and Hunoldt and Rumolt the good knight
Early and late were stirring as briskly as they might;
They rais'd the seats in order, such duty well they knew;
From side to side unwearied the royal servant flew.

XXXVI

Ortwine of Metz and Gary, King Gunther's liegemen bold,
The marriage feast, that forthwith their master was to hold,
Proclaim'd to friends and neighbors; against the festal day
Every noble maiden prepar'd her best array.

XXXVII

Adorn'd was all the palace, and richly every wall
Bedeck'd to grace the strangers; King Gunther's spacious hall
By the skill was furbish'd of many a foreign man;
With merriment and pastime the royal feast began.

XXXVIII

By every road advancing with ceaseless press and din
Flock'd all to Worms together the royal brethren's kin,
Summon'd by hasty message to meet th' expected guests.
Then from the folded wrappers were ta'en the well-stor'd vests.

XXXIX

Sudden spread the tidings, that now one might espy
Brunhild's friends advancing; straight rose a press and cry
'Mong the Burgundian thousands, that waiting stood around.
Ah! what men of valor on either side were found!

XL

Then spake the lovely Kriemhild, " My maidens fair and free,
Who at this reception must bear your part with me,
Let each her choice apparel search out from secret chest;
The matrons too I'd counsel to prank them in their best."

XLI

Then forward came the warriors, and straight th' attendants
    told
To bring forth sumptuous saddles o'erlaid with ruddy gold,
Whereon might ride the ladies from Worms unto the Rhine.
Never was better horse-gear beheld, nor work so fine.

XLII

What store of gold resplendent about the palfreys shone!
From their gorgeous bridles gleam'd many a precious stone.
Richly gilt side-saddles with trappings of bright hue
Were brought forth for the ladies, who gladden'd at the view.

XLIII

Caparison'd all richly with silken housings rare
Was led a gentle palfrey for every lady there.
Each steed a silken pöitral (the silk was of the best
That e'er was spun or fashion'd) had hanging at his breast.

XLIV

Six and eighty ladies, each a married dame,
With hairy bounds in fillets to lovely Kriemhild came,
Each radiant in her beauty, each in rich garb array'd;
Thither too in full adornment came many a blooming maid.

XLV

Fifty and four, the fairest and of the best report
Of all, whose beauty honor'd the proud Burgundian court,
Went forth with glittering laces above their flaxen hair.
What Gunther had requested, all did with all their care.

XLVI

The best stuffs and the richest, that e'er were found, they bore
To meet the stranger heroes; every robe they wore
With care and skill was chosen to suit their lovely hue.
He were a fool, who'd murmur at one of that fair crew.

XLVII

Of sable and of ermine many a robe was there,
And many a sparkling bracelet o'er silken raiment fair
The wrists and arms encircled of many a lady gay.
The care, the taste, the splendor none might at full display.

XLVIII

Many a glittering girdle, that rich and long down hung,
By many a snowy finger o'er gorgeous weed was flung
To bind the far-brought garment of stuff from Araby.
Each noble damsel's bosom swell'd high and joyfully.

XLIX

In the tighten'd bodice many a smiling maid
Had laced herself full deftly; each were ill appaid
Did not her bright complexion outshine her vesture sheen.
A train so fair and graceful now has ne'er a queen.

L

Soon as the lovely ladies for the joyful day
Had donn'd their rich apparel, forthwith, in meet array,
Of bold high-mettled warriors a mighty force drew near,
With many a shield bright-beaming and many an ashen spear.

TENTH ADVENTURE

HOW BRUNHILD WAS RECEIVED AT WORMS

I

BEYOND the Rhine King Gunther, with many a well-arm'd
rank
And all his guests about him, rode toward the river's bank;
You might see by the bridle led forward many a maid.
Those, who were to receive them, were ready all array'd.

II

Soon as the men of Issland came to the shallops down,
And eke the Nibelungers, lieges of Siegfried's crown,
To th' other shore they hasten'd (busy was ever hand)
Where them the friends of Gunther awaited on the strand.

III

Now hear, by wealthy Uta what a device was wrought.
Down with her from the castle a virgin train she brought,
That rode where she was riding in that procession bright;
So many a maid acquainted became with many a knight.

IV

Kriemhild by the bridle the Margrave Gary led.
But only from the castle; then forward Siegfried sped,
And did that gentle service; fair was the blushing maid;
Full well for that thereafter the warrior she repaid.

V

Ortwine, the fearless champion, rode by Dame Uta's rein;
Knights and maids together follow'd, a social train.
At such a stately meeting, all must confess, I ween,
So many lovely ladies were ne'er together seen.

VI

Full many a famous champion careering you might spy
(Ill there were sloth and idless) beneath fair Kriemhild's eye
E'en to the place of landing; by knights of fair renown
There many a high-born lady from steed was lifted down.

VII

The king was now come over, and many a worthy guest.
Ah! before the ladies what spears were laid in rest!
How many went in shivers at every hurtling close!
Buckler clashed with buckler; ah! what a din arose!

VIII

Now might you see the ladies fast by the haven stand.
With his guests King Gunther debark'd upon the strand,
In his hand soft leading the martial maiden fair.
Then each on each flash'd radiance, rich robes and jewels rare.

IX

With that the smiling Kriemhild forth stepp'd a little space,
And Brunhild and her meiny greeted with gentle grace.
Each with snowy fingers back her headband drew,
And either kiss'd the other lovingly and true.

X

Then spoke in courteous manner Kriemhild the fair and free,
" In this our land, dear Brunhild, ever welcome be
To me and to my mother and all by us allow'd
For faithful friends and liegemen." Then each to th' other
      bow'd.

XI

Next to greet Dame Brunhild approach'd Dame Uta too;
Oft she and oft her daughter their arms around her threw,
And on her sweet mouth lavish'd many a loving kiss.
Never was known a welcome so kind and frank as this.

XII

Soon as Brunhild's women were all come to the strand,
Many a courtly warrior took by her lily hand
A lady fair, and gently her mincing steps upstay'd.
Now before Dame Brunhild stood many a noble maid.

XIII

'Twas long before the greeting had gone through all the list.
On either part in plenty rosy mouths were kiss'd.
Still the two fair princesses were standing side by side,
A pair with love and rapture by longing warriors ey'd.

XIV

What erst had been but rumor, was now made clear to sight,
That naught had yet been witness'd so beautiful and bright
As those two lovely damsels; 'twas plain to every eye;
None the slightest blemish in either form could spy.

XV

Whoever look'd on women with but the sight for guide,
Such for her faultless beauty prais'd Gunther's stately bride;
But those, whose thoughts went deeper, and div'd into the mind,
Maintain'd that gentle Kriemhild left Brunhild far behind.

XVI

Now met the dames and damsels in friendly converse free;
Fair robes and fairer beauties were there in store to see;
Many a silk pavilion and many a gorgous tent
The plain before the city fill'd in its whole extent.

XVII

King Gunther's kinsmen ceas'd not to press to that fair show.
And now was begg'd each princess from the sun to go
Close by, with their attendants, where shade was overhead.
By bold Burgundian warriors thither were they led.

XVIII

Then clomb to horse the heroes, and scour'd the sounding field;
Many a joust was practis'd with order'd spear and shield;
Right well were prov'd the champions, and o'er the trampled
    plain,
As though the land were burning, the dust curl'd up amain.

XIX

So all before the ladies display'd their skill and force.
Nor doubt I that Sir Siegfried rode many a knightly course
Before the rich pavilions, and, ever as he sped,
His thousand Nibelungers, a stately squadron, led.

XX

Then came the knight of Trony by the good king's command;
In friendly wise he parted the jousters on the strand,
For fear the dust, now thick'ning, the ladies might molest.
Him with ready reverence obey'd each gentle guest.

XXI

Then spake the noble Gernot, " Let each now rest his steed
Till the air be cooler, 't will then be our's to lead
These lovely ladies homeward e'en to the palace wide.
So keep yourselves all ready till it please the king to ride."

XXII

Thus ended was the tourney, and now the warriors went
To join the dames and damsels beneath each lofty tent,
And there in gentle converse their grace and favor sought;
So flew the hours in pastime till of riding home they thought.

XXIII

Now as drew on the twilight, when cooler grew the air
And the sun was setting, they would not linger there,
But up rose lords and ladies to seek the castle high;
Many a fair dame was cherish'd by many a love-lit eye.

XXIV

So on the fair they waited as from good knights is due.
Then hardy squires, hot-spurring before the nobles' view,
After the country's custom rode for the prize of weed
As far as to the palace, where sprung the king from steed.

XXV

There too the proud queens parted, each taking thence her way.
Dame Uta and her daughter with their handmaids gay
Into a spacious chamber both together went.
There might you hear on all sides the sound of merriment.

XXVI

In hall the seats were order'd; the king would instant hie
With all his guests to table; beside him you might spy
His lovely bride, Queen Brunhild; her royal crown she wore
There in King Gunther's country; so rich was none before.

XXVII

Seats were there plac'd unnumber'd with tables broad and good,
As is to us reported, full heap'd with costly food.
How little there was wanted that passes for the best!
There with the king was seated full many a noble guest.

XXVIII

The chamberlains of Gunther in ewers of ruddy gold
Brought to the guests the water; should you be ever told
That at a prince's table service was better done,
'T were labor lost to say so, 't would be believ'd by none.

XXIX

Then, ere the Lord of Rhineland touch'd the water bright,
Up to him, as befitted, went Siegfried the good knight,
And brought to him remembrance the promise made him there,
Ere yet afar in Issland he look'd on Brunhild fair.

XXX

Said he, " You must remember what swore to me your hand,
That, soon as Lady Brunhild were come into this land,
To me you'd give your sister; your oaths now where are they?
On me throughout your journey much toil and travail lay."

XXXI

" Well did you to remind me," the noble king replied,
" By what my hand has promis'd, I ever will abide,
And in this thing to serve you will do my best, my all."
Then sent he to beg Kriemhild to come into the hall.

XXXII

Straight to the hall came Kriemhild begirt with many a maid,
When from the lofty staircase young Giselher thus said,
" Send back your maidens, Kriemhild, this business is your own;
On this the king our brother would speak with you alone."

XXXIII

Then forward led was Kriemhild, as Gunther gave command,
Where stood the king, and round him from many a prince's land
Were noble knights unnumber'd; at once all silence kept;
At that same instant Brunhild had just to table stepp'd.

XXXIV

Thence came it, she knew nothing of what was to be done.
Then to his gather'd kinsmen spoke Dankrat's royal son,
" Help me to move my sister Siegfried for lord to take."
" Such match," they all gave answer, " with honor she may
   make."

XXXV

Then spoke the king to Kriemhild, " Sister, I ask of thee
From an oath to set me by thy kindness free.
Thee to a knight I promis'd ; if thou become his bride,
Thou'lt do the will of Gunther, and show thy love beside."

XXXVI

Then spake the noble maiden, " Dearest brother mine,
It needed not to ask me ; whate'er command be thine,
I'll willingly perform it ; so now, for thy sake,
Whom thou for husband giv'st me, fain I, my lord, will take."

XXXVII

With love and eke with pleasure redden'd Siegfried's hue ;
At once to lady Kriemhild he pledg'd his service true.
They bade them stand together in the courtly circle bright.
And ask'd her if for husband she took that lofty knight.

XXXVIII

In modest maiden fashion she blush'd a little space,
But such was Siegfried's fortune and his earnest grace,
That not altogether could she deny her hand.
Then her for wife acknowledg'd the noble King of Netherland.

XXXIX

He thus to her affianc'd, and to him the maid,
Straight round the long-sought damsel in blushing grace array'd
His arms with soft emotion th' enamour'd warrior threw,
And kiss'd the high-born princess before that glitt'ring crew.

XL

On this up broke the circle, and to the feast they came ;
There high-advanc'd Sir Siegfried sat with his spoused dame
Right opposite to Gunther ; him many a vassal true
Serv'd at the board, and near him his Nibelungers drew.

XLI

High at the feast sat Gunther and Brunhild by his side,
But woe was then the maiden, when Kriemhild she espied
Sitting by valiant Siegfried ; she straight began to weep,
And her bright visage darken'd with shame and passion deep.

XLII

Then spake the king of Rhineland, "What ails you, lady mine,
That your fair eyes are clouded, and dimm'd their beamy shine?
You rather should be merry, now that my liegemen true,
My country and my castles are subject all to you."

XLIII

"Good cause have I for weeping," return'd the angry fair;
"My very heart is bleeding to see your sister there
Beside your lowly vassal sitting so content;
Never shall I cease weeping for such disparagement."

XLIV

Then spake the noble Gunther, "No more of this, I pray;
You shall be told the reason on some other day,
Wherefore I to Siegfried my sister gave for wife.
May she with him ever lead a happy life!"

XLV

Quoth she, "I sorrow ever for her grace and beauty's sake;
Had I a place to fly to, my flight I hence would take,
For lie will I never, King Gunther, by your side,
Ere I know why Kriemhild is given for Siegfried's bride."

XLVI

Thereto made answer Gunther, "That will I tell you straight.
Know, I have given my sister to no unequal mate:
A mighty king is Siegfried, and unto him belong,
As to their rightful sovran, broad lands and castles strong."

XLVII

Whatever he could tell her, her gloomy mood she kept.
Then from the board to tilting many a warrior stepp'd.
The noise of their tourney made all the castle ring.
His guests and their amusements wearied sore the king.

XLVIII

Thought he, 't were softer lying in a marriage bed.
Then, to beguile annoyance, his longing heart he fed
With thought of future pleasure from love of such a bride,
And ever Lady Brunhild tenderly he ey'd.

XLIX

The guests were bid give over the tourney, as was meet.
The king with his fair lady would now to bed retreat.
Before the hall's grand staircase Kriemhild and Brunhild met;
Bitterness or rancor on neither side was yet.

L

Then came th' attendant courtiers; they linger'd now for
    nought;
Chamberlains well-apparel'd the tapers to them brought.
The followers then divided of the rulers twain;
Then might you see with Siegfried go forth a num'rous train.

LI

And now the royal bridegrooms both to their chambers came;
Each thought with fond caresses to woo his gentle dame,
That both might, as befitted, in love's soft bonds agree.
The night to noble Siegfried was sweet as sweet might be.

LII

There lay he so delighted by lovely Kriemhild's side,
And found such modest graces in his virgin bride,
That he came to love her more than his proper life.
Well she deserv'd his passion as a virtuous wife.

LIII

What more ensued between them it needs not here to say.
Now you must hear the story, how King Gunther lay
By the fair Lady Brunhild. Many a loving swain
By his loving helpmate with more content has lain.

LIV

The crowd had now all vanish'd, that tended them before;
Of the marriage chamber fast was made the door.
He deem'd he now was shortly to win his lovely mate,
But for that happy moment he yet had long to wait.

LV

In robe of whitest linen to the bed she pass'd;
Then thought the noble Gunther, " Now all is mine at last,
That I ever long'd for before in all my life."
Needs must be blest a husband in such a charming wife.

LVI

And now with trembling fingers 'gan he shroud the light,
Then went with glad expectance where lay his lady bright,
And laid him down beside her, nor small the joy he knew,
When his arms around her tenderly he threw.

LVII

Fain would he have caress'd her as gentle love inspires,
Had but the wayward maiden granted his desires;
But there he sore was troubled, so fiercely storm'd his mate.
He look'd for fond affection, and met with deadly hate.

LVIII

" Sir knight," said she, " it suits not—you'd better leave me free
From all your present purpose—it must and shall not be.
A maid still will I keep me (think well the matter o'er)
Till I am told that story."   This fretted Gunther sore.

LIX

Then for her love he struggled e'en till her robe he rent;
With that, up caught the maiden a cord with fell intent
(About her waist she wore it, strong was the same and tough),
And wrought her lord and master shame and wrong enough.

LX

The feet and hands of Gunther she tied together all,
Then to a nail she bore him, and hung him 'gainst the wall,
And bade him not disturb her, nor breathe of love a breath.
Sure from the doughty damsel he all but met his death.

LXI

Humbly to beg began he, who master should have been,
" Untie me, I beseech you, right fair and noble queen !
For your love will I never against your pleasure try,
And ne'er again will venture so close to you to lie."

LXII

How he far'd she reck'd not, while soft herself she lay;
So all night long he dangled perforce till break of day,
When through the chamber window the light began to peep.
That night was Gunther's pleasure as little as his sleep.

LXIII

" Now tell me, good Sir Gunther," began the froward fair,
" Would you like your servants to find you hanging there
The bondsman of a woman? that were a royal view!"
The noble knight made answer, " No credit 'twere to you;

LXIV

" And in good sooth," he added, " 'twere honor none to me;
So of your kindness, lady, be pleas'd to set me free;
Since my love's so distasteful, fear neither harm nor hurt.
Not so much as a finger of mine shall touch your skirt."

LXV

With that the maid unbound him; free stood he, but half dead;
Then all aghast and trembling back totter'd to the bed,
And there lay down so distant that her night-dress fair
He seldom touch'd, if ever; e'en that she well could spare.

LXVI

Now in came their attendants; by these in hand were borne
New gaudy robes in plenty to suit the marriage morn.
Downcast he stood and moody amidst the smiling band.
Their mirth seem'd out of season to the monarch of the land.

LXVII

After the good old custom that in that land was kept,
King Gunther and Queen Brunhild forth from the chamber
    stepp'd,
And hied them to the minster, where the mass was sung.
Thither too came Sir Siegfried; then rose a press the crowd
    among.

LXVIII

Each circumstance of honor for monarch and his mate
Was there in order ready, both crown and robe of state.
Then consecrated were they, and, soon as that was o'er,
With jewel'd crowns conspicuous stood all the goodly four.

LXIX

Bold squires with sword were girded six hundred at the least
In honor of the rulers at that high marriage feast.
Was nought but mirth and joyance in Burgundy to hear,
And swashing of the buckler, and clattering of the spear.

LXX

There too at many a window sat many a laughing maid,
To view in mimic terror far-flashing arms display'd;
But still, whate'er was toward, kept the sad king apart,
With gloom upon his visage and anguish at his heart.

LXXI

'Twixt him and good Sir Siegfried what difference of mood!
Well guess'd what so him fretted that noble knight and good.
To the king he betook him, and ask'd in accents low,
"Last night how far'd it with you? this be pleas'd to let me
    know."

LXXII

Then to his guest said Gunther, "Shame, alas! and strife,
My friend, I home have brought me in my wayward wife.
No sooner came I near her, what did she do, but tie
My feet and hands together, and hang me up on high?

LXXIII

"There like a ball I dangled all night till break of day
Before she would unbind me;—how soft the while she lay!
I breathe my plaint in friendship to thy secret ear."
Then spake the noble Siegfried; "It irks me, what I hear;

LXXIV

"Yet you shall soon be master; lay fear and sorrow by;
This night I'll so contrive it, that close to you she'll lie.
And never more your pleasure with froward freaks delay."
At this from all his troubles wax'd Gunther blithe and gay.

LXXV

"Look at my wrists and fingers swoln with her cursed bands;
She squeez'd them so, I felt me a baby in her hands.
Under each nail forth started the blood beneath her grasp.
As for my life, I thought it e'en then at the last gasp."

LXXVI

Thereto replied Sir Siegfried, "All will again come right;
We two were most unequal in fortune yesternight.
To me thy sister Kriemhild is dear as is my life.
Now must Dame Brunhild also be made a loving wife.

LXXVII

" I will this night," he added, " into your chamber creep,
Envelop'd in my cloud-cloak, in silence still and deep,
That no man may have cunning to guess the trick I'll play;
So send, each to his lodging, your chamberlains away.

LXXVIII

"The tapers I'll extinguish that your pages bear,
And this shall give you notice that I have enter'd there,
Ready and glad to serve you; I'll force her to obey
This night her lord and master, or down my life will lay."

LXXIX

" Spare but to act the husband, and do whate'er thy will
With my loving helpmate, I shall not take it ill,"
Replied the angry monarch; " e'en shouldst thou take her life,
I should not die of sorrow; sooth she's a fearful wife."

LXXX

" Trust me in this," said Siegfried, " my word I'll pledge to thee
That I'll ne'er seek to woo her; thy sister is to me
Beyond all other women that ever met my view."
The king with full affiance took Siegfried's words for true.

LXXXI

The knights were busy tilting with good success or ill;
Straight 'twas bidd'n the tourney should all be hush'd and still,
For to the hall was coming either royal bride.
Then chamberlains advancing bade stand the crowd aside.

LXXXII

The court was clear'd of horses, the crowd no longer seen;
Then forth a reverend bishop led either lofty queen
To where the kings were seated, and tables richly stor'd.
Them many a man of worship follow'd to the board.

LXXXIII

There by his stately consort sat Gunther well appaid,
Musing upon the promise to him by Siegfried made.
That single day to Gunther seem'd thirty days at least.
On the love of Brunhild he thought throughout the feast.

LXXXIV

Scarcely could wait the monarch till from the board they rose;
Brunhild and lovely Kriemhild were summon'd to repose,
Each in her several chamber; ah! what a crowd was seen
Of young and active warriors before each stately queen!

LXXXV

Siegfried was fondly seated by his gentle bride;
Her slender snowy fingers, as leant they side by side
With his were softly toying; in midst of her caress
Suddenly he vanish'd—how, she could not guess.

LXXXVI

As with him she was playing, she miss'd him quite and clean.
"Ha!" to his wilder'd courtiers cried out the wilder'd queen,
"Where's the king? what portent is this? what semblance fine?
He was but now beside me—who snatch'd his hand from
    mine?"

LXXXVII

She stopp'd in speechless wonder; he quick had slipp'd away
To where with lights th' attendants stood ranged in meet array,
And straight 'gan dout the tapers held by the pages there;
Full well that it was Siegfried was Gunther then aware.

LXXXVIII

He knew what was to follow, so sent forth every one,
Maid and dame, from the chamber; then soon as this was done,
With his own hand impatient the king lock'd fast the door,
And two strong bolts of iron shot for assurance more.

LXXXIX

Behind the flowing hangings the lights he huddled all;
Forthwith began a pastime (as could not but befall)
Betwixt the sinewy Siegfried and the maiden fair.
At once with joy and sorrow stood Gunther trembling there.

XC

Adown Sir Siegfried laid him close by the damsel bright.
Said she, "Beware, Sir Gunther, remember yesternight;
Be pleas'd not to disturb me; wake not my wrath anew,
Or at my hands your folly you bitterly shall rue."

XCI

He breath'd no breath in answer, but still was as could be.
Well by the ear knew Gunther, although he could not see,
That nothing pass'd between them the jealous to displease.
Never in couch or chamber dwelt there so little ease.

XCII

Like Gunther he demean'd him, fals mimic of the true;
Around th' unloving damsel his loveless arms he threw.
Him from the bed with fury against a bench she flung.
His head fell on a footstool so hard, that loud it rung.

XCIII

With all his might upstarted again th' undaunted man;
He'd try his fortune better; a struggle stern began,
When he essay'd to quell her; long was his toil and sore;
Such strife, I ween, will never be waged by woman more.

XCIV

As still he would not quit her, up sprung the frenzied fair;
" Sir knight, it ill becomes you a lady's dress to tear.
These are Burgundian manners! but dear it shall be paid;
I'll bring you soon to smart for it," exclaim'd the stormy maid.

XCV

Her arms around the warrior she scrupled not to fling,
And forthwith thought to bind him as though it were the king,
That of the bed sole mistress in quiet she might sleep.
For her injur'd night-dress took she vengeance deep.

XCVI

What booted then his manhood well prov'd in many a fight,
When that heroic maiden put forth her mastering might?
Him by main force she lifted in spite of all he tried,
And 'gainst a press she jamm'd him that stood the bed beside.

XCVII

" Ah!" thought the panting champion, " should I now lose my
    life
By this outrageous damsel, hereafter every wife
Will claim at home the mastery, and, scorning meek accord
And womanly submission, will lord it o'er her lord."

XCVIII

The king with fear and trembling heard all that there befell.
Shame gave fresh strength to Siegfried; furious he wax'd and
    fell.
He with redoubled puissance once more the maid oppos'd.
Fearful was the struggle as he with Brunhild clos'd.

XCIX

Down still she strove to keep him, but wrath and natural might
Combin'd so wrought within him, that soon in her despite
His feet the knight recover'd; sore was his toil, I trow;
In the darken'd chamber they hurtled to and fro.

C

Ill too at ease was Gunther between the struggling pair.
Full oft to shift he needed as strove they here and there.
A wonder 'twas (so fiercely wrestled the mighty foes)
That either 'scap'd uninjured from that tempestuous close.

CI

Sore rued his fate the monarch beset with twofold care;
Still fear'd he most lest Siegfried should chance to perish there,
For now the puissant damsel had all but ta'en his life.
Had he but dar'd, he'd gladly have help'd him in the strife.

CII

Long time endur'd the contest, nor ever seem'd to slack,
Till 'gainst the bed with fury he dash'd the maiden back.
How fierce soe'er she struggled, faint and more faint she grew;
Then many a shrewd suspicion shot Gunther's bosom through.

CIII

Still ever as he listen'd, he thought 'twas wondrous long.
Just then the hands of Siegfried she squeez'd so fierce and
    strong,
That blood from the nails started; the warrior tingled sore;
But soon he brought the damsel to give her frenzy o'er,

CIV

And change her furious passions for love and duty meek.
Whatever pass'd heard Gunther, though daring not to speak
Against the bed he drove her, that loud she shriek'd for pain.
Cruel was her torture from Siegfried's mastering main.

CV

Then grasp'd she at her girdle, and strove to bind her foe,
When down the warrior hurl'd her with such a forceful throw,
That crack'd each bone and sinew; that clos'd at once the
    strife;
The fainting maid submitted to live King Gunther's wife.

CVI

Said she, " Right noble ruler, vouchsafe my life to spare;
Whatever I've offended, my duty shall repair.
I'll meet thy noble passion; my love with thine shall vie.
That thou canst tame a woman, none better knows than I."

CVII

Then up arose Sir Siegfried from where Dame Brunhild lay;
Upon the floor he left her, and noiseless went his way;
But first from her fine finger a golden ring he drew
So gently, that the maiden nothing felt or knew.

CVIII

He took, besides her girdle, with which her lord she tied;
I know not if he did so from triumph and from pride;
To his wife he gave it, a gift that mischief wrought.
Meanwhile the maid and monarch love both together brought.

CIX

They met with mutual passion as man and wife became;
Her stormy rage was soften'd; she was no more the same;
Weak she grew and feeble as in his arms she lay;
All her former puissance flitted straight away.

CX

And now was she no stronger than any dame beside.
Fearless, unfear'd, her husband caress'd his duteous bride.
Why act again the rebel? what boot could thus be won?
So much with alter'd Brunhild King Gunther's love had done.

CXI

How lovingly and fondly he by his lady lay
Till the rosy morning led on the laughing day!
Sir Siegfried thence departed, and back in silence came,
Where tenderly receiv'd him a fair and gentle dame.

CXII

Her questions he evaded, though much to know she sought;
Long time too kept he from her the gifts that he had brought,
Till, crown'd, in his own country she reign'd, his royal bride;
Of all, he else could grant her, how little he denied!

CXIII

Far merrier in the morning than he before had been
Appear'd the good King Gunther; the change with joy was
    seen
By every faithful vassal, and every foreign guest,
Whom he had home invited and feasted with the best.

CXIV

The sumptuous festal lasted e'en to the fourteenth day,
The while was heard unceasing the sound of mirth and play,
That in the crowd of pleasures the wilder'd guests were lost.
Unmatch'd was Gunther's splendor and boundless was his cost.

CXV

By the good king's order, to many a warrior bold
His kinsmen in his honor gave robes and ruddy gold,
And steeds and store of silver, and so their wants supplied,
That not a stranger was there but parted satisfied.

CXVI

As well good King Siegfried, the knight of Netherland,
And his thousand champions their robes, with liberal hand,
And all they had brought thither alike were pleas'd to give,
Fair steeds and costly trappings; like nobles they knew how
    to live.

CXVII

To those, whose thoughts were homeward, the hours seem'd
    all too long,
Ere the rich gifts were lavish'd among the gladsome throng.
Never before was party dismiss'd in merrier plight.
So the high feast concluded; thence off rode many a knight.

ELEVENTH ADVENTURE

HOW SIEGFRIED BROUGHT HIS WIFE HOME

I

THE festal hall was silent, and parted every guest,
When thus the son of Siegmund his loving friends address'd.
" We too must make us ready, and forthwith home return."
Glad was his noble consort her lord's resolve to learn.

II

She thus bespake the warrior, " Since we are home to fare,
Of over-haste in parting, I beg thee, well beware.
First should of right my brethren with me the lands divide."
Sir Siegfried heard with sorrow these words from his fair
    bride.

III

Then came to him the princes, and thus spake all the three,
" Know that for you, King Siegfried, shall ever ready be
Our true and loving service, that e'en of death is vow'd."
To them for their fair promise the stately warrior bow'd.

IV

" With you too we are anxious," said Giselher the young,
" To part the lands and castles that to us all belong.
Of all the broad possessions, o'er which the rule we bear,
We'll yield to you and Kriemhild a good and ample share."

V

Soon as the son of Siegmund their loving offer heard,
To the noble princes this answer he preferr'd.
" God grant you long enjoyment of your possessions fair;
For me and my dear consort, our part wc well can spare.

VI

" The right that you allow her my wife may well lay down;
Henceforth in my country she'll wear the queenly crown,
And, should I live, be richer than any living wight.
In all things else, your bidding I'll do with all my might."

VII

" In th' heritage," said Kriemhild, " though you renounce our
    rights,
Not of so little value are our Burgundian knights;
Them might a king be happy to bring into his land,
And I my portion in them claim at each brother's hand."

VIII

" Take whom thou wilt, fair sister," Sir Gernot straight replied,
" No doubt you'll find abundance, who long with you to ride.
From thirty hundred vassals, each one a chosen man,
Take for thy train a thousand."   Kriemhild to send began

IX

First for Ortwine and Hagan, the noble knights and true,
If they and their bold kinsmen would Kriemhild serve and sue.
Thereat wax'd Hagan wrathful, and frowning thus 'gan say,
" Nor right nor power has Gunther to give us thus away.

X

" For followers and companions seek elsewhere if you will.
As for our Trony customs, sure you must know them still.
At court we guard our princes, nor from this duty swerve.
Thus here we serv'd them ever, thus will we ever serve."

XI

Thereto was made no answer; all on their journey thought.
Her noble train together the lady Kriemhild brought,
Two and thirty maidens and five hundred men.
Eckewart the Margrave follow'd Kriemhild then.

XII

Leave last by all was taken, both by squire and knight
And by dame and damsel, as fitting was and right.
With many a kiss they parted, and many a grasp of hand,
And so not ill contented they left King Gunther's land.

XIII

Far rode their loving kinsmen to bring them on their way;
Each night they found them quarters where'er it pleas'd them
        stay,
While they upon their journey through Gunther's country went
Then messengers were forthwith to old King Siegmund sent,

XIV

To him and to Dame Sieglind the hasty news to bear,
That his son was coming, and with him Kriemhild fair,
The daughter of Dame Uta, from Worms beyond the Rhine.
Ne'er to such welcome tidings did they their ears incline.

XV

"Ah! well is me," cried Siegmund, "that I this day have seen,
That here the lovely Kriemhild should move a crowned queen
My heritage high worship shall hence and honor gain;
Here too my son Siegfried himself a king shall reign."

XVI

Then gave the Lady Sieglind good store of velvet red;
Full weight of gold and silver shower'd she for newsman's
        bread.
Much at the gladsome tidings rejoic'd the royal dame.
Her train themselves apparel'd as nobles well became.

XVII

'Twas told her, who was coming with him into the land.
Then rais'd in haste were sittings, as Sieglind gave command,
Whither crown'd should march Sir Siegfried in front of all his
   train.
Then forth to meet the strangers rode Siegmund's knights
   amain.

XVIII

If e'er was heartier welcome than was receiv'd that day
In good King Siegmund's country, is more than I can say.
To meet the lovely Kriemhild the royal Sieglind came
With many a lovely lady and many a knight of fame.

XIX

A whole day's journey's distance, till came the guests in view.
Then no small toil and trouble both friends and strangers knew
To reach a spacious ortress (Xanten the name it bore),
Where royal crowns thereafter the bride and bridegroom wore.

XX

Sieglind and Siegmund wecom'd fair Kriemhild lovingly;
With laughing mouth full often they kiss'd her tenderly,
And did as much to Siegfried; far flown was all their care.
All the train of followers were warmly greeted there.

XXI

Straight were brought the strangers to Siegmund's royal hall.
Down there the lovely maidens from horse were lifted all
By knights and squires officious, and many a high-born man
To wait on beauteous ladies with courtly zeal began.

XXII

How great soe'er the splendor of Gunther's marriage day,
Yet here were fairer garments profusely given away
Than ever yet at festals had deck'd the warriors bold;
Of their surpassing richness marvels might be told.

XXIII

As sat they in high honor with all delights in store,
What bright gold-color'd raiment their joyful followers wore,
Laces and stones full precious fair work'd in vesture sheen!
Well were the guests entreated by the rich and noble queen.

XXIV

Then spake the good Sir Siegmund before his friends in hall,
" This my resolve declare I to Siegfried's kinsmen all,
That he before these warriors my royal crown shall wear."
The news gave full contentment to the Netherlanders there.

XXV

His crown and power he gave him and seisin of his land;
Their master then became he; zealous was every hand
To execute his judgments; his mouth pronounc'd the law.
To th' husband of fair Kriemhild all look'd with fear and awe.

XXVI

So liv'd he in high honor, a rightful monarch crown'd,
And giving righteous judgment till the tenth year came round,
When the fair queen his consort bore him at last an heir.
Glad were thereat his kinsmen, glad too the royal pair.

XXVII

Forthwith the babe was christen'd, and given him was a name
After his uncle Gunther; it could not bring him shame.
If he his kin resembled, in worth he would excel;
His parents, as became them, train'd up the infant well.

XXVIII

About the self-same season the Lady Sieglind died;
The child of noble Uta her vacant place supplied,
And to the power succeeded that Sieglind held before.
The people deeply sorrow'd that Sieglind was no more.

XXIX

Next messengers came posting the joyful news to bring,
How by the Rhine to Gunther, the stout Burgundian king,
A son was borne by Brunhild the once relentless dame;
He for the love of Siegfried receiv'd the hero's name.

XXX

With every care they train'd him; Gunther his father dear
Bade tutors the young infant in every virtue rear,
That, nurtur'd so to manhood, all worship he might win.
Ah! by mishap thereafter how lost he all his kin!

XXXI

Thenceforward at all seasons full many a tale was told,
How nobly and how knightly the wariors fierce and bold
Liv'd in the land of Siegmund; fame voiced their praises loud.
Like them lived good King Gunther and his noble kinsmen
    proud.

XXXII

Their land the Nibelungers of Siegfried held in fee;
None e'er of all his kindred so wealthy was as he.
His were the knights of Schilbung and both the brethren's store.
Through this the bold Sir Siegfried himself the loftier bore.

XXXIII

The richest of all treasures, that e'er was gain'd by knight,
Save by its former masters, he held by conqueror's right.
The same before a mountain by dint of sword he won.
To win it, many a champion his hand to death had done.

XXXIV

Huge was his wealth and worship; yet, had he naught
    possess'd
Whoever look'd upon him could not but have confess'd,
He was the prowest champion that e'er in saddle sat.
All trembled at his manhood; good cause had they for that.

TWELFTH ADVENTURE

HOW GUNTHER INVITED SIEGFRIED TO THE FESTIVAL

I

Still Gunther's consort ever thought with deep-musing care,
Why should the Lady Kriemhild herself so proudly bear?
And yet her husband Siegfried—what but our man is he?
And late but little service has yielded for his fee.

II

In her heart his thought she foster'd deep in its inmost core;
That still they kept such distance, a secret grudge she bore.
How came it that their vassal to court declin'd to go,
Nor for his land did homage, she inly yearn'd to know.

III

She made request of Gunther, and begg'd it so might be,
That she the absent Kriemhild yet once again might see,
And told him too, in secret, whereon her thoughts were bent.
With the words she utter'd her lord was scarce content.

IV

" How could we bring them hither," the king in turn began,
" Such a length of journey? 'twere past the power of man.
I could not ask it of them, they dwell from us so wide."
Thereto in haughty fashion the frowning queen replied,

V

" How rich soe'er a vassal, how broad soe'er his lands,
Obedience is his duty, whate'er his lord commands."
Sure could but smile Sir Gunther when thus he heard her fret.
'Twas not for suit and service that he and Siegfried met.

VI

Said she, " Dear lord, for my sake thy efforts join with mine,
That Siegfried and thy sister once more may seek the Rhine,
That we again may see them, and all in love unite.
Nothing, I well assure thee, could give me more delight.

VII

"What soft emotion soothes me, whene'er I call to mind
Thy sister's noble graces, her accent soft and kind,
And how, when both were married, we both sat side by side!
No doubt may she with honor be Siegfried's loving bride."

VIII

She press'd so long, that Gunther replied with alter'd cheer,
"Now know that guests so welcome never saw I here.
Much pressing little needed; so messengers of mine
I'll send to bid them hasten hither to the Rhine."

IX

Thereto the queen made answer, "Tell me now, I pray,
When you will send to ask them, and about what day
We may expect the travellers to both of us so dear;
And who will bear your message, I willingly would hear."

X

"So will I do," replied he; "thirty of my men
Shall be commission'd thither." Forthwith he summon'd them
Those by whom his message to Siegfried's land he sent,
Brunhild sumptuous vesture gave them to their full content.

XI

Then spake the king, "Ye warriors, from me this message bear
(That you keep back nothing I bid you well beware),
Which I to valiant Siegfried and to my sister send,
That in this world can no man to both be more a friend;

XII

"And beg them hasten hither us on the Rhine to see;
It shall be well requited both by my wife and me.
By the next midsummer he and his men shall find
From every one among us high honor, welcome kind.

XIII

"Unto the good King Siegmund my service, too, commend;
Say, I and mine shall ever hold him as our friend.
Bid too my sister hasten to meet her kinsmen dear.
Ne'er graced she royal festal like that which waits her here."

XIV

Brunhild and Uta and every lady there
Into the land of Siegfried their greeting bade them bear
To many a noble warrior and many a lady gay.
So with the king's commission the couriers went their way.

XV

To start they now were ready; to each of all the band
Was brought both steed and vesture; so rode they from the
 land.
With happy haste they journey'd, and ever prick'd they hard;
The king had sent an escort his messengers to guard.

XVI

In the weary journey three toilsome weeks they spent.
At last in Niblung's castle, whither they had been sent,
E'en in the march of Norway, they found king Siegmund's son.
Horses alike and riders were travel-tainted and fordone.

XVII

To Siegfried and to Kriemhild forthwith the tidings came,
That knights had journey'd thither, whose venture was the
 same
As what by men of worship was born in Burgundy.
From her day-bed Kriemhild up sprung hastily.

XVIII

Sudden to a window she bade a damsel go,
Who saw bold Gary standing in the court below,
Him, and his valiant comrades on the same errand bound.
For her long-brooded sorrow what rapture then she found!

XIX

Loud call'd she to her husband, " See you, where they stand
Down in the court there waiting, stout Gary and his band,
Whom my good brother Gunther has sent us down the Rhine?"
" Welcome are they," said Siegfried, " welcome to me and
 mine."

XX

Where they saw them standing, all the household ran;
They kindly then saluted, as man encounter'd man,
And, as they best could please them, spoke many a friendly
    word,
With no small joy King Siegmund of their arrival heard.

XXI

Straight were allotted quarters to Gary and his men,
And charge ta'en of their courses; the messengers went then
To where sat bold Sir Siegfried by gentle Kriemhild's side;
They were to court invited, and so they thither hied.

XXII

Uprose, as in they enter'd, the host and his fair dame.
Full well receiv'd was Gary, and all who with him came
His followers, Gunther's liegemen from distant Burgundy.
To a seat the warrior was motion'd courteously.

XXIII

" Nay, deign," said he, " our message to hear before we sit,
And us, way-wearied wanderers, the while to stand permit.
We have to tell you tidings to us committed late
By Gunther and by Brunhild, who are both in best estate;

XXIV

" And from the Lady Uta we come, your mother dear,
And from the good Sir Gernot and youthful Giselher,
And from your choicest kinsmen, who all with kind intent
By us to you their service from Burgundy have sent."

XXV

" Now God then quit!" said Siegfried, " that they're sincere
    and true,
I trust with full assurance, as men with friends should do.
The same too feels their sister. Now further to us tell,
Whether our friends in Rhineland are hearty all and well.

XXVI

" Since we from them departed, has any neighboring foe
Harried my consort's kindred? this let me surely know.
To them by me shall ever such friendly aid be lent,
That their wrong the doers shall bitterly repent."

XXVII

Thereto the Margrave Gary, the good knight, made reply,
" Fraught with all manly virtues they bear them proud and high.
They bid you to a festal, which they at home prepare.
You need not doubt, your kinsmen would gladly see you there.

XXVIII

" They also beg my lady thither with you to wend,
Soon as the blustering winter shall come at length to end,
You both ere next midsummer they all expect to see."
Then said the valiant Siegfried, " That can hardly be."

XXIX

But straight the bold Burgundian Gary gave this reply,
" Surely your mother Uta you never can deny,
Nor Giselher, nor Gernot, who all would meet you fain.
That you dwell so far distant, I hear them daily plain.

XXX

" Brunhild, my noble lady, and all her maidens fair,
Are glad to think that forthwith you thither will repair.
That they once more may see you, fills every heart with glee."
His words to lovely Kriemhild seem'd full good to be.

XXXI

Gary was her kinsman; him begg'd the host to sit,
And straight bade fill the goblets to pledge them, as was fit;
Then too, to meet the envoys, King Siegmund join'd the rest,
And to the bold Burgundians these friendly words address'd:

XXXII

" Welcome, ye men of Gunther! since Siegfried, my good son,
Your noble lady Kriemhild for his wife has won,
You at our court more frequent we should have gladly seen.
Your presence of our friendship the surest bond had been."

XXXIII

They said, whene'er he wish'd it, they willingly would come.
Their toil and teen through gladness forgot they all and some.
Siegfried bade all be seated, and viands of the best,
And in full abundance, be brought to every guest.

XXXIV

Nine days in mirth and feasting the envoys needs must stay.
At length the active warriors could brook no more delay.
Again would they ride homeward; on that their minds were bent
In th' interval King Siegfried for his friends had sent.

XXXV

He ask'd them what they counsel'd; he needs must to the Rhine;
" I bidden am by Gunther that dear friend of mine.
At a high feast my presence he and his kinsmen pray.
Fain would I ride thither, were't not so far away.

XXXVI

" They beg moreover, Kriemhild the journey too may share.
Now, my good friends, advise me; what's best to do, declare.
Should they for them request me to harry thirty lands,
Well they such warlike service might claim at Siegfried's
hands."

XXXVII

Thereto his knights thus answer'd, " As you desire to speed,
If you this feast will visit, hearken to our rede.
Take of your best warriors a thousand by your side.
So 'midst the bold Burgundians in honor you'll abide."

XXXVIII

Then spake the lord of Netherland, Siegmund the frank and
free,
" If you're for this high festal, why say not so to me?
I, if it not displease you, will with you to the Rhine,
And bring, to swell your squadron, a hundred knights of mine."

XXXIX

" Will you too journey with us, my father ever dear? "
Exclaim'd the bold Sir Siegfried; " it glads me this to hear.
Within twelve days at furthest we'll wend upon our way."
To all, who ask'd, then gave he good steeds and garments gay.

XL

When now to take the journey fix'd was the king's design,
He bade the knights of Gunther ride back unto the Rhine,
And sent by them a message to Kriemhild's kinsmen there,
That to the feast, they purpos'd, full fain would he repair.

XLI

Siegfried and Kriemhild (so says the tale) bestow'd
More gifts upon the envoys, than o'er such length of road
Their horses home could carry; a wealthy man was he.
They drove their strong-back'd sumpters merrily o'er the lea.

XLII

Siegfried and eke Siegmund their people cloth'd anew;
Eckewart the Margrave all Siegfried's country through
Bade seek out women's raiment, whate'er was stored in chest
Or could be bought for money, the choicest and the best.

XLIII

Rich saddles were made ready, and shields of glittering pride.
To the knights and ladies, that would with Siegfried ride,
Whate'er they wish'd was granted; none wanted there for
    ought.
To his friends in Rhineland many a lordly guest he brought.

XLIV

Meanwhile homeward speeding prick'd the envoys fast.
Back came the noble Gary to Burgundy at last.
He met with hearty welcome; straight they dismounted all
From war-horse and from palfrey before King Gunther's hall.

XLV

Old and young (as the use is) ran up from every side,
And ask'd what news they brought them? the noble **knights**
    replied,
" When I the king have told it, 'twill spread to all around."
Then went he with his comrades to where the king he found.

XLVI

From sheer pleasure Gunther started from his seat
At the happy tidings; that they had come so fleet,
Much thanks had they from Brunhild.   Gunther straight begun,
" How fares it with Siegfried, who so much for me has done?"

XLVII

" To hear of you," said Gary, " he redden'd with delight,
Both he, and eke your sister; never living wight
Sent his friends a message so tender and so true,
As by me Sir Siegfried and his father have to you."

XLVIII

Then to the valiant margrave the noble queen 'gan say,
" Tell me, is Kriemhild coming? does still her form display
The beauty and soft graces, she well to foster knew?"
The good knight, Gary, answer'd, " She's surely coming too."

XLIX

Then before Dame Uta the messengers were brought;
Well without her asking could Gary guess her thought,
So, ere she put the question, " How did Kriemhild fare?"
He said, how he had found her, and that she'd soon be there.

L

Of all the gorgeous presents nothing was left untold,
Given them by good Sir Siegfried; the raiment and the gold,
That the three brethren's lieges might view them forth were
    laid.
With thanks the gracious giver was by them all repaid.

LI

" Ay! of his own," said Hagan, " full lightly he may give;
'Tis past his power to spend it, should he forever live.
The Nibelungers' treasure holds he by strength of hand.
Ah! would it were brought hither to our Burgundian land!"

LII

The court, both knights and ladies, were all with joy elate
To hear that they were coming.   Early forthwith and late
The friends of the three brethren were busied every man;
Seats with sumptuous trappings to raise they straight began.

LIII

Hunolt and eke Sindolt, the hardy knights and true,
Had not a moment's leisure; full work had they to do
The while, as sewer and butler, and many a bench to raise.
Ortwine for th' aid he gave them had Gunther's thanks and
        praise.

LIV

Sore toil'd the chief cook, Rumolt; ah! how his orders ran
Among his understrappers! how many a pot and pan,
How many a mighty cauldron rattled and rang again!
They dress'd a world of dishes for all th' expected train.

LV

Nor less was then the labor to the fair ladies known,
As they prepar'd their garments; many a precious stone
They set in gold far-beaming, and glitter'd both so bright,
And with such grace they wore them, as ravish'd every sight.

THIRTEENTH ADVENTURE
HOW THEY WENT TO THE FESTIVAL

I

Now we awhile must leave them on household toils intent,
And tell how Lady Kriemhild and her maidens went
From the Nibelungers' country to the Rhine's fair shore.
Such plenty of rich vesture never sumpters bore.

II

Dispatch'd were travelling cases well fraught with precious
　　load ;
Then with his queen and comrades Sir Siegfried forward rode.
Her heart with pleasure's promise was ready to o'erflow ;
All was chang'd thereafter to wail and mortal woe.

III

At home, since so it needed, they left their infant heir,
The son that valiant Siegfried begot on Kriemhild fair.
To the poor boy misfortune that fatal journey bore ;
His father and his mother saw he never more.

IV

And with them good Sir Siegmund prick'd forth in merry
　　mood.
Had he but once foreboded the woes that thence ensued,
At that disastrous festal he ne'er had sat a guest,
Ne'er had he seen the ruin of those he loved the best.

V

Dispatch'd before were couriers to say they were at hand
Straight rode out to meet them a royal vested band,
Many a friend of Uta's, of Gunther's many a knight.
The host himself was stirring to welcome them aright.

VI

Forthwith he sought out Brunhild, where sat the stately dame.
" How did my sister greet you when first you hither came ?
So greet the wife of Siegfried, take care to fail in nought."
" So will I," said she, " gladly ; I love her as I ought."

VII

" To-morrow they'll be with us," said he, " by early day,
So, if you mean to greet them, be stirring while you may.
We must not, sure, be lurking within the castle here.
Never had I the fortune to welcome guests so dear."

VIII

She bade her dames and damsels look out their choicest vests,
The same they wore at festals before high-honor'd guests,
Such were to be expected with to-morrow's sun,
I need not say her bidding right willingly was done.

IX

Then too, to do their service the men of Gunther sped.
With him all his warriors the host in squadron led.
Next the queen came pacing full royally array'd.
To guests belov'd so dearly was goodliest welcome made.

X

With what joy and gladness welcom'd were they there!
It seem'd, when came Dame Brunhild to Burgundy whilere,
Her welcome by Dame Kriemhild less tender was and true;
The heart of each beholder beat higher at the view.

XI

Now too was come Sir Siegfried with all his men around.
You might see the warriors careering o'er the ground,
Now hither and now thither, with fire-sparkling hoof.
From the dust and tumult none could keep aloof.

XII

When Siegfried and eke Siegmund met King Gunther's eyes,
The host both son and father bespoke in loving wise.
" To me you are right welcome, to all my friends as dear.
It is our pride and pleasure as guests to have you here."

XIII

" Now God you quit! " said Siegmund, the grave and reverend
man;
" Ever since my Siegfried you for his comrade wan,
My wish had it been always to see you and to know."
" Right glad I am," said Gunther, " it now has happen'd so."

XIV

Receiv'd was bold Sir Siegfried, as fitted well his state,
With the highest honors; no man bore him hate.
Young Giselher and Gernot proffer'd all courtly care;
Never met friend or kinsman reception half so fair.

XV

Now either king's fair consort nigh to the other came;
Emptied were stor' of saddles; many a smiling dame
To the grass by stalwart champions down was lifted light.
In the ladies' service how busy was many a knight!

XVI

And now the lovely ladies each to the other went.
Thereat was many a chieftain full well at heart content,
When both a welcome offer'd so friendly and so fair.
Meanwhile the warriors ceas'd not to tend the ladies there.

XVII

Chieftain now to chieftain held out the cordial hand;
Low bows were made in plenty by either courtly band.
Amongst the high-born ladies pass'd many a loving kiss.
Both Gunther's men and Siegfried's were fain to look on this.

XVIII

They linger'd there no longer, but toward the city rode.
To his guests King Gunther by every action show'd
How welcome was their presence to all in Burgundy.
Young knights before young maidens ran tilting joyously.

XIX

The power of mighty Hagan and eke of bold Ortwine
Well there might each beholder from what he saw divine.
Whate'er they pleas'd to order, from all obedience won;
To the lov'd guests by either was courtly service done.

XX

The shields they clang'd and clatter'd before the castle gate
With fencing and with foining; long time had there to wait
His guests and good King Gunther ere they could enter in.
They pass'd the time right joyous amidst the press and din.

XXI

So to the spacious palace on rode they merrily.
You might see rich foot-cloths, well cut and artfully,
Down hang from o'er the saddle of many a high-born dame.
Forward to receive them King Gunther's servants came.

XXII

Then to their several chambers the guests were led aside.
From time to time Queen Brunhild with searching glances eyed
The love-enkindling Kriemhild; lovely she was indeed;
Her hue the gold outsparkled that glitter'd in her weed.

XXIII

At Worms through all the city rang the mirthsome shout
Of the rejoicing followers; Gunther the noisy rout
Commended to his marshal, and bade him treat them fair;
Dankwart sought out good quarters and fitly lodg'd them there.

XXIV

Without, within, was feasting; unbounded was the store.
Sure stranger guests were never treated so well before.
It only needed asking, and all was straight supplied;
So rich a king was Gunther that nothing was denied.

XXV

With friendly zeal they serv'd them, with hearts devoid of hate;
Amidst his guests at table the host exulting sate.
To sit was bidden Siegfried where he of yore had done.
With him strode to the banquet proud warriors many a one.

XXVI

Twelve hundred stalwart champions in circle there were seen
With him at table sitting; Brunhild, the watchful queen,
Thought to herself, no vassal could ever wealthier be.
Still him she so far favor'd, that from harm she left him free.

XXVII

All that feastful evening, as sat the king to dine,
Store of the richest vesture was wetted by the wine,
That in hasty hurry the butlers ever pour'd.
Sore toil'd they in their service at that o'ercrowded board.

XXVIII

Then, as is still the custom at each well-order'd feast,
To rest the dames and damsels were in good time releas'd.
All guests with gifts and honors, from whenceso'er they came,
The noble host entreated as well beseem'd his fame.

XXIX

When now the night was over, and reappear'd the dawn,
By the fair hands of ladies was many a jewel drawn,
Sparkling in goodly raiment, from many a travelling chest,
And out was sought and hurried many a lordly vest.

XXX

Ere 'twas full day, came flocking the palace hall around
Knights and squires in plenty; then arose the sound
Of matins sung to Gunther, and, when this was done,
So well rode youthful warriors, that the king's thanks they won.

XXXI

Shrill fifes and loud-voic'd clarions and blaring trumpet-clang
Mix'd with the shouts of thousands, that all the city rang,
And through the startled welkin th' alarum spread around.
Proud knights on strong-hoof'd chargers rode thund'ring o'er
　　the ground.

XXXII

At once without the city a tourney they began.
There his career exulting many a young warrior ran,
Whom his fresh boiling courage impell'd to honor's field.
Many a knight of prowess was there seen under shield.

XXXIII

Many a stately matron and many a smiling maid
Sat at the castle windows in costly robes array'd,
And look'd on while the warriors display'd their skill and force;
The good host with his comrades himself would run a course.

XXXIV

The time seem'd not to linger, so merrily it pass'd.
Pealing from the minster they heard the bells at last.
Then up were led the palfreys; forth rode each lady bright;
The noble queens were follow'd by many a valiant knight.

XXXV

Down before the minster they lighted on the green.
Still to her guests was gracious King Gunther's ·ʼghty queen.
Both crown'd, into the minster they stepp'd with royal state.
Too soon their love was sunder'ḓ and all through jealous hate !

XXXVI

Soon as the mass was over, with regal pomp and pride
Thence came they to the palace, and straight exulting hied
To the joyous banquet, and neither stop nor stay
Was put to the high festal until th' eleventh day.

XXXVII

Then thought Queen Brunhild, " Silent no longer I'll remain.
Howe'er to pass I bring it, Kriemhild shall explain,
Wherefore so long her husband, who holds of us in fee,
Has left undone his service; this sure shall answer'd be."

XXXVIII

So still she brooded mischief, and conn'd her devil's lore,
Till she broke off in sorrow the feast so blithe before.
Ever at her heart lay closely what came perforce to light.
Many a land she startled with horror and affright.

FOURTEENTH ADVENTURE

HOW THE TWO QUEENS REVILED ONE ANOTHER

I

One day at th' hour of vespers a loud alarum rose
From certain lusty champions that for their pastime chose
To prove themselves at tilting in the castle court;
Then many a knight and lady ran thither to see the sport.

II

There were the proud queens sitting together, as befell,
Each on a good knight thinking that either lov'd full well.
Then thus began fair Kriemhild, " My husband's of such might,
That surely o'er these kingdoms he ought to rule by right."

III

Then answer'd Lady Brunhild, " Nay, how can that be shown?
Were there none other living but thou and he alone,
Then might, no doubt, the kingdoms be rul'd by him and thee,
But, long as Gunther's living, that sure can never be."

IV

Thereto rejoin'd fair Kriemhild, " See'st thou how proud he
    stands,
How proud he stalks, conspicuous among those warrior bands,
As doth the moon far-beaming the glimmering stars outshine?
Sure have I cause to pride me when such a knight is mine."

V

Thereto replied Queen Brunhild, " How brave soe'er he be,
How stout soe'er or stately, one greater is than he.
Gunther, thy noble brother, a higher place may claim,
Of knights and kings the foremost in merit and in fame."

VI

Thereto rejoin'd fair Kriemhild, " So worthy is my mate,
All praise that I can give him can ne'er be term'd too great.
In all he does how matchless? in honor too how clear!
Believ'st thou this, Queen Brunhild? at least he's Gunther's
    peer."

VII

" Thou should'st not so perversely, Kriemhild, my meaning take.
What I said, assure thee, with ample cause I spake.
I heard them both allow it, then when both first I saw
And the stout king in battle compell'd me to his law.

VIII

" E'en then, when my affection he so knightly won,
'Twas fairly own'd by Siegfried that he was Gunther's man.
Myself I heard him own it, and such I hold him still."
" Forsooth," replied fair Kriemhild, " they must have used
    me ill.

IX

"How could my noble brethren their power have so applied,
As to make me, their sister, a lowly vassal's bride?
For manners' sake then, Brunhild, this idle talk give o'er,
And, by our common friendship, let me hear no more."

X

"Give o'er will I never," the queen replied again;
"Shall I renounce the service of all the knightly train
That hold of him, our vassal, and are our vassals too?"
Into sudden anger at this fair Kriemhild flew.

XI

"Ay! but thou must renounce it, for never will he grace
Thee with his vassal service: he fills a higher place
Than e'en my brother Gunther, noble though be his strain.
Henceforth thou should'st be wiser, nor hold such talk again.

XII

"I wonder, too, since Siegfried thy vassal is by right,
Since both of us thou rulest with so much power and might,
Why to thee his service so long he has denied.
Nay! I can brook no longer thy insolence and pride."

XIII

"Thyself too high thou bearest," Brunhild answer made;
"Fain would I see this instant whether to thee be paid
Public respect and honor such as waits on me."
Then both the dames with anger lowering you might see.

XIV

"So shall it be," said Kriemhild, "to meet thee I'm prepar'd
Since thou my noble husband a vassal hast declar'd,
By the men of both our consorts to-day it shall be seen,
That I the church dare enter before King Gunther's queen.

XV

"To-day by proof thou'lt witness, what lofty birth is mine,
And that my noble husband worthier is than thine;
Nor for this with presumption shall I be tax'd I trow;
To-day thou'lt see moreover thy lowly vassal go

XVI

" To court before the warriors here in Burgundy.
Assure thee, thou'lt behold me honor'd more royally
Than the proudest princess that ever here wore crown."
The dames their spite attested with many a scowl and frown.

XVII

" Since thou wilt be no vassal," Brunhild rejoin'd again,
" Then thou with thy women must apart remain
From my dames and damsels, as to the church we go."
Thereto Kriemhild answer'd, " Trust me it shall be so.

XVIII

" Array ye now, my maidens," said Siegfried's haughty dame,
" You must not let your mistress here be put to shame.
That you have gorgeous raiment make plain to every eye.
What she has just asserted, she soon shall fain deny."

XIX

They needed not much bidding; all sought out their best;
Matrons alike and maidens each donn'd a glittering vest.
Queen Brunhild with her meiny was now upon her way.
By this was deck'd fair Kriemhild in royal rich array,

XX

With three and forty maidens, whom she to Rhine had brought;
Bright stuffs were their apparel in far Arabia wrought.
So towards the minster march'd the maidens fair;
All the men of Siegfried were waiting for them there.

XXI

Strange thought it each beholder, what there by all was seen,
How with their trains far-sunder'd pass'd either noble queen,
Not walking both together as was their wont before,
Full many a prowest warrior thereafter rued it sore.

XXII

Now before the minster the wife of Gunther stood;
Meanwhile by way of pastime many a warrior good
Held light and pleasant converse with many a smiling dame;
When up the lovely Kriemhild with her radiant meiny came.

XXIII

All that the noblest maiden had ever donn'd before
Was as wind to the splendor her dazzling ladies wore.
So rich her own apparel in gold and precious things,
She alone might out-glitter the wives of thirty kings.

XXIV

Howe'er he might be willing, yet none could dare deny
That such resplendent vesture never met mortal eye
As on that fair retinue then sparkled to the sun.
Except to anger Brunhild, Kriemhild had not so done.

XXV

Both met before the minster in all the people's sight;
There at once the hostess let out her deadly spite.
Bitterly and proudly she bade fair Kriemhild stand;
" No vassalless precedeth the lady of the land."

XXVI

Out then spake fair Kriemhild (full of wrath was she),
" Could'st thou still be silent, better 'twere for thee.
Thou'st made thy beauteous body a dishonor'd thing.
How can a vassal's leman be consort of a king? "

XXVII

" Whom here call'st thou leman? " said the queen again;
" So call I thee," said Kriemhild; " thy maidenly disdain
Yielded first to Siegfried, my husband, Siegmund's son;
Ay! 'was not my brother that first thy favors won.

XXVIII

" Why, where were then thy senses? sure 'twas a crafty train,
To take a lowly lover, to ease a vassal's pain!
Complaints from thee," said Kriemhild, " methinks are much
        amiss."
" Verily," said Brunhild, " Gunther shall hear of this."

XXIX

" And why should that disturb me? thy pride hath thee betray'd.
Why didst thou me, thy equal, with vassalship upbraid?
Know this for sure and certain (to speak it gives me pain)
Never can I meet thee in cordial love again."

XXX

Then bitterly wept Brunhild; Kriemhild no longer stay'd;
Straight with all her followers before the queen she made
Her way into the minster; then deadly hate 'gan rise;
And starting tears o'erclouded the shine of brightest eyes.

XXXI

For all the solemn service, for all the chanted song,
Still it seemed to Brunhild they linger'd all too long.
Both on her mind and body a load like lead there lay.
Many a high-born hero for her sorrow was to pay.

XXXII

Brunhild stopp'd with her ladies without the minster door.
Thought she, " This wordy woman shall tell me something
    more
Of her charge against me spread so loud and rife.
If he has but so boasted, let him look to his life!"

XXXIII

Now came the noble Kriemhild begirt with many a knight;
Then spake the noble Brunhild, " Stop and do me right.
You've voic'd me for a wanton; prove it ere you go.
You and your foul speeches have wrought me pain and woe."

XXXIV

Then spake the Lady Kriemhild, " 'Twere wiser to forbear;
E'en with the gold I'll prove it that on my hand I wear;
'Twas this that Siegfried brought me from where by you he
    lay."
Never liv'd Queen Brunhild so sorrowful a day.

XXXV

Said she, " That ring was stolen from me who held it dear,
And mischievously hidden has since been many a year.
But now I've met with something by which the thief to guess."
Both the dames were frenzied with passion masterless.

XXXVI

" Thief? " made answer Kriemhild, " I will not brook the name.
Thou would'st have kept silence, hadst thou a sense of shame.
By the girdle here about me prove full well I can
That I am ne'er a liar; Siegfried was indeed thy man."

XXXVII

'Twas of silk of Nineveh the girdle that she brought,
With precious stones well garnish'd; a better ne'er was wrought;
When Brunhild but beheld it, her tears she could not hold.
The tale must needs to Gunther and all his men be told.

XXXVIII

Then outspake Queen Brunhild; " Go some one straight and
  call
Hither the Prince of Rhineland; sure will I tell him all,
What infamy his sister has forc'd me to endure,
And how his wife she voices for Siegfried's paramour."

XXXIX

The king with his chieftains up came hastily;
There saw he his beloved weeping bitterly.
" Dearest heart! " soft said he, " who has serv'd you so? "
With many a sob she answer'd, " Deep cause have I for woe.

XL

" Of my good name and honor than life more dear would fain
Thy cruel sister rob me; to thee I needs must plain.
She says her husband Siegfried my virgin favors won."
Thereto replied King Gunther, " Then she foul wrong has
  done."

XLI

" Besides, my long-lost girdle she weareth as in scorn,
My gold adorns her finger;—would I had ne'er been born!
Is not all this an outrage to sting and wound me sore?
King! if thou dost not clear me, I'll never love thee more."

XLII

Thereto return'd King Gunther, " I will do no less;
If Siegfried so has boasted, he shall the same confess,
Or frankly disavow it."   Then turn'd he to his band,
And bade them summon forthwith the Chief of Netherland.

XLIII

No sooner had Sir Siegfried seen them so ill appaid
(He knew not what had happen'd), suddenly he said,
" Why are these women weeping? the cause, I pray you, show,
And why I'm hither summon'd, I should be glad to know."

XLIV

Thereto replied King Gunther, " With anguish I'm oppress'd.
My wife has told me something that's poison in my breast.
She says, thou hast been boasting her virgin love to have won;
So thy wife Kriemhild told her. Hast thou, Sir Knight, so
        done? "

XLV

" Not I," made answer Siegfried, " and if she so did say,
Ere I rest, she surely shall for her folly pay,
And before all thy liegemen my solemn oath I'll take,
That not to her nor others such words I ever spake."

XLVI

Then said the King of Rhineland, " Make this at once appear;
The oath, which thou hast proffer'd, take before us here,
And of all idle charges at once I'll set thee free."
In circle the Burgundians all standing you might see.

XLVII

Straight the noble Siegfried swore with uplifted hand.
" 'Tis enough," said Gunther, " so well I understand
Thy innocence, that freely all doubts I here remit,
My sister did accuse thee, and I with joy acquit."

XLVIII

Then answer'd noble Siegfried, " If it avail her aught
To have griev'd thy gentle consort, and set her thus at naught,
Such gain of her's assure thee, I deeply shall lament."
Then the bold knights fix'd glances each on the other bent.

XLIX

" Women must be instructed," said Siegfried the good knight,
" To leave off idle talking, and rule their tongues aright.
Keep thy fair wife in order, I'll do by mine the same.
Such overweening folly puts me indeed to shame."

L

Hasty words have often sunder'd fair dames before.
Then went on sad Brunhild to weep and wail so sore,
That Gunther's warriors could not but pity such deep grief.
Then to his sovran lady came Hagan, Trony's chief.

LI

He ask'd her, what had happen'd—wherefore he saw her weep
She told him all the story; he vow'd to her full deep,
That reap should Kriemhild's husband as he had dar'd to sow,
Or that himself thereafter content should never know.

LII

Ortwine of Metz and Gernot both came to the debate,
Where the collected chieftains advis'd on Siegfried's fate.
Fair Uta's son, young Giselher, alike the council sought;
He, when he heard the question, thus spoke his honest thought.

LIII

" Ye good knights and noble, why would you do this?
Never sure has Siegfried done so much amiss,
Or merited such hatred, that he should lose his life.
Sure 'tis but a trifle to stir an angry wife."

LIV

" Shall we bring up bastards? " said Hagan furiously;
" That were little honor for knights of our degree.
He hath slander'd my dear lady in his boastful fit.
Die will I in this quarrel, or his life shall answer it."

LV

Then spake himself King Gunther, " Naught has he done but
    give
To us all love and honor; we needs must let him live.
How can it be fitting that I should do him ill?
True was he to us ever alike in deed and will "

LVI

The Knight of Metz in answer, Ortwine, then sternly said,
" That strength of his, so matchless, shall stand him in no stead.
Let but my lord permit me, myself will do the deed."
Against him then the chieftains unrighteous doom decreed.

LVII

None urged the matter further, except that Hagan still,
Kept ever prompting Gunther the guiltless blood to spill;
Saying, that, if Siegfried perish'd, his death to him would bring
The sway o'er many a kingdom.   Sore mourn'd the wavering
    king.

LVIII

Still shrunk they from performance; fair sports meanwhile were
    plied.
Ah! what spears were shiver'd between the palace wide
And the lofty minster Siegfried's fair dame before!
This with angry murmurs the men of Gunther bore.

LIX

Then said the king, " Ye warriors, refrain your murderous hate;
Born was he for the safety and honor of our state.
Besides, so stout of body is he, and so strong of hand;
That, should he come to know it, none durst his fury stand."

LX

" Nay, my good lord," said Hagan, " take comfort and good
    cheer.
The weeping of fair Brunhild, be sure, shall cost him dear.
Trust to my secret practice to guide this matter right.
Ever shall he find in Hagan a fatal opposite."

LXI

Thereto replied King Gunther, " But how can this befall?"
To him straight answer'd Hagan, " List, and I'll tell you all.
Let messengers ride hither, whom here no person knows,
And bid you open battle as if from foreign foes.

LXII

"Before your guests make public, that you and all your men
Must forthwith hence to battle; he will not dally then,
But proffer you his service, and thus will lose his life;
I'll worm us out his secret from his loquacious wife."

LXIII

The king took to his ruin, th' advice his liegeman gave.
The chiefs their horrid treason 'gainst th' innocent and brave
Carried with such close practice, that none the train could spy.
Thus brought two women's quarrel many a good knight to die.

FIFTEENTH ADVENTURE

HOW SIEGFRIED WAS BETRAYED

I

From thence 'twas the fourth morning, when two and thirty men
To the court came riding; 'twas told King Gunther then,
That him and his Burgundians their task was to defy.
Woe were the fearful women from this foul-framed lie.

II

At once they got permission before the king to go,
And told him that from Ludeger they came, his former foe,
Of old o'ercome in battle by Siegfried's conquering hand,
And brought by him a captive into Gunther's land.

III

The messengers he greeted and each bade choose a seat.
Then one among them answer'd "To stand, my lord, is meet,
Till we have told our message, and all our duty done.
Know, that you have for foemen many a mother's son.

IV

"Ludegast and Ludeger you to the death defy,
The kings whom you entreated so hard in years gone by.
In arms into your country they are resolv'd to ride."
Full of wrath seem'd Gunther to hear himself defied.

V

Then were the false pretenders led to guest-chambers fair.
Ah! how could noble Siegfried, or any else beware
The trains of that vile treason, which, for the guiltless spread,
Soon brought down death and ruin on each contriver's head?

VI

The king about went whisp'ring with the friends he loved the
     best.
Hagan, the knight of Trony, never let him rest.
Many of the king's companions to stop the treason tried,
But Hagan from his counsel not once would turn aside.

VII

One day it fell that Siegfried close whisp'ring found the band,
When thus began to ask them the Knight of Netherland,
"Why creep the king and chieftains so sorrowful along?
I'll help you to revenge it, if you have suffer'd wrong."

VIII

"Good cause have I for sorrow," Gunther straight replied,
"Ludegast and Ludeger both have me defied.
With open force they threaten to ravage all my land."
Then spake the dauntless champion, "Their pride shall
     Siegfried's hand,

IX

"Both to your boot and honor, bring lower, and once more
I'll do unto those boasters e'en as I did before.
Ere I end, o'er castles, o'er lands, o'er all I'll spread
Wide waste and desolation, or fortfeit else my head.

X

"Do you and your good warriors sit by the chimney side;
With my knights here about me thither let me ride.
How willingly I serve you, my acts and deeds shall show,
And every one shall feel it who boasts himself your foe."

XI

" Ah! how this promise cheers me!" the king dissembling said,
As though rejoic'd in earnest at that free-proffer'd aid.
Low bow'd to him the false one with fawning semblance fair.
Then return'd Sir Siegfried, " Take now no further care."

XII

For the march the Burgundians prepar'd in show the while,
Yet Siegfried and his warriors 'twas done but to beguile.
Then bade he straight make ready each Netherlandish knight.
They sought out the best harness and surest arms they might.

XIII

Then spake the valiant Siegfried, " Sir Siegmund, father mine,
Best tarry here in quiet till we return to Rhine.
Conquest, if God befriend us. we shortly back shall bring.
Meanwhile live blithe and merry with our good host the king."

XIV

The flags anon were hoisted, and forward all would fare;
Among the men of Gunther many a one was there
Who knew not his lord's secret, and thought no treachery.
There might you see with Siegfried a mighty company.

XV

Their helms and eke their mailcoats upon their steeds were tied.
Many a knight of prowess ready was to ride.
Then Hagan, Lord of Trony, as had before been plann'd,
Went to take leave of Kriemhild ere yet they left the land.

XVI

" Ah! well is me," said Kriemhild, " that I've a lord who lends
Such firm assistance ever to back my dearest friends,
As now does my brave Siegfried for my brethren's sake;
Therefore," said the fair lady, " good courage will I take.

XVII

" My good friend, Sir Hagan, bear in remembrance still
How much I love my kinsmen, nor ever wish'd them ill.
For this requite my husband, nor let me vainly long;
He should not pay the forfeit, if I did Brunhild wrong.

XVIII

" My fault," pursued she sadly, " good cause had I to rue.
For it I have far'd badly; he beat me black and blue;
Such mischief-making tattle his patience could not brook,
And for it ample vengeance on my poor limbs he took."

XIX

" You'll be friends together," said he, " some other day.
But, Kriemhild, my dear lady, tell me now, I pray,
At my hands to your husband what service can be done,
Fain would I do it, lady, better love I none."

XX

The noble dame made answer, " Fear should I not at all,
That by the sword of any my lord in fight would fall,
But that he rashly follows his fiery martial mood.
Else could no harm befall him the noble knight and good."

XXI

" Lady," then answer'd Hagan, " since thus you harbor fear
Lest hostile force should slay him, let me yet further hear,
What best may serve our purpose the warrior to defend.
On foot, on horse, I'll watch him, his guardian and his friend."

XXII

Said she, " Thou art my cousin, and I alike am thine;
To thy good faith commend I this dearest lord of mine.
That thou wilt tend his welfare, assurance firm I hold."
Then told she him the secret far better left untold.

XXIII

Said she, " My husband's daring, and thereto stout of limb
Of old, when on the mountain he slew the dragon grim,
In its blood he bath'd him, and thence no more can feel
In his charmed person the deadly dint of steel.

XXIV

" Still am I ever anxious, whene'er in fight he stands,
And keen-edg'd darts are hailing from strong heroic hands,
Lest I by one should lose him, my own beloved make.
Ah! how my heart is beating still for my Siegfried's sake!

XXV

" So now I'll tell the secret, dear friend, alone to thee
(For thou, I doubt not, cousin, will keep thy faith with me),
Where sword may pierce my darling, and death sit on the thrust.
See, in thy truth and honor how full, how firm my trust!

XXVI

" As from the dragon's death-wounds gush'd out the crimson
        gore,
With the smoking torrent the warrior wash'd him o'er.
A leaf then 'twixt his shoulders fell from the linden bough.
There only steel can harm him; for that I tremble now."

XXVII

Then said the Chief of Trony, " A little token sew
Upon his outer garment; thus shall I surer know
The spot that needs protection as in the fight we stand."
She thought his life to lengthen, the while his death was plann'd.

XXVIII

Said she, " Upon his vesture with a fine silken thread
I'll sew a secret crosslet; by this small token led
Thy hand shall guard my husband, as through the press he goes,
And in the shock of battle confronts his swarming foes."

XXIX

" So will I do," said Hagan, " my honor'd lady dear."
She thought her lord to profit, and keep from danger clear,
But all she did to aid him serv'd but to betray.
Leave then took Sir Hagan, and joyous strode away.

XXX

What he had learn'd from Kriemhild his lord then bade him
        show
" Put off this march," said Hagan, " and let us hunting go;
Now have I all the secret; now in my hand is he;
Could you but contrive it?"   " For that," said Gunther, " trust
        to me."

XXXI

The false king and his courtiers to hear his words were fain.
I ween, so base a treason knight ne'er will do again,
As then was done by Hagan, when to his faith for aid
So fair a lady trusted, and so foully was betrayed.

XXXII

Next morning on his journey in haste Sir Siegfried sped.
Of his men a thousand merrily he led.
He thought his foes to punish who had his friends defied.
Next him rode Sir Hagan, and close his vesture eyed.

XXXIII

Soon as the mark he noted, he bade in secret go
Two of his men some distance, and come as from the foe,
Saying, that only friendship to Burgundy was meant,
And that they to King Gunther from Ludeger were sent.

XXXIV

How then it irk'd Sir Siegfried to turn at once the rein,
Ere he in his friend's quarrel had battled once again!
Scarce could the men of Gunther divert him from his way.
So to the king back rode he, who thus his thanks 'gan pay.

XXXV

" Now God requite you, Siegfried, of all my friends the best!
Since you are always ready to do what I request,
I'll ever do my utmost to merit such good will.
Many are the friends I trust in, but you're the surest still.

XXXVI

" Now that we're free from foemen, and in firm peace abide,
Hence to the Wask forest a-hunting let us ride,
To chase the bears and wild swine, as oft I've done of yore."
The faithless, murderous Hagan had counsell'd this before.

XXXVII

"To all my guests and kinsmen it straight announc'd shall be,
I mean to start full early; whoe'er would ride with me,
Must forthwith make him ready; whoe'er would here abide,
Let him amuse the ladies; with both I'm satisfied."

XXXVIII

Then courteously made answer Siegfried the stout and strong,
" If you're inclined for hunting, gladly will I along.
So lend me but a huntsman and a good brach or two,
And I into the forest will find my way like you."

XXXIX

" If one will not suffice you," the fraudful king replied,
" I'll lend you four good huntsmen, who know the forest wide,
And every track soever where the wild beasts roam.
You'll never, with their guidance, come empty-handed home."

XL

Thence to his gentle lady rode off the warrior bold.
Quick to the king had Hagan the baleful tidings told,
How he would surely trap him, the champion frank and free.
Never was such foul treason, nor ever more will be.

XLI

When now was laid the death-plot by that base traitor pair,
The rest then all consented.   Gernot and Giselher
Neither would join the hunting; I know not through what fear
Or spite they warn'd not Siegfried; soon paid they for it dear.

SIXTEENTH ADVENTURE

HOW SIEGFRIED WAS SLAIN

I

GUNTHER and Hagan, the warriors fierce and bold,
To execute their treason, resolv'd to scour the wold,
The bear, the boar, the wild bull, by hill or dale or fen,
To hunt with keen-edg'd javelins; what fitter sport for valiant
     men?

II

In lordly pomp rode with them Siegfried the champion strong.
Good store of costly viands they brought with them along.
Anon by a cool runnel he lost his guiltless life.
'Twas so devis'd by Brunhild, King Gunther's moody wife.

III

But first he sought the chamber where he his lady found.
He and his friends already had on the sumpters bound
Their gorgeous hunting raiment; they o'er the Rhine would go.
Never before was Kriemhild sunk so deep in woe.

IV

On her mouth of roses he kiss'd his lady dear;
"God grant me, dame, returning in health to see thee here;
So may those eyes see me, too; meanwhile be blithe and gay
Among the gentle kinsmen; I must hence away."

V

Then thought she on the secret (the truth she durst not tell)
How she had told it Hagan; then the poor lady fell
To wailing and lamenting that ever she was born.
Then wept she without measure, sobbing and sorrow-worn.

VI

She thus bespake her husband, "Give up that chase of thine.
I dreamt last night of evil, how two fierce forest swine
Over the heath pursued thee; the flowers turn'd bloody red.
I cannot help thus weeping; I'm chill'd with mortal dread.

VII

"I fear some secret treason, and cannot lose thee hence,
Lest malice should be borne thee for misconceiv'd offence.
Stay, my beloved Siegfried, take not my words amiss.
'Tis the true love I bear thee that bids me counsel this."

VIII

"Back shall I be shortly, my own beloved mate.
Not a soul in Rhineland know I, who bears me hate.
I'm well with all thy kinsmen; they're all my firm allies;
Nor have I from any e'er deserved otherwise."

IX

"Nay! do not, dearest Siegfried! 'tis e'en thy death I dread.
Last night I dreamt, two mountains fell thundering on thy head,
And I no more beheld thee; if thou from me wilt go,
My heart will sure be breaking with bitterness of woe."

X

Round her peerless body his clasping arms he threw.
Lovingly he kiss'd her, that faithful wife and true;
Then took his leave, and parted;—in a moment all was o'er—
Living, alas poor lady! she saw him never more.

XI

Then rode they thence, and hasten'd to a wildering forest drear.
Many a bold knight, on pastime intent and merry cheer,
In the train of Gunther and Siegfried took his way.
Stout Gernot and young Giselher at home preferr'd to stay.

XII

Many a well-laden sumpter before them cross'd the Rhine,
That for the fellow-hunters carried bread and wine.
And flesh and fish in plenty, with every dainty thing
That might become the table of such a mighty king.

XIII

Their course the noble hunters check'd in an open glade,
Where the wild beasts, that haunted the neighboring greenwood
    shade,
Pass'd to and fro by custom; the hunt they here would hold.
Thither at length came Siegfried; straight to the king 'twas
    told.

XIV

Now every path and outlet the huntsmen had beset,
When thus bespake Sir Siegfried the chiefs who there were met.
"Ye bold and dauntless warriors! who will the honor claim
To enter first the forest, and bring us to the game?"

XV

"Ere we begin our pastime," Sir Hagan straight replied,
"Here in this glade together, 'twere better first divide.
We then shall see more clearly, my lords as well as I,
Who's the most cunning sportsman of this fair company.

XVI

"Let us divide among us the huntsmen and the hounds,
Then each, where'er he pleases, beat all these woody bounds,
And who excels his comrades, shall thanks have from the rest."
Not long the hunters linger'd, but started on their quest.

XVII

Then said the good Sir Siegfried, " I do not need a pack;
One well-train'd hound will serve me the lurking beasts to track,
And the close scent to follow through every bush and brake.
We'll now begin our hunting."   So Kriemhild's husband spake.

XVIII

With that an aged huntsman a watchful limehound took,
And shortly brought the champion into a shady nook,
Where store of beasts were couching; as each sprung from his
    lair,
The warriors, like good hunters, fell on and caught them there.

XIX

All, that the limehound started, anon with mighty hand
Were slain by noble Siegfried, the Chief of Netherland.
No beast could there outrun him, so swift his steed could race;
He won from all high praises for mastery in the chase.

XX

Whatever he attempted, he went the best before.
The first beast he encounter'd was a fierce half-bred boar.
Him with a mighty death-stroke he stretch'd upon the ground;
Just after in a thicket a lion huge he found.

XXI

Him the limehound started; his bow Sir Siegfried drew;
With a keen-headed arrow he shot the lion through.
But three faint bounds thereafter the dying monster made.
His wond'ring fellow-huntsmen thanks to Sir Siegfried paid.

XXII

Then one upon another a buffalo, an elk
He slew, four strong ure-oxen, and last a savage shelk.
No beast, how swift soever, could leave his steed behind;
Scarcely their speed could profit the flying hart or hind.

XXIII

Next the sagacious limer a monstrous wild boar trac'd;
Just then the master-hunter came sudden up in haste,
And cross'd his path undaunted as he to fly began.
Straight the churning monster at his opponent ran.

XXIV

Then forward sprung Sir Siegfried, and with his sword him
        slew;
Such feat, I ween, no hunter besides had dared to do.
Then leash'd they the good limehound, and from the thicket led,
And told all the Burgundians how Siegfried's chase had sped.

XXV

Then said his merry huntsmen, " Sir Siegfried, be so kind
As not our wood to empty, but leave some game behind.
There'll else be nothing living on mountain or on wold."
The champion at their jesting his laughter scarce could hold.

XXVI

They heard then all about them, throughout those forest
        grounds,
Such shouting and such baying of huntsmen and of hounds,
That hill and wood re-echoed with the wild uproar.
Th' attendants had uncoupled four and twenty dogs or more.

XXVII

Then full many a monster was doom'd his last to groan.
They thought with glad expectance to challenge for their own
The praise for the best hunting; but lower sunk their pride,
When to the tryst-fire shortly they saw Sir Siegfried ride.

XXVIII

The hunting now was over for the most part at least;
Game was brought in plenty and skins of many a beast
To the place of meeting, and laid the hearth before.
Ah! to the busy kitchen what full supplies they bore!

XXIX

Then bade Gunther summon the noble hunting crew
To the royal breakfast; a horn a huntsman blew
That far and wide re-echoed, and told to all around
That by the tryst-fire ready the king was to be found.

XXX

Said one of Siegfried's huntsmen, " I heard a warning blast,
That thrilling horn assures me our hunting time is past;
We must back to our fellows; answer it will I."
So through the wood resounding rang question and reply.

XXXI

Then spake the good Sir Siegfried, " Well! let us leave the
    wood."
His courser bore him smoothly, fast prick'd his comrades good.
With their noise they rous'd a monster, a wild bear fierce and
    grim.
Said Siegfried o'er his shoulder to those who follow'd him,

XXXII

" Now, comrades, look for pastime! see you yon thicket there?
Slip the dog directly; I spy a monstrous bear.
The same shall instant with us hence to the trysting-place.
To get off in safety swift he indeed must pace."

XXXIII

Straight they slipp'd the limer; off leapt the bear with speed;
Sir Siegfried thought to catch him through swiftness of his
    steed.
He came on fallen timber, so thus it could not be;
Then deem'd himself the monster from his fierce hunter free.

XXXIV

Down sprang from horse Sir Siegfried, and plied on foot the
    chase;
Naught then could aid the monster o'ermaster'd in the race.
Sir Siegfried strongly seized him, and cast a rope around,
And, ere he once could wound him, the struggling bear he
    bound.

XXXV

So fast the warrior bound him, he could nor scratch nor bite,
Then tied him to the saddle, and after mounted light.
So to the tryst-fire laughing with his snorting load,
By way of sport and pastime, the fearless warrior rode.

XXXVI

In his state how lordly thither he came along!
Huge was his mighty boar-spear, weighty and broad and
   strong;
To his spur descended the good sword that he wore;
Of ruddy gold fair glittering a hunting horn he bore.

XXXVII

Of better hunting-vesture never heard I tell.
His coat of darkest samite became the warrior well.
His cap of richest sable sat with a careless grace,
And his death-fraught quiver was bound with many a lace.

XXXVIII

With the skin of a panther the same was cover'd o'er
For its balmy sweetness; a strong bow too he bore,
Which none but with a windlass could draw, howe'er he strove,
Unless himself was present at the mark to rove.

XXXIX

All his outer garment was of a lynx's hide,
From head to foot with cunning 'twas speckled all and pied.
On either side descending of the master-hunter bold
From the rich fur there glitter'd many a bright thread of gold.

XL

Girded he was with Balmung, a broad and mighty blade,
With such keen cutting edges, that straight its way it made
Where'er it smote on helmet, and thousands did to die.
'Sooth was the lordly hunter of bearing proud and high.

XLI

Besides (of this my story to tell you every part)
Fraught was his splendid quiver with many a dreary dart;
The shaft of each was gilded, a hand's-breadth was the steel.
'Twas death of those grim arrows a single wound to feel.

XLII

So stately from the forest rode on the noble knights;
The men of Gunther mark'd him soon as he came in sight,
And ran, and held his courser, and gave him tendance fair.
Meanwhile close to the saddle lay bound the groaning bear.

XLIII

The knight, from horse alighting, soft the band untied
That bound his paws and muzzle; straight when the bear they
        spied,
All the pack of yelpers open'd on him loud.
The beast made for the forest, scattering the startled crowd.

XLIV

Scared by the din and uproar he through the kitchen rac'd.
Ah! how the cooks and scullions from round the fire he chas'd!
Upset were pans and kettles, and store of savory hashes,
Roast, boil'd, and stew'd together were hissing in the ashes.

XLV

From their seats upstarted the lords and all the band;
The bear flew into fury; straight gave the king command
The hounds to uncouple, and slip them on the prey.
Had it all thus ended, it had been a merry day.

XLVI

With bows and mighty boar-spears (no more was quiet there)
Upsprung the light-foot warriors and chas'd the flying bear.
The dogs there were so many, none dar'd a dart to fling.
With shouting and hallooing they made the mountains ring.

XLVII

Before the dogs he scamper'd; they follow'd where he led;
But 'twas the swift-foot Siegfried that caught him as he fled.
Once with his sword he smote him; he wallow'd in his gore.
Back to the scatter'd tryst-fire his friends the monster bore.

XLVIII

Loud shouted each beholder that 'twas a matchless blow.
Now the high-born hunters were bidden to table go.
Down in a flowery meadow sat they right merrily.
Ah! what dainty viands cheer'd that proud company!

XLIX

Still delay'd the attendants the ruddy wine to pour.
Never else were warriors better serv'd before.
But for the heinous treason with which they fram'd their plot,
All that choice band of champions were free from blame or blot.

L

Then said the noble Siegfried, " I needs must wonder here,
That joyous wine is wanting with such abundant cheer.
When so o'erflows the kitchen, how is't the cellar's dry?
Treat merry hunters better, or hunt no more will I.

LI

" I have deserv'd in Rhineland more hospitable care."
Then answering from the table spoke Gunther false and fair.
" This fault shall soon be mended, and reason done you first.
For this we may thank Hagan, who makes us die of thirst."

LII

Then said the Chief of Trony, " My lord and master dear,
I thought that this day's hunting was not to be held here,
But in the wood of Spessart, so thither sent the wine.
The like shall never happen again by fault of mine."

LIII

Then said the Netherlander, " Little thank I such care.
I look'd for seven good sumpters to mend our thirsty fare
With mead and wine of spices; if so we could not dine,
Better by far have placed us close beside the Rhine."

LIV

Then spake the Chief of Trony, " Ye noble knights and bold,
I know just to our wishes a runnel clear and cold
Close by, so be not angry, but thither let us go."
Th' advice brought many a champion sorrow and mortal woe.

LV

Yet could not then his danger the death-doom'd hero spy.
Little thought he so foully by seeming friends to die.
His heart knew naught of falsehood; 'twas open, frank and
    plain.
For his death dear paid thereafter who fondly hop'd to gain.

LVI

The noble knight Sir Siegfried with thirst was sore opprest,
So earlier rose from table, and could no longer rest,
But straight would to the mountain the running brook to find,
And so advanc'd the treason his faithless foes design'd.

LVII

Meanwhile were slowly lifted on many a groaning wain
The beasts in that wild forest by Siegfried's manhood slain.
Each witness gave him honor, and loud his praises spoke.
Alas! that with him Hagan his faith so foully broke.

LVIII

Now when to the broad linden they all would take their way,
Thus spake the fraudful Hagan, " Full oft have I heard say,
That none a match in swiftness for Kriemhild's lord can be,
Whene'er to race he pleases; would he grant us this to see? "

LIX

Then spake the Netherlander, Siegfried with open heart,
" Well then! let's make the trial! together we will start
From hence to yonder runnel; let us at once begin,
And he shall pass for winner who shall be seen to win."

LX

" Agreed! " said treacherous Hagan, " let us each other try."
Thereto rejoin'd stout Siegfried, " And if you pass me by,
Down at your feet I'll lay me humbled on the grass."
When these words heard Gunther, what joy could his surpass?

LXI

Then said the fearless champion, " And this I tell you more,
I'll carry all th' equipment that in the chase I wore,
My spear, my shield, my vesture—leave will I nothing out."
His sword then and his quiver he girt him quick about.

LXII

King Gunther and Sir Hagan to strip were nothing slow;
Both for the race stood ready in shirts as white as snow.
Long bounds, like two wild panthers, o'er the grass they took,
But seen was noble Siegfried before them at the brook.

LXIII

Whate'er he did, the warrior high o'er his fellows soar'd.
Now laid he down his quiver, and quick ungirt his sword.
Against the spreading linden he lean'd his mighty spear.
So by the brook stood waiting the chief without a peer.

LXIV

In every lofty virtue none with Sir Siegfried vied.
Down he laid his buckler by the water's side.
For all the thirst that parch'd him, one drop he never drank
Till the king had finish'd; he had full evil thank.

LXV

Cool was the little runnel, and sparkled clear as glass.
O'er the rill King Gunther knelt down upon the grass.
When he his draught had taken he rose and stepp'd aside.
Full fain alike would Siegfried his thirst have satisfied.

LXVI

Dear paid he for his courtesy; his bow, his matchless blade,
His weapons all, Sir Hagan far from their lord convey'd,
Then back sprung to the linden to seize his ashen spear,
And to find out the token survey'd his vesture near;

LXVII

Then, as to drink Sir Siegfried down kneeling there he found,
He pierc'd him through the crosslet, that sudden from the wound
Forth the life-blood spouted e'en o'er his murderer's weed.
Never more will warrior dare so foul a deed.

LXVIII

Between his shoulders sticking he left the deadly spear.
Never before Sir Hagan so fled for ghastly fear,
As from the matchless champion whom he had butcher'd there.
Soon as was Sir Siegfried of the mortal wound aware,

LXIX

Up he from the runnel started as he were wood.
Out from betwixt his shoulders his own huge boar-spear stood.
He thought to find his quiver or his broadsword true.
The traitor for his treason had then receiv'd his due.

LXX

But, ah! the deadly wounded nor sword nor quiver found;
His shield alone beside him lay there upon the ground.
This from the bank he lifted and straight at Hagan ran;
Him could not then by fleetness escape King Gunther's man.

LXXI

E'en to the death though wounded, he hurl'd it with such power,
That the whirling buckler scatter'd wide a shower
Of the most precious jewels, then straight in shivers broke.
Full gladly had the warrior ta'en vengeance with that stroke.

LXXII

E'en as it was, his manhood fierce Hagan level'd low.
Loud, all around, the meadow rang with the wondrous blow.
Had he in hand good Balmung, the murderer he had slain.
His wound was sore upon him; he writh'd in mortal pain.

LXXIII

His lively color faded; a cloud came o'er his sight;
He could stand no longer; melted all his might;
In his paling visage the mark of death he bore.
Soon many a lovely lady sorrow'd for him sore.

LXXIV

So the lord of Kriemhild among the flowerets fell.
From the wound fresh gushing his heart's blood fast did well.
Then thus amidst his tortures, e'en with his failing breath,
The false friends he upbraided who had contriv'd his death.

LXXV

Thus spake the deadly wounded, " Ay! cowards false as hell!
To you I still was faithful; I serv'd you long and well;—
But what boots all?—for guerdon treason and death I've won,
By your friends vile traitors! foully have you done.

LXXVI

" Whoever shall hereafter from your loins be born,
Shall take from such vile fathers a heritage of scorn.
On me you have wreak'd malice where gratitude was due.
With shame shall you be banish'd by all good knights and true."

LXXVII

Thither ran all the warriors where in his blood he lay.
To many of that party sure 'twas a joyless day.
Whoe'er were true and faithful, they sorrow'd for his fall.
So much the peerless champion had merited of all.

LXXVIII

With them the false King Gunther bewept his timeless end.
Then spake the deadly wounded, " Little it boots your friend
Yourself to plot his murder, and then the deed deplore.
Such is a shameful sorrow ; better at once 'twere o'er."

LXXIX

Then spake the low'ring Hagan, " I know not why you moan.
Our cares all and suspicions are now for ever flown.
Who now are left, against us who'll dare to make defence?
Well's me, for all this weeping, that I have rid him hence."

LXXX

" Small cause hast thou," said Siegfried, " to glory in my fate.
Had I ween'd, thy friendship cloak'd such murderous hate,
From such as thou full lightly could I have kept my life.
Now grieve I but for Kriemhild, my dear, my widow'd wife.

LXXXI

" Now may God take pity, that e'er I had a son,
Who this reproach must suffer from deed so foully done,
That by his murderous kinsmen his father thus was slain.
Had I but time to finish, of this I well might plain.

LXXXII

" Surely so base a murder the world did never see,"
Said he, and turn'd to Gunther, " as you have done on me.
I sav'd your life and honor from shame and danger fell,
And thus am I requited by you I serv'd so well.

LXXXIII

Then further spake the dying, and speaking sigh'd full deep,
" Oh king! if thou a promise with anyone wilt keep,
Let me in this last moment thy grace and favor find
For my dear love and lady, the wife I leave behind.

LXXXIV

" Remember, she's thy sister, yield her a sister's right,
Guard her with faith and honor, as thou'rt a king and knight.
My father and my followers for me they long must wait,
Comrade ne'er found from comrade so sorrowful a fate."

LXXXV

In his mortal anguish he writh'd him to and fro,
And then said, deadly groaning, "This foul and murderous
  blow
Deep will ye rue hereafter; this for sure truth retain,
That in slaying Siegfried you yourselves have slain."

LXXXVI

With blood were all bedabbled the flowerets of the field.
Some time with death he struggled, as though he scorn'd to yield
E'en to the foe, whose weapon strikes down the loftiest head.
At last prone in the meadow lay mighty Siegfried dead.

LXXXVII

When now the chiefs were certain that dead was the good
  knight,
They laid him on a buckler with gold all richly dight,
Then counsel took together the general to mislead,
And keep the shameful secret that Hagan did the deed.

LXXXVIII

Then many said, repenting, "This deed will prove our bale;
Still let us shroud the secret, and all keep in one tale,
That the good lord of Kriemhild to hunt alone preferr'd,
And so was slain by robbers as through the wood he spurr'd."

LXXXIX

"I'll bring him home, and gladly," said Hagan, frowning stern;
"As to his wife, I reck not whether the truth she learn,
Who slander'd gentle Brunhild, and wrought her so much ill.
I care not for her weeping, do she whate'er she will."

XC

Of that same little runnel where Siegfried murder'd fell,
The true and rightful story you now shall hear me tell.
In th' Odenwald is a village, Odenheim is its name.
There still the brook is running; doubt not it is the same.

SEVENTEENTH ADVENTURE

HOW SIEGFRIED WAS BEWAILED AND BURIED

I

TILL nightfall there they tarried, and then the Rhine recross'd;
Never yet hunted warriors at such a grievous cost.
Many a fair lady sorrow'd for a hart they slew that day;
The life of many a champion must for that hunting pay.

II

Of overweening outrage now must tell my strain,
And dire revenge remorseless; the dead, thus foully slain,
As though athirst for horrors, Hagan bade bear away,
And cast before the chamber where unweeting Kriemhild lay.

III

He bade his followers darkling down lay him at the door,
That she might surely find him, as she stepp'd the threshold o'er.
Going forth to matins ere the dawn of day,
For from a single service she seldom kept away.

IV

The minster bells were ringing at th' early 'custom'd hour.
Upstarted then fair Kriemhild, and wak'd each maid in bower.
For light she call'd and vesture that she might straight be
    gown'd.
A chamberlain hasten'd thither, and there Sir Siegfried found.

V

He saw him blood-bespatter'd, with weed all dabbled o'er;
He knew not 'twas his master stretch'd on the reeking floor;
In went he to the chamber; with him the light he took,
By which on such deep horror sad Kriemhild was to look.

VI

As she now with her maidens to church would take her way,
The chamberlain bespoke her; "Lady, a little stay;
A murder'd knight is lying close before the sill."
"O woe!" cried fearful Kriemhild, "what means this tale of
    ill?"

VII

Ere yet she could see clearly 'twas her lord who lay there lay
    slain,
The question put by Hagan rush'd to her mind again,
How he could guard her husband; then anguish first she felt.
From his death for ever with lingering grief she dwelt.

VIII

To earth down sank she senseless, that not a word she spoke.
There lay the fair, the friendless, beneath that mortal stroke.
Then, from her swoon reviving, up from the ground she sprang,
And shriek'd so shrill and sudden, that all the chamber rang.

IX

Then said her trembling maidens, " What stranger here lies
    slain ? "
From her mouth a bloody torrent burst through heart-quelling
    pain.
" No, no! " said she, " 'tis Siegfried, my love, that there lies
    low.
'Twas Brunhild gave the counsel, and Hagan struck the blow."

X

Thither where the corpse was lying, her maids their lady led;
With her lily hand, all trembling, she raised his languish'd head;
Howe'er with blood 'twas dabbled, her lord at once she knew.
There lay the Chief of Netherland, a piteous sight to view.

XI

Then weeping thus and wailing the queen her sorrows pour'd;
" Woe's me, woe's me for ever! sure no fair foeman's sword
Shiver'd thy failing buckler; 'twas murder stopp'd thy breath;
O that I knew who did it! death I'd requite with death."

XII

Then wept and wail'd full shrilly her gentle maidens all
With their beloved mistress; woe were they for the fall
Of their noble master there in his blood embrued.
Hagan the wrath of Brunhild had wreak'd with deadly feud.

XIII

Then spake the sorrow-laden, " Go hence with your best speed,
Quick call up Siegfried's liegemen, his warriors good at need;
To Siegmund, too, let tidings of my deep loss be borne,
That he may help his daughter his murder'd son to mourn."

XIV

A messenger ran quickly, and came where slept the band
Of Siegfried's chosen champions from the Nibelunger's land.
Their merry cheer his tidings chang'd to sorrow deep.
His tale they would not credit until they saw him weep.

XV

Thence quickly came he running where aged Siegmund lay
From the king's aching eyelids sweet sleep was far away.
His heart, I ween, foreboded the deed that had been done,
And that the childless father no more should see his son.

XVI

" Wake, wake! Sir King! Sir Siegmund! Kriemhild, my
        lady dear,
In haste hath sent me hither; she's plung'd in doleful drear;
Woe, that all woe surpasses, wrings her inmost heart.
Help her to mourn the misery, whereof you own a part."

XVII

Then said the king, half-rising, " What has happ'd of woe
To the fair Lady Kriemhild, which here thou com'st to show?"
" Alas!" replied he weeping, " concealment here is vain;
The noble Netherlander, Siegfried, thy son, is slain."

XVIII

Then said the good King Siegmund, " Leave off such idle sport;
For my sake spread no further this mischievous report.
Were't true indeed that Siegfried my son were made away,
Ne'er could I cease from wailing e'en to my dying day."

XIX

" If me you will not credit, but still will doubt my tale,
Hark then yourself to Kriemhild, hear her so wildly wail,
Her and her band of maidens, for noble Siegfried dead."
Then sorely shudder'd Siegmund; deep cause had he for dread.

XX

Straight from his bed up sprang he, and his hundred warriors
    too;
Their long sharp-edged weapons with hasty hand they drew.
Where they heard the wailing, headlong they thither ran;
Thither too Siegfried's thousand, each a chosen man,

XXI

Led by the shrieks of horror, ran with like eager speed.
Some of the household fancied, they came for funeral weed.
Well might they be confounded, and from their senses start.
The sting of deadly sorrow was deep in every heart.

XXII

Then said the good King Siegmund, when Kriemhild he had
    seen,
" Woe worth our journey hither! would it had never been!
'Midst such good friends and kinsmen, who has this murder
    done,
Which thee hath cost thy husband, and me, alas! my son?"

XXIII

The noble lady answer'd, " Could I the murderer find,
I'd wreak on him such vengeance with all my heart and mind,
That all his friends should sorrow at the woful tale,
While they had eyes for weeping, while they had tongues to
    wail."

XXIV

His arms round the dead champion Sir Siegmund trembling
    threw;
Thereat so loud the sorrow of each beholder grew,
That the proud hall of Gunther and the palace high
And Worms, through all his quarters, rung to the thrilling cry.

XXV

But none there could bring comfort to Siegfried's lady true.
Out from his bloodied vesture his comely limbs they drew,
And wash'd his wound wide-gaping, and laid him on the bier.
Woe were his weeping followers through heart-consuming
    drear.

XXVI

Out then spake his warriors from the Nibelungers' land;
" Revenge will we our master each with his own good hand
This very house must harbor him who has done the deed."
Then hasten'd Siegfried's meiny to don their warlike weed.

XXVII

Now did the chosen squadron each with his buckler stand,
Eleven hundred champions; at head of all the band
Was seen the reverend Siegmund; to faith and honor true
Fain would he take vengeance on those who Siegfried slew.

XXVIII

With whom they were to battle they could not yet discern,
Unless it were with Gunther and his Burgundians stern,
For with them did Siegfried to the fatal hunting go.
When Kriemhild saw them weapon'd, 'twas ill on ill, 'twas woe
    on woe.

XXIX

However deep her anguish, however great her need,
She fear'd to see her followers the Nibelungers bleed
Beneath her brother's numbers; so, their stout minds to bend,
She gave them gentle counsel, as friend should deal with friend.

XXX

Thus said the mournful lady, " Siegmund, my lord, give ear.
What is it you are doing? some rash resolve I fear.
King Gunther has about him full many a man of might;
You and all must perish in such unequal fight."

XXXI

Each had bound on his buckler; each held his sword in hand;
They yearn'd for blood and vengeance; with prayer and with
    command
She press'd th' impatient warriors to choose the milder part;
They call'd for instant battle; that cut her to the heart.

XXXII

She spake, " My good lord Siegmund, lay thoughts of vengeance by
Till some more fitting season; then with you fain will I
Revenge my murder'd husband; could I but come to know
Who has made me thus a widow, woe•should be his for woe.

XXXIII

" Many are the haughty warriors here on the banks of Rhine,
So keep peace for the present; such sure advice is mine;
The match is too unequal, thirty at least to one;
God do to them hereafter as they to us have done.

XXXIV

" Stay here, and in my sorrow be pleas'd a part to take,
Mine and my lord's revengers, till day begin to break,
And help me then to coffin my lord who there lies low."
Then all the warriors answer'd, " Dear lady, be it so."

XXXV

In sooth it was a wonder that none can tell aright,
How wept and loud lamented many a dame and many a knight,
That e'en unto the city the rueful wail was borne;
In haste the noble burghers came when they heard them mourn.

XXXVI

They with the guests lamented, for sore they griev'd as well.
What was the offence of Siegfried, none of them could tell,
For which by stroke so sudden the chief had lost his life.
There with the high-born ladies wept each good burgher's wife.

XXXVII

Joiners and smiths were summon'd to frame a coffin strong,
Beset with gold and silver, massy and broad and long,
And braced with bars of iron to guard the frailer wood.
Then all the crowd about it in dreary sorrow stood.

XXXVIII

'And now the night was over; forth peep'd the morning fair;
Straight bade the noble lady thence to the minster bear
The matchless champion Siegfried, her husband lov'd so dear.
All her friends close follow'd with many a sigh and tear.

XXXIX

When they the minster enter'd, how many a bell was rung!
How many a priest on all sides the mournful requiem sung!
Then thither with his meiny came Dankrat's haughty son,
And thither too grim Hagan; it had been better left undone.

XL

Then spoke the king, " Dear sister, woe worth this loss of thine!
Alas that such misfortune has happ'd to me and mine!
For sure the death of Siegfried we ever both must rue."
" Nay," said the mournful lady, " so without cause you do,

XLI

" For if you really rued it, never had it been.
I know you have your sister forgotten quite and clean,
So I and my beloved were parted as you see.
Good God! would he had granted the stroke had fall'n on me!"

XLII

Firmly they made denial; Kriemhild at once replied,
" Whoe'er in this is guiltless, let him this proof abide.
In sight of all the people let him approach the bier,
And so to each beholder shall the plain truth appear."

XLIII

It is a mighty marvel, which oft e'en now we spy,
That, when the blood-stain'd murderer comes to the murder'd
nigh,
The wounds break out a-bleeding; then to the same befell,
And thus could each beholder the guilt of Hagan tell.

XLIV

The wounds at once burst streaming fast as they did before;
Those, who then sorrow'd deeply, now yet lamented more.
Then outspake King Gunther, " I give you here to know,
He was slain by robbers; Hagan struck ne'er a blow."

XLV

" Ay! well know I those robbers," his widow'd sister said;
" By the hands of his true comrades may God revenge the dead!
False Gunther, and false Hagan! 'twas you, your friend that
    slew."
Thereat the knights of Siegfried gripp'd to their swords anew.

XLVI

This more distracted Kriemhild; when in her anxious pain
Two friends she saw approaching to seek and mourn the slain,
Gernot her good brother, and Giselher the young.
Their eyes were blind with weeping; true grief their bosoms
    wrung.

XLVII

They wept for Kriemhild's husband, and inly sorrowed too.
Mass now all would be singing; the doors they open threw,
And straight into the minster both men and women press'd.
Those, who could well spare Siegfried, mourn'd for him with the
    rest.

XLVIII

Gernot then and Giselher thus spake, " My sister dear!
For this sad death take comfort, all must have sorrow here.
We'll do our best to help thee as long as we have life."
Yet could not they nor others console the widow'd wife.

XLIX

His coffin now was ready; it was about midday;
From the bier he was lifted whereon till now he lay.
Yet would not his pale lady have him laid at once in ground.
His friends and faithful followers to further toil were bound.

L

In richest stuff, deep sighing, they wrapp'd the clay-cold dead;
Not one, I ween, was present, but bitter tears he shed.
Then wail'd the high-born Uta; deep teen in heart she bore;
And all her dames lamented that Siegfried was no more.

LI

Soon as 'twas heard, the murder'd had now been laid in chest,
And that the mass was singing, to church the people press'd.
For his soul what offerings were brought in all men's view!
E'en 'midst foes so deadly, friends had he firm and true.

LII

Then the wretched Kriemhild her chamberlains bespake,
" Now must you toil and trouble suffer for my sake.
To those who honor'd Siegfried, and dear his widow hold,
For the soul of the departed deal out his treasur'd gold."

LIII

No child, howe'er so little, just knowing wrong from right,
But brought an offering thither; ere buried was the knight,
At least a hundred masses they sang the whole day long;
Thither all friends of Siegfried's flock'd in, a numerous throng.

LIV

When now the chants were over, the crowd would wend away;
Then spake the sobbing Kriemhild, " Ah! leave me not, I pray,
This night alone to sorrow, and watch th' unheeding dead.
With him, my own beloved, all my joys lie withered.

LV

" Three nights, three days, I'll keep him, and gaze upon him
      still,
Till of the dearly dear one I thus have had my fill.
What if God be willing that me, too, death should seize?
Then well at once were ended poor Kriemhild's miseries."

LVI

The people of the city went home as darkness fell;
The priests and monks attendant, and all the train, who well
Had serv'd the champion living, fair Kriemhild begg'd to stay.
Their night was full of sorrow, of dreariment their day.

LVII

Many of the woful mourners nor meat nor drink would taste,
But for all such as needed at hand was ready plac'd
Good store of each provision; this Siegmund took in hand.
There mickle toil awaited the Nibelungers' band.

LVIII

For three whole days together, as we have heard men say,
Whoe'er had skill in singing, on them hard labor lay.
Sore were their hearts afflicted, as for the soul they pray'd
Of that redoubted champion, who there a corpse was laid.

LIX

There, too, the poor and needy, who of his own had nought,
In hand, by Kriemhild furnish'd, a golden offering brought
From Siegfried's proper treasure; when his body lifeless lay,
Marks full many a thousand for his soul were given away.

LX

Landed rents and revenues she scatter'd wide around,
Wherever sacred convents and holy men were found,
And to the poor gave silver and clothes in plenteous store.
She proved by all her actions what love to him she bore.

LXI

On the third morn when duly the mass was to be sung,
With country folk all weeping (such grief their bosoms wrung)
The churchyard of the minster was fill'd from end to end.
Each wail'd the dead, each sorrow'd as for his dearest friend.

LXII

In four days successive were scattered 'mongst the poor
Marks some thirty thousand for Siegfried's soul, or more.
To the good knight such honor his friends desir'd to pay,
When his life was brought to nothing, and his beauty passed
   away.

LXIII

The singing now was over, God had been serv'd as due;
Then with o'ermastering sorrow strove that empassion'd crew.
Next to the grave they brought him from out the minster near.
One weeping, one wild wailing was then alone to hear.

LXIV

Loud shrieking, mov'd the people around the bearers slow;
None there, nor man nor woman, but wore one face of woe.
'Twas sung; 'twas said, as fitted, ere he in ground was laid.
Ah! what good priests to Siegfried the last sad duties paid!

LXV

Ere to the grave advancing his own true lady came,
Her sense-o'erpowering sorrow so shook her wasted frame,
That oft was need to sprinkle her from the cool-springing well.
Boundless was her distraction; the like no tongue can tell.

LXVI

'Twas strange, such utter anguish dislodged not the frail life.
With eager haste to help her flock'd many a wailing wife.
Then spake the queen, " Ye warriors! My murder'd Siegfried's
    best,
By your love to your master grant me this last request.

LXVII

" Let me have one small pleasure 'mid pains so manifold;
The stately head of Siegfried I would once more behold."
She begg'd so long, so wailful, that less they could not do
Than force the coffin open, and give the corpse to view.

LXVIII

So thither they led the lady, where lay the clay-cold dead.
With her fine snowy fingers she rais'd his stately head,
And kiss'd him lifeless lying; long bending there she stood;
Her fair eyes for anguish wept o'er him tears of blood.

LXIX

How woful was their parting! Borne was she thence away,
Walk she could no longer; insensible she lay
Through bitterness of sorrow, so lovely and so still,
As if Death would have smitten, yet wanted heart to kill.

LXX

When now the noble champion was duly laid in ground,
O'erwhelm'd with boundless sorrow the valiant chiefs were
    found,
That from the land of Nibelung had come with him erewhile;
King Siegmund too thereafter was seldom seen to smile.

LXXI

Many were there among them who made unceasing moan,
Nor ate nor drank for anguish till three whole days were gone.
Then hard constraint compell'd them to life against their will,
And they from grief recover'd, as haps to thousands still.

LXXII

In deadly swoon unconscious the widow'd Kriemhild lay,
Both day and night unalter'd e'en to the second day,
Nor heard whate'er was spoken, nor mark'd what pass'd around;
In like unheeding sorrow was eke King Siegmund drown'd.

LXXIII

With pain back to his senses return'd the childless chief;
Shrunk were his powers, and weaken'd through the strong dint
    of grief,
Nor was there ground for wonder.   Then said his liegemen near
" My lord, best travel homeward; we must not tarry here."

EIGHTEENTH ADVENTURE
HOW SIEGMUND RETURNED HOME

I

THE father-in-law of Kriemhild to the pale mourner went,
And kindly thus bespake her, " Our thoughts are homeward
    bent;
Unwelcome guests in Rhineland I ween we needs must be,
So, Kriemhild, dearest lady, ride to my land with me.

II

" Thou must not here dwell helpless among thy foemen left,
Where both of us of Siegfried foul treason hath bereft.
I'll guard thee with firm friendship and honor undefil'd
For love of thy good husband and of his noble child.

III

" All power, beloved lady, shall be thine again,
And, as thy lord intended, royally shalt thou reign.
The land, the crown, thou ownedst, thou both, as erst, shalt
    sway.
To thee shall Siegfried's liegeman a willing service pay."

IV

Forthwith 'twas told his followers that they must hence with
    speed;
Each straight to the stable hurried for his steed.
To dwell with deadly foemen scorn and shame they thought;
Matrons and maids were stirring, and out their vesture sought.

V

When now the good King Siegmund ready was to ride,
Her mother sued to Kriemhild among her kin to bide,
That still her only daughter her aged eyes might see.
The joy-bereft made answer, " Nay, that can hardly be.

VI

" With my eyes could I ever the fawning friend behold,
Who wrought me, wretched woman, sorrows so manifold?"
Then spake the youthful Giselher, " Dear sister, why away?
For love's sake and for duty's, here with thy mother stay.

VII

" Who have weigh'd thee down with sorrow and wreak'd on thee
    their hate,
Of them thou need'st no service; live from my sole estate."
She answer'd thus the warior, " No! no! it cannot be.
Die should I straight of horror, if I should Hagan see."

VIII

" From that thou may'st be certain I'll shield thee, sister dear,
With me shalt thou dwell ever, thy brother Giselher,
Who, if love can bring comfort, will thy sad loss supply."
" Ah! " said the heaven-forsaken, " Of that sore need have I."

IX

Soon as this gentle proffer the youthful knight had made,
Next Uta and good Gernot and their true cousins pray'd
The joy-deserted mourner among them there to stay.
" Her kin 'mong Siegfried's followers were few and far away."

X

" To you they all are strangers," said Gernot, drawing nigh;
" No man there lives so mighty but he must some time die;
Consider this, fair sister, and comfort to you take;
Here with your friends 'twere better your fix'd abode to make."

XI

At last she promised Giselher that she would there abide.
Meanwhile the knights of Siegmund ready were to ride
To the Nibelunger's country; their steeds were led from stall,
And on the sturdy sumpters was laid their raiment all.

XII

The venerable Siegmund went up to Kriemhild then,
And with these words address'd her: " Lady, Siegfried's men
Are waiting with the horses; part must we instantly;
It irks me every moment we stay in Burgundy."

XIII

Then answer'd Lady Kriemhild, " Such friends as wish me well
And bear me love, advise me among them here to dwell,
Since in the land of Nibelung nor kith nor kin have I."
Woe was the noble Siegmund at hearing her reply.

XIV

" In this at least," return'd he, " trust not their offers fair.
Thou before all my kindred the royal crown shalt wear
With the same pride and puissance as ere our joys were crost,
Nor want of aught remind thee that Siegfried we have lost.

XV

" Come then, return among us for thy fair infant's sake;
Desert not the young orphan; a mother's duty take.
When he grows up to manhood, he'll comfort thy sad cheer;
Meanwhile good knights shall serve thee, who held thy husband
    dear."

XVI

Said she, " My good lord Siegmund, from home I cannot ride.
Whatever hence befall me, here must I still abide
Among my proper kinsmen, who'll help me to lament."
Her words gave the good warriors sorrow and discontent.

XVII

With one accord they answer'd, " We must in truth confess,
That never till this moment we felt true bitterness,
If thou persist to tarry among our foemen here.
Sure for a peaceful journey knights never paid so dear."

XVIII

" Hence without thought of danger ride home with God to
    friend,
Your steps a fitting escort shall through this land attend
E'en to your native country.   Farewell, good knights and true;
My dear, my orphan'd infant I trust, my friends, to you."

XIX

When they perceiv'd for certain that she her purpose kept,
The warriors of King Siegmund with one accord they wept.
With what heart-rending sorrow the reverend Siegmund, too,
Parted from Lady Kriemhild! then what was grief he knew.

XX

"Woe worth this dreary festal!" the hoary monarch cried,
"To kings nor to their kinsmen shall never more betide
From merriment and pleasure such heart-devouring teen.
In Burgundy shall Siegmund never more be seen."

XXI

Then said and frown'd indignant the knights of Siegfried's
        train,
"Nay, into this same country we well may come again
To seek and find the traitor who laid our master low.
Among the kin of Siegfried they have many a mortal foe."

XXII

Lovingly kiss'd he Kriemhild, and sadly thus 'gan say,
When he could see too clearly that she was fix'd to stay,
"Now home, bereav'd and joyless, a weary way we go.
'Tis only now I'm feeling the fulness of my woe."

XXIII

They rode without an escort from Worms beyond the Rhine.
Sorrowful and silent they mov'd in lengthen'd line,
Nor fear'd assault or ambush by lurking foemen plann'd;
Secure each Nibelunger felt in his own right hand.

XXIV

From all they kept disdainful, leave of none they took;
Giselher and Gernot such parting could not brook.
But lovingly approach'd them; woe were they for their woe;
That for their loss they sorrow'd, they gave their guest to know.

XXV

Then gently spoke Prince Gernot, and heav'd full many a sigh,
"God in heaven is my witness, nor part the guilt had I
In the death of Siegfried, nor had I heard before
That any him bore malice; I sorrow for him sore."

XXVI

To them was given good escort by Giselher the young.
Deep-sorrowing altogether he brought them safe along,
Both king and loyal liegemen, home to Netherland.
There met they all their kindred; small joy was in the band.

XXVII

What happ'd to them thereafter is more than I can say.
At Worms still heard was Kriemhild complaining, day by day.
That none her sorrow pitied, or brought her comfort due,
Save Giselher her brother; he still was good and true.

XXVIII

Meanwhile sat misproud Brunhild in haughtiness uncheck'd;
Of Kriemhild's tears and sorrows her it nothing reck'd.
She pitied not the mourner; she stoop'd not to the low.
Soon Kriemhild took full vengeance, and woe repaid with woe.

NINETEENTH ADVENTURE

HOW THE TREASURE OF THE NIBELUNGERS WAS BROUGHT TO WORMS

I

WHILE thus the mourning Kriemhild remain'd in widow'd state,
Count Eckewart upon her did ever constant wait
With all his men about him; he serv'd her without fail,
And help'd his weeping lady his murdered lord to wail.

II

At Worms fast by the minster was fram'd for her to dwell
A building high and spacious, and thereto furnish'd well,
Where sat she joyless ever among her joyless train.
To church she oft betook her, and there would linger fain.

III

How oft, weigh'd with sorrow (she seldom miss'd a day),
Thither would she go faintly where her beloved lay,
And God for grace and mercy upon his soul implore,
And with true love unfailing beweep him evermore!

IV

Queen Uta and her ladies to sooth the mourner sought,
But still take could she never the comfort that they brought;
The sting of deadly sorrow had pierc'd her heart too deep;
Nor love had she, nor longing, but for her lord to weep.

V

Such grief as Kriemhild's never wife for her husband knew;
Thence might be seen how faithful her heart was, and how true.
E'en to her day of dying her life in woe she pass'd.
She took for her slain Siegfried a dread revenge at last.

VI

So after her bereavement she sat, for three long years
And half another, ever in sorrow and in tears,
Nor once spoke word to Gunther, albeit in blood so nigh,
Nor on her foeman Hagan ever once set eye.

VII

Then said the Knight of Trony, " Your best attention bend,
How you may hereafter your sister make your friend.
So might the wondrous treasure come to this land, I ween.
'Twould much be to your profit, could we appease the queen."

VIII

" We'll try," replied King Gunther, " my brothers with her bide
Perhaps by their persuasion she may be pacified,
And e'en in our possession the hoard contented see."
" I can't believe," said Hagan, " that that can ever be."

IX

Then to the Margrave Gary in haste King Gunther sent;
Ortwine to court was summon'd to further their intent,
And Gernot and young Giselher were both together brought.
The boon from Lady Kriemhild with friendly prayer they
  sought.

X

Then first the good Burgundian the valiant Gernot spake.
" Lady, too long you're wailing for your lost husband's sake.
Sure proof the king will give you, he ne'er the warrior slew;
Why then with such deep passion his death forever rue? "

XI

Said she, " Who charges Gunther? 'twas Hagan struck the blow.
He gain'd from me the secret, where steel could lay him low.
Could I suspect, that treason lurk'd such fair words among?
Else, be sure, had silence sat ever on my tongue.

XII

" Ah! had I ne'er betrayed him, but still his secret kept,
I had not now, poor widow! thus lamentably wept,
But ne'er will I forgive them, who this foul deed have done."
Then the stout knight, young Giselher, to intercede begun.

XIII

" Ay," said she, " I must greet him, you press and urge me so;
The more your fault and folly; such bitterness of woe
Hath the king brought upon me with no guilt on my part;
My mouth it may forgive him, but never will my heart."

XIV

" Matters may mend hereafter," her kin said with one voice,
" What if his future kindness should make her yet rejoice?
" Needs must he," said good Gernot, " make up for former ill."
" See! " said the sorrow-laden, " I'll do what'er you will.

XV

" Yes! I will greet King Gunther." She scarce had given
        consent
When with his best friends Gunther unto his sister went.
Yet durst not stern Hagan before the mourner go.
He knew himself blood-guilty, he had wrought her mortal woe.

XVI

When she had pardon'd Gunther all that had pass'd amiss,
He thought it fitting kindness the gentle dame to kiss.
Had he the deed not counsell'd which all that ill had wrought,
With freedom oft and boldness her presence he had sought.

XVII

Sure ne'er was reconcilement 'twixt friends too long apart
By such full tears cemented; her loss she took to heart,
Yet all concern'd she pardon'd, all, save only one.
Never had been the murder, if not by Hagan done.

XVIII

'Twas no long time thereafter when this device they wrought,
That from the land of Nibelung should to the Rhine be brought
By the command of Kriemhild the wondrous treasure bright;
'Twas her morning-gift at marriage and so was hers by right.

XIX

For it the youthful Giselher and eke good Gernot went;
Eighty hundred warriors with them their sister sent,
To bring it from the mountain, where close conceal'd it lay,
Watch'd by the stout dwarf Albric and his best friends alway.

XX

When now came the Burgundians the precious hoard to take,
Albric, the faithful keeper, thus his friends bespake:
" This far renowned treasure we can't withhold, I ween,
The marriage-morning present claim'd by the noble queen.

XXI

" Yet should they have it never, nor should we thus be cross'd,
Had we not the good cloud-cloak to our misfortune lost
Together with Sir Siegfried, who gain'd it here of yore;
For Kriemhild's noble husband the same at all times wore.

XXII

" Now ill, alas! has happ'd it to Siegfried the good knight,
That from us the cloud-cloak he took by conquering might,
And all this land to serve him as lord and master bound."
Then went the chamberlain sadly, where soon the keys he found.

XXIII

And now the men of Kriemhild before the mountain stood,
And some, too, of her kinsmen; the hoard, as best they could,
Down to the sea they carried; there in good barks 'twas laid,
Thence o'er the waves, and lastly up the Rhine convey'd.

XXIV

The tale of that same treasure might well your wonder raise;
'Twas much as twelve huge wagons in four whole nights and
     days
Could carry from the mountain down to the salt-sea bay,
If to and fro each wagon thrice journey'd every day.

XXV

It was made up of nothing but precious stones and gold;
Were all the world bought from it, and down the value told,
Not a mark the less thereafter were left, than erst was scor'd.
Good reason sure had Hagan to covet such a hoard.

XXVI

And there among was lying the wishing-rod of gold,
Which whoso could discover, might in subjection hold
All this wide world as master, with all that dwell therein.
There came to Worms with Gernot full many of Albric's kin.

XXVII

When Gernot and young Giselher had thus possession gain'd
Of that power-giving treasure, the rule they straight obtain'd
Of the country and the castles and many a warlike knight;
All was constrain'd to serve them through terror of their might.

XXVIII

When they had brought the treasure thence to King Gunther's
      land,
And had their charge deliver'd into fair Kriemhild's hand,
Cramm'd were the towers and chambers wherein the same they
      stor'd.
Ne'er told was tale of riches to match this boundless hoard.

XXIX

Yet had she found the treasure a thousand-fold as great,
Could she have seen but Siegfried restor'd to life's estate,
Bare as her hand had Kriemhild preferr'd with him to live,
Renouncing all the puissance which all that hoard could give.

XXX

Now she had gain'd possession, so liberal was the dame,
That foreign knights unnumber'd into the country came.
All prais'd her generous virtues, and own'd they ne'er had seen
Lady so open-handed as this fair widow'd queen.

XXXI

To rich and poor together began she now to give;
Thereat observ'd Sir Hagan, " If she should chance to live
Some little season longer, so many should we see
Won over to her service, that ill for us 'twould be."

XXXII

Thereto made answer Gunther, " The hoard is hers alone;
How can I check her giving?   She gives but from her own.
Scarce could I gain forgiveness for my offence of old.
I care not how she scatters her jewels and ruddy gold."

XXXIII

" A prudent man," said Hagan, " not for a single hour
Would such a mass of treasure leave in a woman's power.
She'll hatch with all this largess to her outlandish crew
Something that hereafter all Burgundy may rue."

XXXIV

Thereto replied King Gunther, " An oath to her I swore,
That I would ne'er offend her nor harm her any more;
And I'm resolv'd to keep it; my sister too is she."
At once Sir Hagan answer'd, " Then lay the blame on me."

XXXV

Too many of the chieftains their plighted faith forsook;
The powerful hoard the perjur'd from the poor widow took;
Sir Hagan straight made seizure at once of every key.
When her brother Gernot heard it, bitterly wroth was he.

XXXVI

Then spake the young Sir Giselher, " Hagan the fierce and rude
Hath foully wrong'd my sister; this I should have withstood;
But that he is my kinsman, it should cost his life."
Then afresh all vainly wept noble Siegfried's wife.

XXXVII

Then said the good Sir Gernot, " Ere this pernicious mine
Confound us any further, better beneath the Rhine
Sink it altogether, and tell no mortal where."
Then sadly went fair Kriemhild to her brother Giselher.

XXXVIII

She wept and said, " Dear brother, pray take some thought
        of me;
Of my person and possessions thou should'st the guardian be."
Then spake he to his sister, " I will, whate'er betide,
Soon as we come back hither, for now we hence must ride."

XXXIX

King Gunther and his kinsmen they forthwith left the land.
The very best among them he took to form his band.
There stay'd behind but Hagan; fierce hate and malice still
He bore the weeping Kriemhild, and sought to work her ill.

XL

Ere back the king came thither, impatient of delay
Hagan seiz'd the treasure, and bore it thence away.
Into the Rhine at Lochheim the whole at once threw he!
Henceforth he thought t' enjoy it, but that was ne'er to be.

XLI

He never more could get it for all his vain desire;
So fortune of the traitor cheats of his treason's hire.
Alone he hop'd to use it as long as he should live,
But neither himself could profit, nor to another give.

XLII

Once more return'd the princess, and with them all their train.
Forthwith began sad Kriemhild her heavy loss to plain
With ladies and with maidens; their grief indeed was strong.
In all good faith was Giselher ready to venge her wrong.

XLIII

Then said they altogether, " Much evil hath he done."
So for a time Sir Hagan retir'd their wrath to shun,
Till he regain'd their favor; at last they look'd it o'er.
Thereat to him fair Kriemhild yet deadlier hatred bore.

XLIV

Ere thus the Knight of Trony had hidd'n the wondrous hoard,
They all an oath together had sworn with one accord
To keep it in concealment while one of them should live,
So none himself could take it, nor to another give.

XLV

With this new weight of anguish surcharg'd was Kriemhild left,
Of her bold husband widow'd, and of the hoard bereft
By such o'erweening outrage; in tears the mourner lay,
Nor ever ceas'd to sorrow e'en till her dying day.

XLVI

From the death of Siegfried for thirteen years she dwelt
On her wrongs ever brooding, nor joy one moment felt.
The murder of her husband she could not once forget.
To him she still was faithful; that praise is Kriemhild's yet.

XLVII

The wealthy Lady Uta, when death took Dankrat hence,
A sumptuous monastery rais'd at her own expense,
Endow'd with rich revenues, which yet its coffers fill;
The abbey of Lorsch they call it; 'tis high in honor still.

XLVIII

Thereto the mourning Kriemhild no little part supplied
Both for the soul of Siegfried and for all souls beside.
She gave both gold and jewels; a wife more chaste and true,
And a more liberal giver man surely never knew.

XLIX

Since Kriemhild had King Gunther once to her grace restor'd,
And yet by his connivance next lost the precious hoard,
A thousand-fold more sorrow at her heart there lay.
The proud and high-born lady would gladly thence away.

L

Meanwhile for Lady Uta was built with skill and care
At Lorsch, fast by her abbey, a sumptuous palace fair.
The widow left her children, and there seclusion found.
Still lies she in her coffin deep in that hollow'd ground.

LI

Then said the queen to Kriemhild, " List to me, daughter dear,
Come to Lorsch, to my palace, thou canst not linger here;
And dwell with me thy mother, and cease to weep and grieve."
" To whom then," answer'd Kriemhild, " Shall I my husband
leave? "

LII

The Lady Uta answer'd, " Here let him still abide."
" Now God in heaven forbid it! " the faithful wife replied;
" No! my beloved mother, I must not have it so;
If Kriemhild hence must journey, with her must Siegfried go."

LIII

Then gave command the mourner up to take the dead;
His noble bones were forthwith transferr'd to their last bed
At Lorsch beside the minster in many-honor'd guise.
There yet in a long coffin the stately warrior lies.

LIV

Just then, when sorrowing Kriemhild was ready to depart,
And hop'd with her fond mother to ease her aching heart,
She yet was forc'd to tarry and that last hope resign.
'Twas caus'd by sudden tidings, that cross'd from far the Rhine.

TWENTIETH ADVENTURE

HOW KING ETZEL SENT INTO BURGUNDY TO PROPOSE FOR KRIEMHILD

I

'Twas of yore, in the season when Dame Helca died,
And the stout King Etzel would take another bride,
His friends all gave him counsel his marriage troth to plight
To a proud Burgundian widow, that Lady Kriemhild hight.

II

His courtiers thus, when Helca had ended now her life,
Bespoke him, " Would you ever take a noble wife,
The best with whom a monarch could share his royal state,
Make choice of this fair lady; bold Siegfried was her mate."

III

Then answer'd stout King Etzel, " How can succeed the plan,
For me, that am a heathen, and not a christen'd man,
To woo a Christian woman? never consent will she;
Sure 'twere a very marvel if this could ever be."

IV

Thereto his knights made answer, " What if she yet consent
Mov'd by your name so glorious and potent regiment?
'Twere well to make the trial whatever thence accrue;
For such a fair companion a king might gladly sue."

V

The noble king then question'd, " Who among you knows
The people and the country where Rhine's fair current flows? "
Said Rudeger of Bechlaren, " For that trust me alone;
I from earliest childhood the noble kings have known.

VI

" Gunther and Gernot, good knights as e'er can be;
The third is the young Giselher; each of the brethren three
Does all, whereby clear honor and high repute are won,
Just as their brave forefathers down to our times have done."

VII

Thereto gave answer Etzel, " Friend, do to me declare,
If she indeed be worthy here the proud crown to wear;
And, if she be so lovely as by report is borne,
My best friends may be certain, they'll have no cause to mourn.

VIII

" For peerless grace and beauty with Helca she may vie,
My lady ever-honor'd; saw yet never eye
In all this world a fairer; she's of all queens the best;
The lord of such a lady must be supremely blest."

IX

" Then, as thou lov'st me, Rudeger, go, court her for my bride,
And if I should come ever to lie by Kriemhild's side,
Assure thee, to my utmost I will thy pains requite;
Well thou hast ever serv'd me, and done my will aright.

X

" Out of my treasure-chamber whate'er thou wilt I'll give,
That thou and thy companions merrily may live.
Clothes, horses, all thou needest, I'll willingly defray.
Of such make full provision, and speed thee on thy way."

XI

Thereto in answer Rudeger, the wealthy margrave, spake,
" Surely 'twould ill beseem me ought from the stores to take.
Fain will I bear thy message to the Rhenish brethren bold
From my own rich possessions, that of thee I have and hold."

XII

Then spake the mighty monarch, " Now when will you ride
To seek my love and lady? God be your guard and guide,
And keep you both in safety through all the paths you trace,
And fortune speed my wooing, that I may win my lady's
    grace."

XIII

Then Rudeger made answer, " Ere this land we quit,
With weapons and with raiment our band we out must fit,
That we before the princes in splendor due may shine.
Five hundred stately warriors I'll lead unto the Rhine;

XIV

" That, when the stout Burgundians me and mine shall see,
It by all beholders at once confess'd shall be,
That ne'er despatch'd a monarch, on distant wooing bent,
A band more choice and numerous than thou to Rhine hast sent.

XV

" And, noble king, remember whom thou desir'st to wed;
The first of martial champions, Sir Siegfried, shar'd her bed,
The son of royal Siegmund; thou hast seen him here before;
From all, the highest honors, and well deserv'd, he bore."

XVI

Then replied King Etzel, " If she was Siegfried's wife,
So honor'd was her husband, while he was yet in life,
That at my hands his consort will meet true love and care.
Heaven grant that I may find her as gracious as she's fair! "

XVII

Then spake the noble margrave, " Thus then at once I say,
We'll fix for our departure the four and twentieth day.
Straight to my dear wife Gotelind I'll send to let her know,
That on this quest for Kriemhild I must in person go."

XVIII

Rudeger to Bechlaren bade a courier speed amain;
The margravine his message fill'd both with joy and pain.
He told her he was going for the king to woo;
Fair Helca she remember'd with tender love and true.

XIX

Glad was she from her husband such tidings to receive,
And yet in part she sorrow'd; she could not choose but grieve,
In doubt to find a mistress so gracious as before,
And when she thought on Helca, her very heart was sore.

XX

Seven days Sir Rudeger in Hungary abode;
Well pleas'd was stout King Etzel when forth his envoy rode.
In the city of Vienna was order'd all their weed.
The margrave would not tarry, but ever on would speed.

XXI

Right gladly at Bechlaren he and his men were seen;
Him waited there Dame Gotelind and the young margravine
Rudeger's gentle daughter, and many a noble dame
Was there with fitting welcome as home the warriors came.

XXII

Ere the noble Rudeger to Bechlaren took his way
From the city of Vienna, the raiment rich and gay
Had safe arriv'd to meet them, full many a sumpter's load;
So strong they march'd, that little was robb'd upon the road.

XXIII

When they came to Bechlaren, to his companions brave
A warm and hearty welcome, the host, as fitted, gave,
And in commodious chambers lodg'd them all and some.
Dame Gotelind the wealthy rejoic'd to see him come.

XXIV

And so did his dear daughter, the fair young margravine.
Never were guests so welcome as these to her, I ween.
The chiefs that came from Hungary how gladly she survey'd!
Then thus with smiling aspect spake the noble maid.

XXV

" Welcome home, dear father, welcome thy comrades too! "
Fair thanks were paid the damsel by all that knightly crew,
As them and her befitted, for her reception kind.
Well to Lady Gotelind was known her husband's mind.

XXVI

As by the side of Rudeger that night awake she lay,
Thus in soft accents asking the margravine 'gan say,
" Whither have you been order'd by the King of Hungary? "
Said he, " My Lady Gotelind, I'll tell you willingly.

XXVII

" Our king again would marry now that fair Helca's dead,
And I must go a-wooing in royal Etzel's stead.
To ask the hand of Kriemhild hence to the Rhine I ride.
Here will she rule as lady with queenly power and pride."

XXVIII

" God grant it! " answered Gotelind, " So 'twill be surely best.
We hear her praise and honor by every tongue confess'd.
She'll be to us hereafter what Helca was whilere.
We the proud crown of Hungary may gladly see her wear."

XXIX

Then said the noble margrave, " Love and lady mine,
To the good knights, that with me prick hence unto the Rhine,
Give friendly gifts in plenty from our abundant store.
Fair robes and rich equipments the bold embolden more."

XXX

" Whoe'er will take a present," she answer'd, " not a guest
Shall go by me unguerdon'd of what may suit him best.
Whoever poor dismounted, rich shall return to selle."
Thereto replied the margrave, " Your words content me well."

XXXI

Ah! what rich stuffs the warriors then from her chamber bore!
'Mong the good knights were mantles shar'd out in copious
       store,
Each with the patient needle well sewn from throat to spur.
Therefrom whatever pleas'd him chose out Sir Rudeger.

XXXII

'Twas on the seventh fair morning that from Bechlaren rode
The host and his companions; they through Bavaria yode
With store of arms and raiment, yet such was their array,
That robbers rarely ventur'd to assail them on their way.

XXXIII

Within twelve days of journey by Rhine they drew the rein.
The news of their arrival no secret could remain.
To the king and his liegemen at once the tidings ran,
That come were certain strangers; the host to ask began,

XXXIV

If they were known to any; who knew, should say so straight
'Twas seen their sturdy sumpters bore many a heavy weight;
So, that they were wealthy, each took at once for known.
Forthwith were they to chambers in the wide city shown.

XXXV

Since no man knew the strangers who to the land were come,
Narrowly was each chieftain observ'd by all and some.
They wonder'd wherefore came they, and from what distant
        coast.
The same of stout Sir Hagan inquir'd the anxious host.

XXXVI

Then said the Knight of Trony, " I have not seen them yet;
I can inform you better when I and they have met.
Whatever be their country, how far soe'er it be,
They must indeed be strangers, if they're unknown to me."

XXXVII

Now were in fitting chambers bestow'd the noble guests. ·
The margrave and his comrades all donn'd their choicest vests,
And rode to court attended; all gaz'd on them their fill;
Right gorgeous was their raiment, and cut with curious skill.

XXXVIII

Straight cried the nimble Hagan, " If I conjecture right,
(Though now 'tis many a summer since last I saw the knight),
So moves yon gallant squadron, that we must needs have here
The mighty Hunnish margrave redoubted Rudeger."

XXXIX

" Nay! how can I believe it," said Gunther instantly,
" That he of Bechlaren has come to Burgundy?"
The king had scarce well ended, when they had drawn so nigh,
That Hagan could for certain good Rudeger descry.

XL

He and his friends ran forward, and flock'd the guests around.
Five hundred knights together sprung from horse to ground.
The valiant chiefs of Hungary were welcom'd o'er and o'er.
Messengers yet never such goodly raiment wore.

XLI

Then the stout Knight of Trony spoke these fair words aloud,
" Now in God's name welcome all ye champions proud,
The Lord of Bechlaren and his followers bold."
The warlike Huns were greeted with honors manifold.

XLII

King Gunther's nearest kinsmen to see them forward press'd.
Ortwine of Metz thus friendly Sir Rudeger address'd,
" We ne'er have seen so gladly on any former day
Guests in the bounds of Rhineland; this can I truly say."

XLIII

Much thanks for their fair welcome return'd the warriors all.
Thence forthwith stepp'd they forward into the spacious hall,
Where the king was seated amidst his chivalry.
He rose as in they enter'd, such was his courtesy.

XLIV

With what kind condescension to the messengers he went!
Gunther and Gernot welcom'd with friendly warm intent
Their guest and his companions, and made them fitting cheer.
By the hand then took King Gunther the noble Rudeger.

XLV

To the seat he brought him whereon himself he sat.
Then bade he hand the strangers (a joyful task was that)
Cups of his best metheglin and of the choicest wine
That ere was made from vineyards in the land all round the
Rhine.

XLVI

Giselher and Gary had both arriv'd at court,
Dankwart too and Folker had heard the glad report
Of such fair guests come thither; before the king they stood,
And joyously saluted the noble knights and good.

XLVII

Then to his lord Sir Hagan the Knight of Trony spake,
" These chiefs to Gotelind's husband a fit return should make
For all the friendly service he did to us of yore.
We should at full requite him, and love him still the more."

XLVIII

Then thus began King Gunther, " This now I needs must ask
How are they both who sent you (to tell me be your task),
King Etzel and Queen Helca, who reign in Hungary?"
The noble margrave answer'd, " I'll tell you willingly."

XLIX

Then from his seat the warrior uprose with all his train,
And thus bespake King Gunther, " If you, Sir King, are fain
To grant me gracious audience, nothing will I withhold.
The message, that I bring you, it shall be freely told."

L

Said he, " Whate'er the message that Etzel by you sends,
I give you leave to speak it without consulting friends.
At once then let me hear it, and these my comrades too.
All power you have with honor your business here to do."

LI

Then spake the noble envoy, " My mighty sovran sends
His love sincere and service to you and all your friends.
Here in distant Rhineland, and I in honor bring
A true and faithful greeting from a true and faithful king.

LII

" The noble king entreats you his sorrow to deplore;
His vassals all are mourning; my lady is no more,
Helca the fair and virtuous, who shar'd his royal bed.
Many a young maid is orphan'd now the good queen is dead.

LIII

" Children of noble princes she train'd with fostering care;
Whom have they now, so truly a mother's charge to bear?
The land is all in sorrow, the king can nought but plain;
'Twill be long time, I fear me, ere he be blithe again."

LIV

" Now heaven him quit," said Gunther, " that with so fair
    intent
To me and mine so distant his service he hath sent.
I take his greeting kindly; henceforth, as best they may,
My kinsmen and my servants his favor shall repay."

LV

Then spake the bold Burgundian, Gernot the stout and true,
" The death of fair Queen Helca the world may ever rue.
Beauty and worth together are buried in her grave."
To the words of Sir Gernot assent Sir Hagan gave.

LVI

Thereon the high-born envoy his message freely told,
" King, since you have permitted, I'll to your ears unfold,
Wherefore my royal master me to your court has sent,
Plung'd as he is in sorrow and doleful dreariment.

LVII

" It has been told my master, Sir Siegfried now is dead,
And Kriemhild left a widow; if thus they both have sped,
Would you but permit her, she the crown shall wear
Before the knights of Etzel, this bids me my good lord
    declare."

LVIII

Thereto the king made answer, with courteous kind intent,
" She will perform my pleasure if she to this consent.
Within three days I'll tell you whether her mind be so.
How can I promise Etzel; till first her will I know?"

LIX

Meanwhile the guests were feasted and furnish'd with the best,
And all so well entreated, that Rudeger confess'd
That among Gunther's vassals true friends he sure had won.
With zeal him serv'd Sir Hagan, as he once to him had done.

LX

So to the third day rested Sir Rudeger and his crew.
Meanwhile the king took counsel ('twas wisdom so to do),
And ask'd, what thought his kinsmen, if 'twere a fitting thing,
That Kriemhild for her husband should take the noble king.

LXI

All with one voice advis'd it; Hagan alone said nay;
Then to the bold knight Gunther thus 'gan the warrior say,
" If you are in your senses, beware what I foresee.
E'en with consent of Kriemhild ne'er let this marriage be."

LXII

" Wherefore," return'd King Gunther, " should I oppose her
        will?
Whate'er may please fair Kriemhild, I'll grant it freely still.
Remember, she's my sister; let her this crown obtain.
Ourselves should seek th' alliance, if honor thence she gain."

LXIII

Thereto replied Sir Hagan, " Let this no farther go;
If you knew King Etzel as I King Etzel know,
You ne'er would let him wed her as now I hear you say,
But rather look for ruin from this same marriage day."

LXIV

" What should I fear?" said Gunther, " Safe can I keep me
        still.
I dwell from him so distant, he ne'er can work me ill.
E'en though he wed my sister, I'll never come him nigh."
Once more rejoin'd Sir Hagan, " This ne'er advise will I."

LXV

For Gernot and young Giselher in haste King Gunther sent,
To learn of both the brethren whether they were content
That their fair sister Kriemhild should be King Etzel's bride.
Still gainsaid Sir Hagan, and not a soul beside.

LXVI

Then spake the bold Burgundian, Giselher the good knight.
" Now may you, friend Hagan, do what is just and right.
Make her full atonement, whom you have caus'd such pain,
Nor of the gift of fortune deprive her once again.

LXVII

" Yes, you have cost my sister so many a bitter tear,"
Thus further spoke the warrior redoubted Giselher,
" That she has cause to hate you; this must yourself confess,
For ne'er by man was woman spoil'd of such happiness."

LXVIII

" What I foresee for certain, that give I you to know.
If she but wed King Etzel and to his country go,
Some way she'll work us mischief, and bring revenge to bear.
She'll have all at her service many a good warrior there."

LXIX

Thereto the bold Sir Gernot thus in answer said,
" All then may rest in quiet e'en till they both are dead.
For wherefore should we ever set foot on Etzel's ground?
But yet to serve her truly we're all in honor bound."

LXX

Thereto thus answer'd Hagan, " For that I little care;
Let but the noble Kriemhild the crown of Helca wear,
Howe'er she plot our ruin, 'twill sure and sudden fall.
So let alone this matter; 'twere better so for all."

LXXI

Then spake in wrath Sir Giselher, fair Uta's youngest son,
" We must not sure like traitors demean us every one.
Her good should make us happy, her hopes we should fulfil.
Howe'er you murmur, Hagan, I'll serve her truly still."

LXXII

Ill pleas'd thereat was Hagan, and darkly frowning stood.
Gernot straight and Giselher, the noble knights and good,
And the rich King Gunther in this conclusion met,
T' assent, if Kriemhild wish'd it, and all ill will forget.

LXXIII

" I'll go and tell my lady," said Gary there in place,
" That forthwith to King Etzel she may accord her grace.
He holds such countless warriors beneath his awful sway;
Full well may he requite her for many a mournful day."

LXXIV

Swift went the chief to Kriemhild, exulting for her sake;
Gladly she receiv'd him; how quickly then he spake!
" Well may you greet me, lady; my newsman's guerdon give;
You and your woes are parted—henceforth with pleasure live.

LXXV

" One of the mightiest monarchs that ever sceptre bore
Of far-extended kingdoms, or crown imperial wore,
Now for your love is suing; noble knights, his friends,
Are hither come to woo you; this news your brother sends."

LXXVI

Then spake the sorrow-laden, " Now God in heaven forfend
That you, or any other that calls himself my friend,
Should mock a lonely widow! Who once has gain'd the free
And virgin love of woman, how can he think of me?"

LXXVII

Firmly she made denial; together came to her
Next her two faithful brethren, Gernot and Giselher.
With loving words they cheer'd her, and kindly urg'd her, too,
To take the king for husband; right well she thus would do.

LXXVIII

Yet could not all persuasion the faithful mourner bring
To choose a second lover, and yield unto the king.
Then begg'd the noble warriors, " If nothing more can be,
Consent at least a moment the messengers to see."

LXXIX

" I'll not deny," soft sighing the noble dame replied,
" But that I'd fain see Rudeger renown'd so far and wide
For all his many virtues: 'tis due to him alone;
Were't any other envoy, to him I'd ne'er be known.

LXXX

"So beg him," said she further, "to let me see him here
In my bower to-morrow; then I'll acquaint his ear
Myself with all my wishes and tell him all my tale."
Then bitterly began she once more to weep and wail.

LXXXI

Nothing the noble Rudeger had more desir'd, I ween,
Than to obtain an audience of that fair widow'd queen.
Such he well knew his wisdom and smooth persuasive skill,
He doubted not, to reason he'd bend her stubborn will.

LXXXII

So early on the morrow, about the matin song,
Forth came the noble envoys; there was a mighty throng;
To court with the good margrave there went a gorgeous
  crowd,
In glittering weed accoutred, of high-born knights and proud.

LXXXIII

Kriemhild, the fair, the spotless, amidst her ladies stood,
Waiting for Sir Rudeger the noble envoy good.
He found her in the vesture that every day she wore;
Her dames stood by in raiment all work'd and proider'd o'er.

LXXXIV

To the door to meet him with stately step she went,
And well and warmly welcom'd the chief from Etzel sent.
Eleven good knights were with him, himself the twelfth was
  there.
Ne'er came such high-born suitors to woo a queen so fair.

LXXXV

They bade the chief be seated, and with him all his band.
There the two noble margraves were seen before her stand,
Eckewart and Gary; none there was blithe or glad;
All wore one face of mourning, e'en as their lady sad.

LXXXVI

Before her meekly seated many a fair maid was seen,
Pale sorrowful companions of that woe-wither'd queen.
The cloth, that veil'd her bosom, with scalding tears was wet.
Well saw the noble margrave, her grief was lively yet.

LXXXVII

Then spake the high-born envoy, " Fair child of mightiest
    kings,
To me and to my comrades after our wanderings,
Vouchsafe now your permission before you here to stand,
And tell what brought us hither from our far-distant land."

LXXXVIII

" Now take my full permission," the queen said with a sigh,
" And speak your wishes freely; not ill inclin'd am I
To hear you, honor'd margrave! You are an envoy good."
Thereby her firm reluctance the rest well understood.

LXXXIX

Then the Prince of Bechlaren, Sir Rudeger, thus spake,
" The mighty monarch Etzel, lady! for your fair sake
Has bidd'n me journey hither, and many a good knight too
Has sent with me to Rhineland all for your hand to sue.

XC

" True love to you he proffers, pleasure unmix'd with pain,
A firm unswerving friendship, that shall to death remain;
Such love he bore Dame Helca; deep in his heart she lay;
He now for her lost virtues leads many a joyless day."

XCI

Then thus the queen made answer, " Margrave Rudeger,
If man could feel my sorrows, no suit would vex my ear,
Again to take a husband, and be again undone.
More have I lost already than woman ever won."

XCII

" What more amends for anguish," the warrior answer'd kind,
" Than faithful love unchanging, could one the blessing find,
Choosing the heart's beloved and choosing not amiss?
For life-consuming sorrow what sweeter balm than this?

XCIII

" To love my noble master should you consenting deign,
You o'er twelve mighty kingdoms a crownéd queen shall reign.
And more than thirty princedoms he at your feet will lay,
Won by his matchless puissance in many a bloody fray.

XCIV

" To you, besides, obedience many a good knight shall do,
That to my Lady Helca were wont to serve and sue.
And all the dames and damsels, that once swell'd Helca's state,
Daughters of high-born princes, shall now on Kriemhild wait.

XCV

" Thereto my lord will give you (this bade he me declare),
If you vouchsafe beside him the queenly crown to wear,
The highest rights and honors that once were Helca's due;
All these before his liegemen shall be transferr'd to you."

XCVI

" How can I feel contented," the mourning queen replied,
" To wed another hero, a widow and a bride?
Grim Death in one already has wounded me so sore,
That nought can now await me, but sorrow evermore."

XCVII

" Fair queen," the Huns made answer, " if only you consent,
Your days will with King Etzel so royally be spent,
That each will, as it passes, some varied pleasure bring;
Such store of courtly warriors has our redoubted king.

XCVIII

" Together Helca's damsels and your fair maids will vie
In zeal to do you service, one blooming company;
Good knights will there be merry amid so bright a train;
Be well advis'd, high lady! in sooth 'twill be your gain."

XCIX

" Well," said she, soft and courteous, " this converse now give
        o'er
Until to-morrow morning, then hither come once more,
And then your monarch's message I'll answer as I may."
The high-descended warriors could not but obey.

C

So to their several chambers the lofty strangers went.
Straight to her brother Giselher the noble lady sent,
And eke to her good mother; to both them 'gan she say,
That nothing now became her but to weep her life away.

CI

Then spake her brother Giselher, " Sister, I have been told,
And I would fain believe it, that all thy griefs of old,
Etzel will turn to joyance if thou with him wilt dwell.
Whatever others counsel, I like this marriage well.

CII

" Thee will he sure," he added, " for all the past repay,
For there reigns ne'er a monarch of such redoubted sway
From Rhone to Rhine, believe me, from th' Elbe to the salt sea.
With such a king for husband needs must thou happy be."

CIII

" Ah! why," said she, " dear brother, advise me to my bale?
Sure it befits me better ever to weep and wail.
How could I ever venture to yonder court to go?
If I once had beauty, 'tis wither'd all with woe."

CIV

Thereat to her dear daughter, the Lady Uta spake,
" Give ear unto thy brethren, dear child, their counsel take;
Do what thy friends advise thee, 'twill to thy profit be.
Thy never-ending sorrow it has griev'd my heart to see."

CV

Full oft she God entreated, nor ceas'd for wealth to pray,
That she might give to others gold, silver, garments gay,
As erst, ere noble Siegfried, her warlike lord, was slain,
Yet never liv'd the mourner such happy hours again.

CVI

Then to herself thus thought she, " How can I Etzel wed?
I, a Christian woman, share a heathen's bed?
Throughout the world dishonor would surely be my due.
No—not for all his kingdoms thus could I ever do."

CVII

So let she rest the matter. All night till break of day
With troublous thoughts companion'd on her weary couch she
    lay,
Nor ceas'd the tears a moment from her fair eyes to flow,
Till early dawn to matins bade the pale mourner go.

CVIII

Just at mass time returning the kings her brethren came;
To their reluctant sister their suit was still the same;
To wed the King of Hungary they urg'd her o'er and o'er,
But not a whit more yielding they found her than before.

CIX

Then summon'd were the warriors that came on Etzel's part;
They sought a farewell audience ere they should home depart,
Successful or successless, as it might chance to fall.
To court straight came Sir Rudeger and his valiant comrades
    all.

CX

These press'd their noble leader ever by the way
To learn the mind of Gunther, and that without delay,
For they had far to travel back to their homes, they said.
Straight was good Sir Rudeger to Kriemhild's presence led.

CXI

With soft persuasive accents the knight began to pray
The fair and high-born lady, that she to him would say,
What answer to King Etzel she to return would deign.
Naught, ween I, but denial he from her lips could gain.

CXII

" She'd take no second husband, love she could feel for none."
" Nay," said the noble margrave, " that were unwisely done.
Why such surpassing beauty waste in a mourning bed?
'Twould sure be to your honor a loving lord to wed."

CXIII

In vain they her entreated, in vain to her they pray'd,
Till to the queen the margrave this secret promise made,
" He'd full amends procure her for past or future ill."
Those words her storm-toss'd bosom had power in part to still.

CXIV

Then spoke he to the princess, " Cease now to weep and moan;
Among the Huns to friend you had you but me alone,
And my fearless vassals, and eke my kinsmen true,
No one should work you mischief, but he should dearly rue."

CXV

That still the more attemper'd her coy reluctant mood.
" Swear then, whoe'er may wrong me," the lofty dame pursued,
" You will be first and foremost revenge on him to take."
" Fain will I," said the margrave, " high lady, for your sake."

CXVI

Then swore to her Sir Rudeger and all his knightly train
To serve her ever truly, and all her rights maintain,
Nor e'er of her due honors scant her in Etzel's land.
Thereto gave the good margrave th' assurance of his hand.

CXVII

Then thought the faithful mourner, " With such a host of
　　friends,
Now the poor lonely widow may work her secret ends,
Nor care for what reflections the world on her may cast.
What if my lost beloved I may revenge at last?"

CXVIII

Thought she, " The halls of Etzel such countless heroes fill,
That I if I should rule them, may do whate'er I will.
Beside, the king's so wealthy, to give I shall have store,
As though injurious Hagan had robb'd me ne'er before."

CXIX

So thus she spake to Rudeger, " If I only knew
That he was not a heathen, I'd go, and gladly too,
Wherever he requested, and be his faithful bride."
" Nay, lady," said the margrave, " such scruples cast aside.

CXX

" He is not quite a heathen, this take for truth you may;
My good lord was converted, as I have heard him say,
And then the faith abandon'd he had awhile profess'd.
This, if you love him, lady, may be with ease redress'd.

CXXI

" Of Christian faith moreover so many knights has he,
That at his court you'll ever be blithe and sorrow-free.
Perhaps, if you desire it, he may be christen'd too.
For this then scorn not Etzel, nor let him vainly woo."

CXXII

Soon as ceas'd the margrave, once more her brethren sued,
" Grant us this favor, sister, cheer up thy mournful mood."
So long they begg'd and pray'd her, that in the end they sped,
And, sighing soft, she promis'd that she would Etzel wed.

CXXIII

She said, " You will I follow, poor, widow'd, lonely queen!
I'll to the Huns betake me, and here no more be seen,
If I've but friends to guide me hence to King Etzel's land."
Thereto before the heroes fair Kriemhild gave her hand.

CXXIV

Then spake the noble margrave, " If you have but two men,
I have more to join them; 'twere well adviséd then
Over the Rhine to bring you attended honorably;
You must not, lady, longer tarry here in Burgundy.

CXXV

" Men have I five hundred, and kinsmen not a few,
All at your service, lady, both here and yonder too,
Whatever you command them; myself will foremost be;
If aught you will henceforward, speak but the word to me.

CXXVI

" Now bid your steeds be saddled, fair dame, and quickly too
(Ne'er shall Rudeger's counsels give you cause to rue),
And tell the gentle damsels who bear you company,
On the road good knights will meet us, the flower of chivalry."

CXXVII

Still had they many a trinket, in Siegfried's time uplaid
To guerdon the best rider; thus could she many a maid
Lead forth in fitting splendor, when hence to fare she sought;
Ah! what goodly saddles for the fair dames were brought!

CXXVIII

If ever they had prank'd them in gay apparel dress'd,
Sure for the present journey her maids prepar'd their best;
They had heard of Etzel's splendor such tales as credence
    mock'd.
Every chest flew open, before kept closely lock'd.

CXXIX

They rested not a moment for four whole days and more.
Forth from the veiling wrappers the gorgeous vests they bore.
Kriemhild her treasure-chamber now to unlock began.
She long'd t' enrich the comrades of Rudeger, every man.

. CXXX

Gold had she yet remaining from the Nibelungers' land;
All wish'd she to th' Hungarians to give with lavish hand;
Sturdy mules a hundred could not have borne the same.
But the tale of this huge treasure to th' ear of Hagan came.

CXXXI

Said he, " She'll ne'er forgive me, that need I not be told;
So safe with us Burgundians shall stay Sir Siegfried's gold.
Why should I let such treasure to deadly foes accrue?
I know full well what Kriemhild with all this wealth will do.

CXXXII

" If once she hence could fetch it, I guess her whole intent;
I doubt not, every farthing would to my hurt be spent.
Besides, they have not horses such weight to undergo;
So Hagan here will keep it, and that shall Kriemhild know."

CXXXIII

When she heard the tidings, she felt it grievous bale;
To the three kings together full soon was told the tale.
They wish'd they could avert it, but nothing hence ensued.
Then thus the noble Rudeger spoke in right merry mood.

CXXXIV

" Rich and noble princess, why sorrow for the gold?
Let but the eyes of Etzel your peerless fair behold,
So much the king adores you (for this on me depend)
He'll give you far more treasure than you can ever spend."

CXXXV

Thereto the queen made answer, " Right noble Rudeger,
More wealth had never princess in kingdom far or near,
Than this outrageous Hagan has foully reft from me."
Then came her brother Gernot to her chamber hastily.

CXXXVI

The king's key in a moment he dash'd into the door.
The gold of Lady Kriemhild, thirty thousand marks or more,
Out was laid in order from the secret cell.
He bade the strangers take it; that pleas'd King Gunther well.

CXXXVII

Then he of Bechlaren, fair Gotelind's husband, spake:
" If my Lady Kriemhild had power with her to take
All that from Nibelung's country was ever brought to Rhine,
Yet touch'd should it be never by her hand or by mine.

CXXXVIII

" So let it here be treasur'd, for none of it will I.
From home I have hither brought such a large supply,
That on the road full lightly we can with this dispense,
So amply are we furnish'd for all the journey hence."

CXXXIX

Twelve chests of gold, the choicest that e'er was seen of eye,
Her maidens had kept ever in close reserve laid by.
Now with them, as they parted, they took the precious load,
With store of women's trinkets, to serve them on the road.

CXL

Still she look'd for violence from Hagan bad and bold.
She had yet for pious uses a thousand marks of gold.
These for the soul of Siegfried, her dearest lord, she gave.
" Her love," thought noble Rudeger, " lives e'en beyond the
    grave."

CXLI

Then spake again the mourner: " Where are my friends," said
    she,
" Who will a life of exile endure for love of me?
They with the banish'd widow to Hungary must ride;
Let them take of my treasures, and clothes and steeds provide."

CXLII

Then spake to the sad princess the Margrave Eckewart,
" Since of your royal household first I form'd a part,
I've done you loyal service; this can I truly say,
And will the like do ever e'en to my dying day.

CXLIII

" Of my men, too, five hundred to guard you I will lead,
All at your disposal, faithful and good at need.
Us from the side of Kriemhild death alone shall part."
She bow'd to him in silence; his words went to her heart.

CXLIV

Then forth were led their horses; start must they presently;
There all around them flocking their friends wept bitterly.
Surely did wealthy Uta with her fair maidens show
How deeply they lamented that Kriemhild was to go.

CXLV

A hundred high-born damsels begirt the parting queen,
All clad, as well became them, in robes of glittering sheen.
Full many a tear of sorrow from their bright eyes was shed.
At Etzel's court soon after a joyous life they led.

CXLVI

Then in place young Giselher and Gernot you might view;
They came, through love to Kriemhild, with all their followers
    true.
On her way the brethren to bring their sister sought,
And with them well accoutred a thousand warriors brought.

CXLVII

Then came the active Gary, Ortwine was present too,
And there the steward Rumold his duty had to do.
These found them fitting quarters e'en to the Danube's shore.
A little from the city rode Gunther, and no more.

CXLVIII

Ere from the Rhine for ever their eastward steps they bent,
They to the Huns beforehand swift messengers had sent,
To tell the stout King Etzel what Rudeger had done,
And how he peerless Kriemhild for his lord had woo'd and
    won.

CXLIX

The messengers spurr'd hotly; no time had they to lose;
They rode at once for honor and the guerdon of good news.
When home they brought the tidings, and all the truth made
    clear,
Word surely never sounded so sweet in Etzel's ear.

CL

For joy of such fair tidings the king was pleas'd to give
The messengers such presents, that thenceforth each might
    live
Merrily for ever, e'en to his dying day.
Through love the king's long sorrow vanish'd at once away.

TWENTY-FIRST ADVENTURE

HOW KRIEMHILD DEPARTED

I

ENOUGH now of the messengers; we'll tell you, as we may,
How the queen through the country went riding on her way,
And where Gernot and Giselher, who forth with her had passed,
And serv'd her well and truly, took leave of her at last.

II

On rode they to the Danube, and Vergen now was near
When leave they took, lamenting of the queen their sister dear,
For to the Rhine together they would retrace their road.
As such nigh kindred parted, many a sad tear there flow'd.

III

As leave took Sir Giselher, to his sister thus said he,
" Lady, if hereafter thou e'er have need of me,
Whatever be thy danger, if thou but let me know,
Straight to the land of Etzel to serve thee will I go."

IV

All those, who were her kinsmen, kiss'd on her mouth the
    queen.
That day a loving farewell 'twixt Kriemhild's friends was seen
And the good margrave's vassals; they thence asunder sped.
The high-born queen right onward many a fair maiden led.

V

Fivescore and four together, a richly vested throng
In stuffs of divers colors; many a buckler strong
Follow'd the lovely lady, while many a knight of pride,
At length from her departing, turn'd rein and homeward hied.

VI

Thence down the stream advancing, they rode Bavaria
    through;
Then all around spread tidings, that with hot haste a crew
Of strangers on were coming. Where now an abbey stands,
And where to reach the Danube the swift Inn scours the lands,

VII

There sat in Passau city a bishop of good report.
Straight empty was each chamber, and eke the prince's court.
All were forthwith pricking to Bavarian ground,
Where the good Bishop Pilgrin the Lady Kriemhild found.

VIII

The good knights of the country were not ill pleas'd, I ween,
To see so many a beauty about the stately queen.
With loving looks they courted the maids of lofty race.
Then led was every stranger to seemly resting-place.

IX

They there at Pledelingen were lodg'd as best might be.
On all sides all came flocking the noble guests to see.
Whome'er they met, were ready alike to give or do
Whate'er was to their honor, both there and elsewhere too.

X

With his niece, the bishop straight to Passau sped.
Forthwith the merry tidings among the burghers spread,
Kriemhild was thither coming, their prince's sister's child;
The merchants well receiv'd her, the queenly lady mild.

XI

Much desir'd the bishop that they awhile would stay;
Then said the good Sir Eckewart, " No, we must hence away
(Howe'er well pleas'd to linger), down to Rudeger's land.
His knights await our coming, and think us close at hand."

XII

Already had fair Gotelind the joyful tidings heard;
She and her noble daughter quick themselves bestirr'd.
She had been advis'd by Rudeger, her lord and master dear,
It seem'd him right and fitting, that, the sad queen to cheer,

XIII

She should ride and meet her with his vassals every one,
Up to the Ems advancing. This was no sooner done,
Than, afoot or in saddle, all together ran;
The roads throughout the country were alive with horse and
man.

XIV

To Efferding fair Kriemhild had now her journey made;
Many a Bavarian pricker his hands had gladly laid
On the costly baggage as is their custom still,
And thus the noble travellers would have suffer'd loss and ill,

XV

But those light-finger'd rovers the margrave could not brook.
A thousand knights and better to guard his march he took;
Thither, too, his consort fair Gotelind had come,
And in bright array around her his vassals all and some.

XVI

Thence o'er the Traun they hasten'd, and forthwith all around
With tents and huts bespotted the plain of Ems they found.
There the noble travellers that night their lodging made.
The bands of knights their charges by Rudeger were paid.

XVII

No longer in her quarters fair Gotelind abode;
Many a wanton palfrey pranc'd in the crowded road,
Every bridle jingling, and glittering every selle.
Right hearty was the welcome; it pleas'd the margrave well.

XVIII

Now on both sides advancing the gorgeous trains drew near.
Many a good knight between them forth prick'd in full career,
And waged the mimic battle; their knightly sports, I ween,
Drew many a damsel's glances, nor irk'd the stately queen.

XIX

When met the noble strangers and Rudeger's vassals true,
Up in the air, loud crashing, many a splinter flew
From the hands of heroes in knightly exercise.
Well before the ladies rode they for the prize.

XX

Soon was o'er the tourney; the knights together sped,
Each friendly greeting other; then Gotelind forth was led,
Her duty to Queen Kriemhild in humble guise to pay.
The skill'd in ladies' service, scant leisure sure had they.

XXI

To meet his wife, the margrave rode forward from the queen.
Not ill pleas'd was surely the noble margravine,
That back from Rhine so hearty had come her own good
    knight.
Her long-brooded sorrows vanish'd in delight.

XXII

When now had pass'd the welcome the loving pair between,
He bade her with her ladies alight upon the green.
None then was idle standing among the nobles there;
All busily bestirr'd them in the service of the fair.

XXIII

Soon as the Lady Kriemhild beheld the margravine
There with the ladies standing, rode on a space the queen;
Then sudden check'd her palfrey (the bit he answer'd well)
And instant bade her servants lift her down from selle.

XXIV

Then might you see the bishop, already sprung from steed,
Him and good Sir Eckewart, his niece to Gotelind lead.
All there made way before them as softly on they came.
Then on the mouth the wanderer kiss'd the good margrave's
    dame.

XXV

Then said the wife of Rudeger, with tender love and true,
" Now well is me, dear lady, that one so fair as you
Here at last in our country I with my eyes have seen.
Ne'er in these times, be certain, so happy have I been."

XXVI

" Now heaven you quit," said Kriemhild, " for all that you
    have done.
Should we live, noble Gotelind, both I and Botlung's son,
You may indeed be thankful that you have look'd on me."
'Twas all unknown to either what after was to be.

XXVII

Courteously one to another went many a blooming maid;
Young knights to yield them service with ready zeal essay'd;
So after kindly greeting (though erst unknown I ween)
They soon came friends together close sitting on the green.

XXVIII

With wine were serv'd the ladies; by this 'twas height of noon;
The noble knights and damsels again were moving soon.
Thence rode they to a meadow where spacious tents were
    pight,
And all within made ready for solace and delight.

XXIX

There through the dark they rested till morn began to smile.
They of Bechlaren bestirr'd themselves the while,
For such guests and so many fittingly to prepare.
The margrave so had order'd, little was wanting there.

XXX

There might you see wide open every window in every wall;
The gates of Bechlaren were back thrown one and all;
In rode the guests; loud shouted the townsmen least and
    most;
Choice quarters were prepar'd them by the care of the noble
    host.

XXXI

Sir Rudeger's fair daughter with her maidens went
Where the queen she greeted with loving kind intent;
There found she, too, her mother, who had with Kriemhild
    stay'd.
Meanwhile to each fair damsel was joyous welcome made.

XXXII

So either party mingled, and each went hand in hand
Into a spacious palace with curious cunning plann'd;
Beneath it roll'd the Danube; there took they all their ease,
In gentle pastime sitting, fann'd by the river breeze.

XXXIII

What further pass'd among them is more than I can say.
Sore murmur'd Kriemhild's followers that they must hence
    away,
And leave the pleasant city where such kind friends abode.
Ah! what good warriors with them from Bechlaren rode!

XXXIV

To them much loving service the noble margrave paid;
Then to fair Gotelind's daughter the queen a present made;
She gave her twelve red armlets, and robes so richly wrought,
That with her nothing better to Etzel's land she brought.

XXXV

Albeit the wondrous treasure now was hers no more,
Still, from the small remainder of her once boundless store,
Whome'er she saw, her bounty made every one content,
And now to Rudeger's household right precious gifts she sent.

XXXVI

In turn, as well befitted her state and lofty line,
So well Dame Gotelind treated the strangers from the Rhine,
That few were there among them, but from her copious store
Precious stones in plenty or gorgeous raiment bore.

XXXVII

When they their fast had broken, and ready were to part,
Then the noble hostess with true and faithful heart
Proffer'd her constant service to Etzel's stately queen,
Who much caress'd and fondly the fair young margravine.

XXXVIII

To the queen said the damsel, " If it seem you well,
Of the mind of my father this I can truly tell,
That he would gladly send me among the Huns to you."
That the young maiden lov'd her, how well fair Kriemhild
    knew!

XXXIX

Their horses now were saddled, and brought before the town.
Thither the noble Kriemhild came from the castle down,
And bade farewell to Gotelind and to her daughter dear.
Many a maid of many a maiden took leave with many a tear.

XL

They look'd on one another but seldom from that day.
At Medilich to the strangers were handed on the way
Rich golden cups, well fashion'd, and thereto, as a sign
Of free and hearty welcome, fill'd to the brim with wine.

XLI

Here held his wary station a host that Astolt hight;
From him the road to Austria the travellers learn'd aright,
Toward Mautern down the Danube; all anxious there were
    seen
To meet with zealous service King Etzel's gracious queen.

XLII

There lovingly the bishop parted from his niece,
How strongly he advis'd her to live in joy and peace,
And gain fair fame and credit as Helca did of yore!
Ah! what high honors thenceforth among the Huns she bore!

XLIII

Thence their way to the Traisem the noble strangers made.
The men of the good margrave all fair attendance paid,
Till the Huns to meet them came riding o'er the green.
Then with royal honors was welcom'd the fair queen.

XLIV

Fast beside the Traisem the King of Hungary
Possess'd a famous castle kept well and warily;
It's name was Zeissenmauer; there Helca once did dwell,
Displaying such high virtues, that none could her excel,

XLV

Save only peerless Kriemhild, who well knew how to give;
Sure, after all her sorrows, she might contented live,
Such crowds of Etzel's warriors were proud on her to wait,
Adorers of her beauty and vassals of her state.

XLVI

Wide was the rule of Etzel, and wider his renown;
The most redoubted champions from castle and from town
Were at his court assembled; together, all and some,
Christian knights and Paynim, they now with him were come.

XLVII

With him at every season was many a prowest chief
Alike of heathen doctrine and of the true belief.
Whate'er his faith, each warrior was prompt at Etzel's call,
And the king was so gracious, he gave enough to all.

TWENTY-SECOND ADVENTURE

HOW THE HUNS RECEIVED KRIEMHILD

I

KRIEMHILD at Zeissenmauer remain'd till the fourth day;
On the roads, while there she rested, the dust no moment lay.
It seem'd the land was burning, so smok'd each hoof-beat plain,
As Etzel's men through Austria came trampling on amain.

II

When to the monarch's hearing the joyful tidings came.
How stately through his country rode the Burgundian dame,
All sorrow in a moment was from his heart effac'd;
To meet his love and lady he spurr'd with burning haste.

III

Good knights of many a region and many a foreign tongue
Prick'd before King Etzel, that all the champaign rung;
Christian and heathen squadrons, careering wide around,
Advanc'd in dazzling splendor to where the queen they found.

IV

Chiefs from Greece and Russia in crowds were there to meet;
Polacks and Wallachians there were spurring fleet.
Each his fiery charger had in due command;
Each display'd the customs of his own native land.

V

From Kiev came many a champion, each in fair array,
And savage Petchenegers, that ever on their way
Kept shooting from the saddle at wild birds as they flew;
The arrow-head full strongly to the bend of the bow they drew.

VI

Fast by the flowing Danube there stands on Austrian ground
A city that hight Tulna; there first fair Kriemhild found
Many an outlandish custom, and was with welcome sought
By many a knight, whom after to doom and death she brought.

VII

Before King Etzel riding his household forward came,
Four and twenty princes of loftiest birth and name,
Merry, and rich, and courtly, and glittering all with gold,
Who long'd for nothing better than their lady to behold.

VIII

Duke Ramung of Wallachia rode trampling o'er the plain;
Seven hundred chosen warriors behind him held the rein;
You might see them speeding like wild birds in their flight.
Thither came Prince Gibek with many a squadron bright.

IX

Swift Hornbog, with a thousand trampling the dusty green,
Left the side of the monarch, and gallop'd toward the queen.
After their country's fashion they shouted shrill and loud.
Hotly was also ridden by Etzel's kinsmen proud.

X

Hawart was there of Denmark (a champion bold was he),
And the nimble Iring from falsehood ever free,
And Irnfried of Thüringia, a stern and stately knight.
These receiv'd fair Kriemhild with all the pomp they might.

XI

With men at arms twelve hundred advanc'd they o'er the lea.
Thither too from Hungary rode on with thousands three
Sir Blœdel, Etzel's brother, for knightly deeds renown'd;
He mov'd with princely splendor to where the queen he found.

XII

Last the great King Etzel and eke Sir Dietrich came
With all his brave companions; there many a knight of fame
And proud descent was present, prudent, and bold, and true,
High beat the heart of Kriemhild their wide array to view.

XIII

Then to the queen beside him thus spoke Sir Rudeger;
"Lady, with your permission the king I'll welcome here.
Whome'er to kiss I bid you, let it straight be done.
It fits not, such a favor be granted every one."

XIV

Straight from her sleek palfrey the queen was lifted down;
No longer dallied Etzel, the king of wide renown;
From horse with many a warrior he lighted on the green,
And merrily went forward to meet the noble queen.

XV

Two great and mighty princes, as has to us been told,
Advanc'd with the fair lady in raiment rich with gold,
As the wide-ruling Etzel approach'd his bride to meet,
When she deign'd the monarch with a loving kiss to greet.

XVI

With that her veil back threw she; forth beam'd her rosy hue
From the gold around it; many were there to view;
All own'd Dame Helca's beauty scarce with hers could vie.
There the king's brother Blœdel close was standing by.

XVII

Him the first kiss'd Kriemhild as bade the margrave good,
And next to him King Gibek; there too Sir Dietrich stood.
Twelve, the chief and noblest, were kiss'd by Etzel's bride.
With courteous grace she welcom'd many a good knight
    beside.

XVIII

All the while that Etzel talk'd with his lady true,
The young knights were doing as young knights now will do.
They tried their skill in tilting as best they could devise,
Christian alike and heathen each in his country's guise.

XIX

In Dietrich's men bold bearing and knightly you might spy.
How high above the bucklers they made the splinters fly
(So mighty was their puissance) and deafen'd all the field!
By the German strangers pierc'd through was many a shield.

XX

The crash of spears resounded as band encounter'd band.
Thither were come from all sides the warriors of the land,
And the king's guests together, nobles in proud array;
Thence now with Lady Kriemhild King Etzel went his way.

XXI

Close by, a rich pavilion for their retreat they found;
Crowded with tents and cabins was all the field around.
There, after all their labors, their languid limbs they laid.
Many a good warrior thither led many a gentle maid,

XXII

Where on a cushion'd sofa rich beyond compare
The stately queen was seated: the margrave's anxious care
For all things most convenient to pomp and ease had sent,
And so at once serv'd Kriemhild, and gave the king content.

XXIII

The tale then told by Etzel is more than I can say;
Soft in his hand reposing her snowy fingers lay.
So sat they gentle toying, for Rudeger, I ween,
Left not the king a moment in secret with the queen.

XXIV

Then o'er the spacious meadow they bade the tourney cease;
With honor all that tumult now was hush'd in peace.
Then Etzel's men betook them to cabin, booth, or tent;
Fit and convenient harbor they found where'er they went.

XXV

The day at last was ended, then took they their repose,
Till, at her hour returning, the cheerful dawn arose.
Then hasten'd many a warrior to horse at once to spring.
Ah! what pastimes plied they in honor of the king!

XXVI

The king his Huns exhorted to do as honor bade.
From Tulna to Vienna their journey then they made.
There found they many a lady adorn'd in all her pride
To welcome with due honor King Etzel's noble bride.

XXVII

In overflowing fulness all, that could each delight,
To his wish was ready; exulting many a knight
Look'd forward to the revels; joy smil'd on most and least;
With mirth and gladness open'd King Etzel's marriage-feast.

XXVIII

The numbers now assembled the city could not hold,
So all, who were not strangers, the noble margrave told
To seek convenient quarters in all the country round.
Still constant in attendance on the fair queen were found

XXIX

The valiant chief, Sir Dietrich, and many a knight besides;
Needful rest and solace each himself denied
To cheer the noble strangers and give them full content.
Sir Rudeger and his comrades had heartiest merriment.

XXX

Held was the marriage festal on a Whitsuntide;
'Twas then that royal Etzel embrac'd his high-born bride
In the city of Vienna; I ween she ne'er had found,
When first she wed, such myriads all to her service bound.

XXXI

With gifts she made acquaintance of those she ne'er had seen;
" Kriemhild," said many a stranger, " is sure a royal queen;
She had lost, we thought, the treasures that she before had
    won;
Yet here with her rich presents what wonders she had done!"

XXXII

For seventeen days did Etzel his marriage festal hold;
Never to us of monarch, I ween, before was told,
Who so proudly feasted, in old or modern lore.
The guests, who there were present, all their new raiment wore.

XXXIII

Of old, I ween, in Netherland she ne'er at board had sat
With such a host of warriors; well can I vouch for that;
For ne'er so many champions had Siegfried at command,
With all his wealth, as Kriemhild saw before Etzel stand.

XXXIV

Never king before him so many mantles brave,
For length and breadth conspicuous, at his own wedding gave,
Nor such store of rich vesture, enough for each to take;
All this was freely lavish'd for lovely Kriemhild's sake.

XXXV

There of a mind together were friends and strangers too;
Neither their goods nor chattels kept that free-handed crew.
Whate'er was ask'd, was granted; they gave till they were
    bare.
Many a one, through kindness, not a coat had left to wear.

XXXVI

How once by Rhine she tarried, the bride a moment thought,
With her first noble husband; to her eyes the tears it brought;
Yet she so well conceal'd it, the feasters mark'd her not;
Now, after all her sorrows, what glory was her lot!

XXXVII

All was but a trifle, that by the rest was done,
To the liberal deeds of Dietrich; whatever Botlung's son
In former days had giv'n him, went scatter'd through the land;
Marvels too of bounty were wrought by Rudeger's hand.

XXXVIII

Prince Blœdel, too, of Hungary vied nobly with the best;
He bade his comrades empty full many a travelling chest
Cramm'd with gold and silver; the whole was giv'n away;
The warriors of King Etzel a merry life led they.

XXXIX

Werbel as well as Swemmeline, the minstrels of the king,
To them no little profit did this fair marriage bring.
They gain'd, I ween, in largess a thousand marks or more,
When Kriemhild fair with Etzel the crown imperial wore.

XL

'Twas on the eighteenth morning, they from Vienna rode;
Pierc'd was many a buckler in tilting on the road
By spears which valiant champions level'd dexterously.
So back return'd King Etzel to the land of Hungary.

XLI

The walls of ancient Haimburg they reach'd by fall of night,
So that scarce 'twas easy to estimate by sight
How huge a strength of warriors the country round beset;
Ah! what fair troops of ladies each, home returning, met!

XLII

At Misenburg the wealthy, on shipboard went the band;
From bank to bank the river, as though 'twere firm dry land,
With man and horse was cover'd that floated as it flow'd;
Rest had the way-worn ladies, borne on their liquid road.

XLIII

Many a good ship together was lash'd and firmly bound,
Lest the damp spray should harm them from billows dashing
    round;
Many a good tent above them kept off the sun and breeze,
As if they in a meadow were sitting at their ease.

XLIV

When to King Etzel's castle the joyful tidings came,
Right merry were to hear it many a knight and many a dame.
The courtly train, accustom'd Queen Helca to obey,
In after time with Kriemhild led many a happy day.

XLV

In anxious doubt there waiting stood many a noble maid,
All, since the death of Helca, down by deep sorrow weigh'd
Seven, of proud kings the daughters, Kriemhild found there
    in place,
Of all King Etzel's country the ornament and grace.

XLVI

Of this fair train of damsels Dame Herrat had the care,
Helca's sister's daughter, renown'd for virtues rare,
Wife of good Sir Dietrich, daughter of King Nentwine;
Her after honors suited well with her lofty line.

XLVII

That the high guests were coming, it joy'd her much to hear;
Straight she bade make ready good store of choicest cheer.
How then King Etzel feasted, no tongue may hope to tell.
E'en in the days of Helca they scarcely far'd so well.

XLVIII

As from the shore with Kriemhild rode on King Etzel bold,
Who forward led each damsel, straight to the queen was told,
And thus each lord and lady she welcom'd as was meet;
Ah! with what power thereafter she sat in Helca's seat!

XLIX

Their true and loyal service all vow'd to her alone;
Silver, and gold, and raiment, and many a precious stone,
She freely shar'd among them; on that auspicious day,
All she had brought from Rhineland was giv'n at once away.

L

To her, as to their mistress, whoe'er the king obey'd,
His kinsmen and his vassals, true liegemen's service paid,
That never Lady Helca ruled with such mighty sway.
Such service held Queen Kriemhild e'en to her dying day.

LI

So court and country flourish'd with such high honors
    crown'd,
And all at every season fresh joy and pastime found.
Every heart was merry, smiles on each face were seen;
So kind the king was ever, so liberal the queen.

TWENTY-THIRD ADVENTURE

HOW KRIEMHILD THOUGHT OF REVENGING HER INJURIES

I

KING Etzel and Queen Kriemhild in proudest honor dwelt
For seven whole years together, nor woe nor sorrow felt;
Meanwhile to her fond husband the queen produced a boy;
Never before did Etzel exult so high with joy.

II

She never ceas'd entreating till her good lord she won
To have the right of baptism giv'n to her infant son
After the Christian custom; Ortlieb call'd was he;
Thereat all Etzel's kingdoms were fill'd with mirth and glee.

III

Whatever queenly virtues had fame to Helca brought,
Dame Kriemhild daily practis'd, and love, like Helca, sought.
From the foreign maiden Herrat, who still in secret yearn'd
For Helca's loss, the customs of all the land she learn'd.

IV

Her praise both friends and strangers alike were glad to tell;
'Twas own'd that never kingdom so graciously and well
By queen had e'er been governed; so much to all was clear.
This fame she bore in Hungary e'en to the thirteenth year.

V

When now she knew for certain that none would thwart her
    will
(So deal with wives of princes their husbands' vassals still),
And saw twelve kings for ever standing her before,
Her home-bred wrongs and sorrows again she brooded o'er.

VI

She thought how all the honors of the Nibelungers' land,
That once were her possession, fierce Hagan's rugged hand,
After the death of Siegfried, had torn from her away,
And how the proud wrong-doer with wrong she might repay.

VII

" 'Twere done, if I could only lure him to this land!"
Still would she dream, that often she wander'd hand in hand
With Giselher her brother, and often on the mouth
Kiss'd him in her slumber; too soon came bale on both.

VIII

Sure the foul fiend possess'd her, and lurking in her heart
Prompted her from King Gunther so lovingly to part,
Kissing, but not forgiving, close harboring still the feud.
Hot tears of wrath and malice once more her vesture dew'd.

IX

At her heart for ever early and late it lay,
How, guiltless, from her country she had been driven away,
And forc'd to take for husband a man of heathen creed.
Gunther and bloody Hagan had brought her to such need.

X

One long and dreary yearning she foster'd hour by hour;
She thought, " I am so wealthy and hold such boundless power,
That I with ease a mischief can bring on all my foes,
But most on him of Trony, the deadliest far of those.

XI

" Full oft for its beloved my heart is mourning still;
Them could I but meet with, who wrought me so much ill,
Revenge should strike at murder, and life atone for life;
Wait can I no longer." So murmur'd Etzel's wife.

XII

All the great king's vassals much love unto her bore,
And to do her service were ready evermore.
Her chamberlain was Eckewart, who thus made hosts of
　　friends;
So none could thwart her pleasure, whate'er might be her ends.

XIII

Ever was she thinking, " I'll ask the king a boon,
Which he, I know, will grant me readily and soon,
To bid my friends and kinsmen hither to Hunnish ground,"
None guess'd her secret malice, or harm in Kriemhild found.

XIV

So on a night reposing, as by the king she lay
(He in his arms embrac'd her, and bless'd the happy day,
That gave him such a consort, dear to him as his life;
She on her foes was thinking and th' old intestine strife),

XV

Thus spake she to the monarch, " Dear lord, full fain would I
Entreat of thee a favor, which thou wilt not deny
If thou think'st I deserve it, to let me see aright
If my friends in good earnest have favor in thy sight."

XVI

Then spake the mighty monarch (kind was his heart and true),
" Of that can I assure thee; whatever good accrue
To those bold knights, be certain to me content it lends;
Never through love of woman acquir'd I better friends."

XVII

Then thus made Kriemhild answer, " 'Tis true, as thou dost
    know,
Right noble are my kinsmen, yet ever am I woe
That still they keep so distant nor I by them am seen.
I'm told, for a mere outcast people report your queen."

XVIII

Then answer'd thus King Etzel, " Dear love and lady mine,
If they regard not distance, I'll send beyond the Rhine.
And hither bid whomever thou here to see art fain."
Much joy'd the vengeful lady thus his consent to gain.

XIX

Said she, " Would'st thou but please me, dear lord and master
    mine,
Despatch from hence thy envoys to Worms beyond the Rhine.
Such friends as most I long for, I hither will invite,
And straight will come among us full many a noble knight."

XX

Said he, " As thou would'st have it, so let the matter be;
Assure thee, thou wilt never thy friends so gladly see
As I shall gladly see them, noble Uta's children dear;
It irks me much and deeply, they've been such strangers here.

XXI

" So, if it thus content thee, dear love and lady mine,
I'll gladly send my minstrels for those good friends of thine.
They this very morning shall start for Burgundy."
With that, the king his minstrels bade summon instantly.

XXII

They hasten'd at the summons where, newly ris'n from bed,
The king sat with his consort; thus to both he said,
" Hence you with a message to Burgundy must ride."
With that, the richest vesture, he bade for them provide.

XXIII

For four and twenty warriors fit raiment was prepar'd.
Moreover to his envoys his will the king declar'd,
How they should to Hungary bid Gunther and his folk.
But what the queen enjoin'd them close apart she spoke.

XXIV

Thus them address'd King Etzel, " I'll tell you what to do;
To my good friends go tender my love and service true,
And bid them deign ride hither, and taste our Hunnish cheer.
Guests have I none other whom I hold so dear.

XXV

" So if they will do me the favor which I pray,
Entreat them not to linger; speed makes the surest way.
At my high feast this summer I trust to see my friends,
And on my wife's fair kinsmen much of my joy depends."

XXVI

Thereto replied the minstrel, the haughty Swemmeline,
" When in this land of Hungary your feast do you design?
That to your friends exactly your purpose we may say."
" About," replied King Etzel, " next midsummer day."

XXVII

" We'll surely do your bidding," Werbel made reply.
Into her inmost chamber the queen bade by and by
In secret bring the envoys, and there her will 'gan tell,
Whence death and grim destruction many a good knight befell.

XXVIII

She said to both the envoys, " Now only serve me true,
And as I command you my will discreetly do,
And, when you come to Rhineland, speak but my bidding
      there,
And I'll give you gold and raiment plenty and to spare.

XXIX

" To my friends, whomever you meet with, more or less,
At Worms, as there you tarry, be sure you ne'er confess
That ever you beheld me moody or sorrow-worn;
Only let my service to the good knights be borne.

XXX

" Beg them to grant the favor for which the king hath sent,
And so at once will vanish my only discontent.
I here am fancied friendless, and scarce esteem'd aright.
I'd go myself to visit them if I but were a knight.

XXXI

" And also to Sir Gernot, my noble brother, say,
That none can love him better than his sister far away,
And bid him bring me hither our friends most prov'd and true,
That all may here accord us the honor that's our due.

XXXII

" And say, too, to young Giselher that he should bear in mind,
That he never wrong'd me, but still was good and kind.
My eyes are ever yearning to look upon him here,
For dearly do I love him, as I to him am dear.

XXXIII

" And tell my noble mother what honors here I bear.
Then, if Hagan of Trony resolve to tarry there,
Who will there be to guide them through lands so waste and
    lone?
But he the roads to Hungary e'en from a child has known."

XXXIV

Not a whit the envoys could guess her deep design
In keeping him of Trony from tarrying by the Rhine.
It irk'd them sore thereafter, when their unconscious breath
With him had drawn the guiltless into the toils of death.

XXXV

Letters and goodly greetings the king was prompt to give;
And riches bore they with them right sumptuously to live.
So leave they took of Etzel, and of his noble queen;
Adorn'd were they with raiment as rich as e'er was seen.

TWENTY-FOURTH ADVENTURE

HOW WERBEL AND SWEMMELINE DELIVERED THE MESSAGE

I

When Etzel had his envoys for the Rhenish border bown'd,
From land to land the tidings at once flew wide around.
He pray'd and eke commanded by many a nimble post
Guests to his gorgeous festal; 'twas the doom of death to most.

II

So from the realm of Hungary forth the envoys went
To the bold Burgundians; thither were they sent
To three royal brethren and their warriors wight
To bid them come to Etzel; fast prick'd they as they might.

III

Thence came they to Bechlaren as on the spur they rode;
There all were glad to tend them, and naught but kindness
    show'd.
Rudeger and Gotelind by them their service true
Sent to their friends in Rhineland, so did their daughter too.

IV

Thence without many a present they would not let them part,
So that the men of Etzel might go with merrier heart.
Rudeger bade tell Uta and her children three,
That sure no other margrave lov'd them so well as he.

V

And eke they sent to Brunhild their service and best will,
Their loyalty devoted, and love enduring still.
So, thus at full commission'd, the envoys sprung to selle;
The margravine at parting pray'd God to guard them well.

VI

Ere the despatchful minstrels had ridd'n Bavaria through,
Swift Werbel found the bishop, Queen Kriemhild's uncle true.
What to his Rhenish kinsmen by their mouths he said
Came never to my knowledge; but th' envoys gold so red

VII

He gave for a remembrance ere he let them part;
But first thus spake good Pilgrin, " 'Twould gladden sure my
    heart
To see them in Bavaria, these sister's sons of mine,
Since I can hope so seldom to seek them by the Rhine."

VIII

What roads they took yet further, as to the Rhine they far'd,
Is more than I can utter; none sure to pilfer dar'd
Their silver or their raiment; Etzel all had dread;
His majesty and puissance so wide around were spread.

IX

Within twelve days, so riding, they came unto the Rhine,
E'en to Worms, the minstrels Werbel and Swemmeline.
To the kings and their liegemen forthwith the tidings ran,
That come were foreign envoys.   Gunther to ask began.

X

Thus said the Lord of Rhineland, " I fain would understand,
Whence have the strangers journey'd who thus have sought
    our land."
Not one to his inquiry could satisfaction bring,
Till they were seen by Hagan, who thus bespake the king;

XI

" These must be weighty tidings; that can I vouch for true;
Sure they are Etzel's minstrels whom here I have in view.
Your sister sends them hither unless I much mistake;
Let's give them hearty welcome for their great master's sake."

XII

At once up to the palace in fair array they rode;
Never prince's minstrels before so lordly show'd.
Forth stepp'd King Gunther's servants with courteous act
    and look,
And led them to fit chambers, and in charge their raiment
    took.

XIII

So rich and so well fashion'd were the riding-vests they wore,
That in them they with honor might go the king before;
Still they resolv'd no longer the same at court to wear,
But ask'd, "Who would accept them?" of those who loiter'd
    there.

XIV

It chanced that there were many, who were right well content
To take their proffer'd bounty; to these they straight were
    sent.
Then robes of such rare splendor put on the lofty guests,
That well might royal envoys keep state in meaner vests.

XV

Straightway, with leave accorded, Etzel's servants went
To where the king was sitting; kind looks were on them bent.
To them in courteous fashion up stepp'd Sir Hagan brave,
And warmly bade them welcome; due thanks in turn they
    gave.

XVI

Much after news inquir'd he, much after great and small,
How it was with Etzel, how with his warriors all.
The minstrel thus made answer, "The land was ne'er so well,
The people ne'er so happy; this I for truth can tell."

XVII

To the host then went the envoys; throng'd was the palace
    wide;
They met right courteous greeting from knights on every side,
Such as in distant countries to noble guests is due.
Werbel there found with Gunther many a champion bold and
    true.

XVIII

Courteously King Gunther greeted them as they stood;
"Welcome to Worms, both welcome, ye Hunnish minstrels
    good,
You and your worthy comrades; wherefore from Hungary
Has noble Etzel sent you so far to Burgundy?"

XIX

Low bow'd they to King Gunther, then Werbel spake, " By
me
My good king and thy sister their service send to thee,
And their fraternal greeting with kind sincere intent.
We to you knights of Rhineland in love and truth are sent."

XX

Then said the puissant Gunther, " This news I'm glad to hear;
And how," asked he, " is Etzel, whom long I've held so dear,
And my fair sister Kriemhild, who reigns in Hungary?"
Then answer'd thus the minstrel, " I'll tell you faithfully.

XXI

" This take for true and certain, that never yet were seen
People so blithe and merry as our good king and queen,
Their vassals, and their kinsmen, and knights in bower and
hall;
The tidings of our journey rejoic'd them one and all."

XXII

" Thanks for his friendly message, which you so far have
brought,
And also for my sister's; it glads my inmost thought
To find they all live happy, both king and liegemen bold.
I ask'd with fear and trembling before your tale was told."

XXIII

The two young kings together alike the presence sought.
But just before, the tidings had to their ears been brought.
Right glad to see the envoys for his dear sister's sake
Was the young knight Giselher, and friendly them bespake.

XXIV

" Welcome, ye noble envoys, welcome to me and mine;
Should you be pleas'd more frequent to travel to the Rhine,
Friends you would meet with ever who'd see you still with joy,
And little you'd encounter to cause you here annoy."

XXV

" For that we freely trust you," straight answer'd Swemmeline;
" Express ne'er could I fitly by wit or words of mine
What kind and friendly greetings I from King Etzel bear,
And from your noble sister, who reigns so proudly there.

XXVI

" Your love and old affection she bids you keep in mind,
And how to her you ever in heart and soul were kind.
But first to the king and foremost we come by high command,
To beg you'd deign to travel hence into Etzel's land.

XXVII

" In strictest charge 'twas given us by our redoubted king,
Unto you all this message on his account to bring,
If you your loving sister are so resolv'd to shun,
Yet fain would learn King Etzel, what he to you has done,

XXVIII

" That you to him such strangers and to his land have been;
E'en were you distant aliens, nor kinsmen of his queen,
He at your hands might merit that you his guests should be,
And if this e'er should happen, right well content were he."

XXIX

Thereto replied King Gunther, " Before this sennight's end,
I'll tell you, after counsel first ta'en with many a friend.
What I shall have determin'd; meanwhile for you 'twere best
To go back to your quarters and there in pleasure rest."

XXX

Then said the minstrel Werbel, " And might it also be,
That you would permit us a little space to see
My gracious Lady Uta ere we retire to rest?"
Thereto assent Sir Giselher thus courteously express'd.

XXXI

" That no one will refuse you, and, would you thither go,
Full well you'd please my mother, that for a truth I know;
Surely for my sister the Lady Kriemhild's sake
She will behold you gladly, and friendly welcome make."

XXXII

Giselher then led them where he the lady found;
Full gladly she beheld them, the chiefs from Hunnish ground.
She gave them friendly greeting, for she was good and wise;
They then their charge deliver'd in grave and courtly guise.

XXXIII

" To you the queen my lady," thus noble Swemmeline spake,
" Commends her love and duty; this you for truth may take,
That if your royal daughter her mother oft could see,
In all the world no pleasure more dear to her would be."

XXXIV

Thereto the queen made answer, " That cannot be, I fear;
Much as 'twould glad me, often to see my daughter dear,
She dwells from hence too distant, the noble Etzel's wife.
May she and he together ever lead a happy life!

XXXV

" I pray you, give me notice, e'er you from Rhineland go,
When you begin your journey; this too for certain know,
That I never envoys with more content have seen."
The squires to do her pleasure made promise to the queen.

XXXVI

The messengers from Hungary thence to their chambers went;
Meanwhile in haste King Gunther round to his friends had
     sent,
And, when all were assembled, inquir'd of every man,
What thought they of the message; many then to speak began.

XXXVII

That into Etzel's country be might in safety ride,
This all the best advis'd him, who stood there by his side,
Save only stern Sir Hagan; he drew the king apart,
And grimly frowning mutter'd, " You strike at your own heart.

XXXVIII

" You sure must still remember what we ere now have done.
We must beware of Kriemhild for ever, every one.
To the death her husband I smote with this good hand;
How then can we with prudence set foot in Etzel's land?"

XXXIX

Then spake the mighty monarch, " She thinks no more of this;
At parting she forgave us, with many a loving kiss,
All we had done against her; her wrath is overblown.
If she bear malice, Hagan, 'tis sure 'gainst you alone."

XL

" Trust not, Sir King," said Hagan, " how smooth soe'er they
    be,
The messengers from Hungary; if Kriemhild you will see,
You put upon the venture your honor and your life.
A nurse of ling'ring vengeance is Etzel's moody wife."

XLI

Then took the word Prince Gernot, and in the council spake,
" Because you with good reason believe your life at stake
In yonder Hunnish kingdoms, must we too Kriemhild shun,
And visit not our sister? that sure were wrongly done."

XLII

Then to the frowning warrior Prince Giselher turn'd his rede,
" Since you know yourself guilty, friend Hagan, in this deed,
Better stay here in safety, and of your life take care,
And with us to our sister let journey those who dare."

XLIII

Thereat the Knight of Trony to kindle wrath began,
" Never shall you, never, lead with you hence a man
That with you dare ride readier to visit your worst foe;
Since you will not hear counsel, this I ere long will show."

XLIV

Then spake the steward Rumolt, a hardy knight and true;
" You can dispose in Rhineland of friends and strangers too
After your own good pleasure; abundance have you here;
No one, I ween, in Hungary has bound you to appear.

XLV

" Since you will not hear Hagan, to my advice attend;
This is what Rumolt counsels, your firm and faithful friend;
Stay here in peace and plenty; let those who need it roam,
And let the great King Etzel cheer his fair queen at home.

XLVI

" Where can you be better for pleasure or repose?
Where more with friends surrounded, and more secure from
    foes?
So be wise and merry, the richest raiment wear,
Drink the best wine in Rhineland, and woo the fairest fair.

XLVII

" Store have you too of dainties, the best and most to prize
That ever feasted monarch, and, if 'twere otherwise,
At home you still should tarry for love of your fair wife,
Nor in such childish fashion expose your precious life.

XLVIII

" Stay here then, I beseech you; rich are your lawns and leas,
Here every pledge of pleasure you may redeem with ease,
Far better than in Hungary; who knows what there may rise?
Stay here, my lord, and stir not; this is what I advise."

XLIX

" Stay will we not, assure thee," Prince Gernot answer'd
    straight;
" How can we, when my sister and the great king, her mate,
Have bidd'n us by a message so loving and so kind?
Who will not freely with us may safely stay behind."

L

Thereto made Hagan answer, " Be not displeas'd at all
With what I now shall counsel, whatever hence befall.
In faith and truth I warn you; would you in safety go,
Ride well array'd to Hungary, and arm'd from top to toe.

LI

" Since you still will forward, for all your warriors send,
For every valiant stranger and every trusted friend.
From all I'll choose a thousand, each a well-proved knight;
Thus you may rest in safety from moody Kriemhild's spite."

LII

" I gladly take thy counsel," the king at once replied;
Throughout his lands despatch'd he his messengers far and
    wide.
Three thousand knights or better came on with proud intent.
Little thought they to purchase such doleful dreariment.

LIII

With jollity and joyance to Gunther's land they rode;
On all, that proffer'd service, was horse and weed bestow'd,
For soon were they to travel far from Burgundian ground.
Many a good knight to join him the king right willing found.

LIV

Then Hagan told Sir Dankwart, his brother good at need,
Eighty of their warriors forth to the Rhine to lead.
Thither they came full knightly; the well-appointed band
Harness with them, and raiment, brought into Gunther's land.

LV

Folker, a noble minstrel, and eke a hardy knight,
Came to partake their journey with thirty men of might,
All clad in such apparel as well a king might wear;
He bade announce to Gunther, to Hungary he'd fare.

LVI

Now, who was this same Folker, I'll tell you faithfully.
He was a high-born warrior, and had in Burgundy
Many good knights for vassals of honor undefil'd.
For playing on the viol the minstrel he was styl'd.

LVII

Hagan chose out a thousand whom well before he knew
In stern assaults and forays for valiant men and true,
And in all forms of battle their worth he oft had tried.
Their well-approved prowess by none could be denied.

LVIII

Sore irk'd it Kriemhild's envoys to make so long a stay;
They fear'd their lord's displeasure, and fain would speed away.
They daily were entreating for leave at once to part,
But Hagan still refus'd it through subtlety of heart.

LIX

To his lords he thus gave warning, " We must well beware
Of letting these ride homeward, unless ourselves we fare
Within a sennight after straight into Etzel's land.
We shall be thus the safer if any fraud be plann'd.

LX

" With all her thirst for vengeance, Kriemhild will want the
    time
To weave a web of mischief, and muster strength for crime,
Or, if she strike too early, she'll be the sufferer then,
Since we shall bring to Hungary such a host of chosen men."

LXI

Forthwith for many a champion, who thence would soon away,
Prepar'd were shields and saddles and all the proud array
That to the land of Etzel each was with him to bring;
Meanwhile Queen Kriemhild's envoys were call'd before the
    king.

LXII

Then thus began Sir Gernot to th' envoys there in place,
" The king will do the bidding of royal Etzel's grace.
Fain will we seek his festal, which it were ill to miss,
And see once more our sister; she may depend on this."

LXIII

Then spake to them King Gunther, " Could you to us declare
The time of this high festal, and when we should be there
With all our following present? " then Swemmeline made reply,
" For the next midsummer is fix'd the festal high."

LXIV

The king then gave permission, not granted till that hour,
If they wish'd to visit Dame Brunhild in her bower,
With his free allowance thither at once to go,
Then interpos'd Sir Folker (the queen would have it so).

LXV

" Just now my Lady Brunhild is not so well of cheer,"
Said the good knight, " that strangers before her can appear.
Wait until to-morrow; then you the queen may see."
Much wish'd they to behold her, yet never could it be.

LXVI

Then in his gracious fashion commanded straight the king
Through kindnes to the envoys forth his gold to bring
Spread out on massy bucklers; good store thereof had he.
Rich gifts his friends too gave them with liberal hand and free.

LXVII

Gernot alike and Giselher and Gary and Ortwine
Show'd, they as well could lavish the treasures of the mine.
Such rich gifts on the envoys were shower'd with one accord,
That they durst not accept them through terror of their lord.

LXVIII

On this the messenger Swemmeline thus to the king 'gan say,
" Sir King, needs must your presents here in your country stay;
We cannot take them with us; our king has so decreed,
And strictly that forbidden; besides, we've little need."

LXIX

Not little wonder'd Gunther, and felt displeasure more,
That they refus'd such presents given from his royal store.
Still he at last constrain'd them his gold and weed to take,
And to the land of Etzel to bear them for his sake.

LXX

An audience of Queen Uta, ere they set out, they sought.
Young Giselher the minstrels before his mother brought.
The lady to her daughter by them this message sent,
To hear of all her honors, it gave her full content.

LXXI

Girdles and gold she lavish'd, sure more than I can tell,
Both for the sake of Kriemhild (for her she lov'd full well)
And also of King Etzel, on those same minstrels brave;
They willingly accepted what she sincerely gave.

LXXII

Their leave then took the envoys, well-gifted as might be,
Of every noble warrior and every lady free.
Thence on they rode to Swabia; Sir Gernot sent along
So far his knights to guard them, that none should do them
     wrong.

LXXIII

When from the friends they parted, who had assur'd their way,
In peace they went thenceforward, safe under Etzel's sway,
That no man dar'd to pilfer their horses or their weed.
So to the land of Etzel they prick'd with fiery speed.

LXXIV

Whom true they found and friendly, them told they all and
        some,
That the bold Burgundians would shortly thither come
From the Rhine into Hungary, as Etzel them had pray'd.
Also to Bishop Pilgrin like tidings were convey'd.

LXXV

As they nigh to Bechlaren came riding down the road,
Twas told to good Sir Rudeger, who there in peace abode,
And to the Lady Gotelind, the noble margravine.
To hear she soon would see them, right glad was she, I ween.

LXXVI

On went they with the tidings, fast sped they horse and man;
The minstrels found King Etzel in his good town of Gran.
Greetings upon greetings were sent from Rhine, they said,
All there were at his service; for joy he glow'd a merry red.

LXXVII

When the queen heard for certain (what she so long had
        plann'd)
That her long absent brethren would come into the land,
She swam in joy and rapture; richly for service done
The minstrels she requited; high honor thus she won.

LXXVIII

Then thus she spake, " Now tell me, Werbel and Swemmeline,
Who to our feast are coming of kin and friends of mine,
Into this land invited with many a friendly word;
And tell, too, what said Hagan, when he the tidings heard."

LXXIX

" Early upon a morning to the council-board he came;
Little there he utter'd but words of gloom and blame;
And when the jaunt to Hungary was voted in a breath,
He grimly smil'd and mutter'd, ' This jaunt's a jaunt to death.'

LXXX

" There are your brethren coming, the noble kings all three,
In lofty mood and joyous; who there besides may be,
We could not learn for certain, else would we nothing hide.
The valiant gleeman Folker agreed with them to ride."

LXXXI

" I could have spar'd full lightly the minstrel's presence here,"
Replied the wife of Etzel; " this gives me little cheer;
I'm well inclin'd to Hagan; he is of courage high;
To have him here among us right well content am I."

LXXXII

Then in haste went Kriemhild where sat King Etzel near;
How kindly she bespake him! " My lord and husband dear,
What thinks't thou of these tidings, thou, who this feast hast
    will'd?
My heart's long lingering wishes shall now be all fulfill'd."

LXXXIII

" Thy wishes are my pleasure," the smiling king replied,
" Ne'er with my own good kinsmen was I so satisfied,
Whene'er into my country they have been pleas'd to fare;
Through love of thy brave brethren has vanish'd all my care."

LXXXIV

The officers of Etzel forthwith bestirr'd them all,
With fitting seats to furnish palace as well as hall
For the dear guests, approaching the merry feast to keep.
They gave him cause thereafter full bitterly to weep.

TWENTY-FIFTH ADVENTURE

HOW THE LORDS ALL CAME INTO HUNGARY

I

BUT let us tell no further how there the work they plied.
Never to a king's country were known before to ride
Such well-appointed squadrons as thither were to speed.
They had whate'er they wanted, both weapons and eke weed.

II

The King of Rhine apparel gave to his liegemen bold,
To threescore and a thousand, as I have heard it told,
Beside nine thousand yeomen, on mirth and revel bent.
Those, whom they left behind them, soon rued that e'er they
    went.

III

In Worms, as their equipment was carrying through the court,
From Spire an aged bishop, of reverend report,
Thus bespake fair Uta, " Our worthy friends prepare
To yonder feast to travel; God watch and ward them there!"

IV

Thereon the noble Uta bespake her children dear,
" Far better stay, good heroes, and tend your safety here.
I had last night, my children, a dream of ghastly dread,
How all the birds, that flutter throughout this land, were dead."

V

" Who cares for dreams," said Hagan, " and thinks by them
    to walk,
Ne'er in the path of honor with sturdy steps can stalk,
Or breathe the voice of reason, but wavers to and fro.
I rede, my noble master take leave and forward go.

VI

" Yes, we shall ride full gladly hence into Etzel's land.
There kings need for their service many a good hero's hand,
And this fair feast of Kriemhild's awaits us there to view."
So Hagan urg'd the journey, which soon he came to rue.

VII

He ne'er had giv'n such counsel but for what late had pass'd,
When scorn on him Sir Gernot had so unseemly cast,
Reminding him of Siegfried, and what had erst been done,
As though for that dislik'd him the journey to the Hun.

VIII

Then answer'd he of Trony, " Fear prompts not what I rede.
If so you'll have it, heroes, fall to the work and speed;
You'll find me not the hindmost to ride to Etzel's realm."
Soon shatter'd he thereafter many a shield and many a helm.

IX

The boats were waiting ready, the band was muster'd there;
Thither his choice apparel each one made haste to bear.
Their toil was scarce well over ere eve fell on the lea;
So from their homes they parted as merry as might be.

X

Beyond the Rhine's fair current their hasty camp was seen;
There tents and proud pavilions bespotted all the green.
The lovely queen her husband detain'd for that one night,
The last they spent together, dole mingling with delight.

XI

At early dawn there sounded sweet flute and trumpet-clang;
'Twas the hour of parting; to work the warriors sprang.
With a hasty kiss fond lovers were then constrain'd to sever.
With woe and death fell Kriemhild soon sunder'd them for ever.

XII

The children of fair Uta a man had at their court,
Bold alike and faithful, in all of best report.
The same, as they were going, drew the king aside.
" Woe's me," said he, " dear master, you to this feast will ride."

XIII

The good knight's name was Rumolt, a tall man of his hands.
Said he, " To whom commit you your people and your lands?
Would one could turn your warriors to do what best you
　　　should;
This message of your sister's it never seem'd me good."

XIV

" This is my will and pleasure; to thee my infant heir,
To thee I trust my country; of the women take good care;
Whomever thou see'st weeping, his woe with comfort charm.
Sure at the hands of Kriemhild we ne'er can come to harm."

XV

For the kings and for their liegemen the steeds were ready
    ranged;
How many then, with kisses of true love interchanged,
Full flown with lively vigor, athirst for bold emprise,
Left each a stately lady to droop in tears and sighs.

XVI

When light into their saddles up sprang the warriors good,
Then might you see the women how sorrowful they stood.
All felt, they did for ever, and to their doom, depart,
A dreary, dark foreboding, that shakes the firmest heart!

XVII

As the bold Burgundians rode forth in gallant show,
To see them all the country ran hurrying to and fro.
On either side the mountains both men and women wept.
Little reck'd they the weepers; their joyous course they kept.

XVIII

In habergeons a thousand the knights of Nibelung's reign,
Who many a lovely lady they ne'er should see again
Had left at home in sorrow, rode gaily with the rest.
The wounds of Siegfried fester'd in Kriemhild's throbbing
    breast.

XIX

So went they ever onward until the Main they spied,
Thence up through Eastern Frankland the men of Gunther
    hied.
Well knew the roads Sir Hagan, who led their steps aright;
Their marshal was Sir Dankwart, the stout Burgundian knight.

XX

As on from Eastern Frankland to Schwanfeld still they rode,
Their grace and stately courtesy and knightly bearing show'd,
The princes and their kindred deserv'd their lofty fame.
The king on the twelfth morning unto the Danube came.

XXI

A space the Knight of Trony rode on before the host;
He still the Nibelungers best cheer'd and aided most.
The fear-defying champion alighted on the lea,
And fast beside the river his horse tied to a tree.

XXII

Swoln was the roaring river, bark was there none to spy;
Every bold Nibelunger look'd on with wistful eye
In doubt how to pass over, the surges spread so wide.
Many a good knight from saddle down sprung the stream
        beside.

XXIII

" Good Lord of Rhine," said Hagan, " much mischief here may
        be,
Much may'st thou have to suffer, as thou thyself may'st see.
Strong is the flood and furious, the stream can ill be cross'd.
Many a good knight, I fear me, will here to-day be lost."

XXIV

" Why dost thou check me, Hagan ? " the troubled king 'gan
        say;
" Do not, as thou are valiant, the daunted more dismay.
Look out a ford up higher, above these lower meads,
Where we may pass in safety our baggage and our steeds."

XXV

" I never," answer'd Hagan, " my life so weary found,
But in these burly billows 'twould irk me to be drown'd.
Many a knight of Etzel's, ere yet my day be o'er,
By this good hand shall perish; that, 'faith, would please me
        more.

XXVI

"So here beside the water, ye noble knights, abide;
Myself will seek the ferrymen along the river side,
And bid them bring us over hence into Gelfrat's land."
With that the sturdy Hagan took his good shield in hand.

XXVII

Well arm'd was the stern champion; he bore a shield of might;
Strongly lac'd was his helmet, well-temper'd, burnish'd bright;
His broadsword in a baldric hung o'er his armor sheen;
Wounds could it cut full ghastly with both its edges keen.

XXVIII

As there and here for boatmen look'd out the warrior good,
He heard a splash of water; listening awhile he stood.
The sound came from wise women, who took their pleasure
near,
Bathing for refreshment in a fountain cool and clear.

XXIX

'Ware of them was Hagan; nigh he closely crept;
Sudden they espied him,—how away they swept!
That they had so escap'd him, their bosoms swell'd with joy;
He seiz'd upon their raiment, nor wrought them more annoy.

XXX

Then one of them bespake him (Hadburg was her name),
"Noble knight, Sir Hagan, go seek a worthier game.
Give us back our raiment, and we will tell thee all
That from this march to Hungary shall thee and thine befall."

XXXI

Like water-hens they floated before him on the wave.
Him seem'd, their well-known wisdom of truth assurance gave;
Hence what they chose to tell him, he took with more belief.
Then thus they of the future resolv'd the listening chief.

XXXII

Said th' one, "To Etzel's country (doubt not what Hadburg
        saith)
You well may ride and safely, for that I pledge my faith,
And never band of heroes sought kingdom far or near
To win such height of honor; 'tis true as we are here."

XXXIII

Well pleas'd her speech Sir Hagan, his heart wax'd light and
        gay;
He gave them back their vesture, and would no longer stay;
But when again the mermaids had donn'd their wondrous weed,
They told in truth, how Gunther in Hungary should speed.

XXXIV

And then the other mermaid, that Sieglind hight, began,
"I will warn thee, Hagan, thou son of Aldrian;
My aunt has lied unto thee her raiment back to get;
If once thou coms't to Hungary, thou'rt taken in the net.

XXXV

"Turn, while there's time for safety, turn, warriors most and
        least;
For this, and for this only, you're bidden to the feast,
That you perforce may perish in Etzel's bloody land.
Whoever rideth thither, Death has he close at hand."

XXXVI

Thereto gave answer Hagan, "In vain you cheat and lie,
How can it ever happen that there we all shall die,
However fierce the hatred that one to us may bear?"
They then began the future more fully to declare.

XXXVII

Then thus the first bespake him, "Yet so it needs must be;
Not one of you his country again shall ever see,
Not one but the king's chaplain; this well to us is known;
To Gunther's land in safety return shall he alone."

XXXVIII

Then angrily Sir Hagan bespake her, frowning stern,
" 'Twere ill to tell my masters what they'd disdain and spurn,
That we should all in Hungary death and destruction find.
Now show us o'er the water, wisest of womankind."

XXXIX

Said she, " Since from this journey, it seems, thou wilt not turn,
Up yonder by the river an inn thou may'st discern.
A ferryman there dwelleth; no others here abide."
The knight believ'd her answer, and took her words for guide.

XL

Him then the first call'd after as gloomily he went,
" Stay yet awhile, Sir Hagan, why so on haste intent?
Hear better our instructions to reach the farther strand.
A margrave, that hight Elsy, is lord of all this land.

XLI

" He has a valiant brother (Sir Gelfrat men him call),
A great lord in Bavaria; ill might it you befall,
If through his march you travel; your course with caution
    plan,
And smoothly deal and gently with yonder ferryman.

XLII

" He scarce will leave you scathless (so fierce is he and rude),
Unless with sound discretion you temper his rough mood.
Would you he'd put you over, pay down at once the fare.
He is a friend of Gelfrat's and of this land has care.

XLIII

" And, should the ferryman tarry, across the river shout,
And say your name is Amelrich, whom late a feud drove out
Perforce from this, his country, a knight of birth and fame.
Good speed will make the ferryman when once he hears the
    name.

XLIV

For all reply Sir Hagan to the wise ladies bow'd;
Then in his gloomy silence strode off the warrior proud.
Still higher up the river along the shore he hied,
Until a lonely hostel on th' other bank he spied.

XLV

He straight across the water 'gan call with all his might,
" Come, carry me over, ferryman," shouted the lusty knight.
" Of ruddy gold an armlet I'll give thee for thy meed.
Come, carry me, well thou knowest how pressing is my need."

XLVI

The ferryman was wealthy, to serve he scarce could bear,
And hence it seldom happen'd he deign'd to take a fare.
His men were like their master, as moody and misproud.
Still on this side Sir Hagan stood ever shouting loud.

XLVII

So loud and strong he shouted, that all the water rung,
While the deep-chested warrior thus thunder'd from his tongue,
" Come, put me o'er, I'm Amelrich, who Elsy serv'd and sued,
The same who from this country fled for a mortal feud."

XLVIII

High on his sword an armlet held out the champion bold
(Bright was it and glittering and ruddy all with gold)
That he might be put over thence into Gelfrat's land.
Then took the burly boatman himself an oar in hand.

XLIX

He was in sooth, that boatman, an ill-condition'd elf.
Nothing leads men to ruin like hankering after pelf.
He thought by ferrying Hagan his ruddy gold to get;
A sword-stroke for an armlet, and death for gain he met.

L

With sinewy might the boatman row'd o'er to yonder strand,
But not the man he heard of sprung to the boat from land.
The ferryman wax'd furious when Hagan there he found;
Thus he bespake the hero, and speaking darkly frown'd.

LI

" Your name it may be Amelrich for ought I know," said he,
" But you're like him I look'd for as little as can be.
In sooth he was my brother, by father and mother's side
You've put a trick upon me, so on this bank shall bide."

LII

" Nay, think again, for heaven's sake," Sir Hagan made reply,
" In pain for sundry comrades a foreign knight am I;
So take my fare contented, and kindly put me o'er;
You'll bind me to your service, your friend for evermore."

LIII

" No, no," replied the ferryman, " it must not, faith, be so;
My good lords all around them have many a deadly foe;
For this, I ne'er put over strangers into this land,
So, as your life you value, out with you to the strand."

LIV

" Nay, speak not so," said Hagan, " you see my drooping
        cheer;
Take of me, and welcome, the gold I hand you here,
And ferry a thousand horses and as many knights of pride."
" That will I do never," the ferryman grim replied.

LV

With the word up caught he an oar both broad and long,
And lent the knight a buffet so sturdy and so strong,
That in the boat he brought him at once upon his knee.
Such a boisterous boatman never before met he.

LVI

Yet more the haughty stranger to wrath would he provoke,
So on the head of Hagan a boat-pole next he broke,
The ferryman of Elsy was sure a lusty wight,
Yet naught but loss and ruin got he by all his might.

LVII

The grim knight up starting ended soon the fray;
To the sheath quick gripp'd he wherein his weapon lay.
Off he his head has smitten, and to the bottom thrown.
Soon were the glad tidings to the bold Burgundians known.

LVIII

The boat meanwhile, ere Hagan its master yet had slain,
Had dropp'd into the current; this wrought him mickle pain,
For ere he round could bring it, faint he to wax began,
Yet strongly row'd and stoutly King Gunther's large-limb'd
     man.

LIX

The brawny stranger turn'd it with many a sturdy stroke,
Till in his grasp o'ermaster'd the oar asunder broke.
He long'd to reach his comrades at a near landing-place,
But oar had ne'er another, so this he join'd apace.

LX

With a shield-thong together (poor cord, but workman good!)
And then adown the river made for a neighboring wood.
There his good lords the warrior found waiting on the strand;
Many a bold knight ran toward him as he drew nigh the land.

LXI

Him well his comrades greeted beside the foamy flood,
But when they saw the shallop reeking all with blood
From that grim wound, that sudden the ferryman did to death,
They put a thousand questions to Hagan in a breath.

LXII

When beheld King Gunther the hot blood, how it ran
About the heaving ferry, thus he straight began.
" Here's a boat, Sir Hagan, but where's the boatman left?
Your sturdy strength, I fear me, the wretch's life hath reft."

LXIII

With lying tongue he answer'd, " The shallop I espied
Fast by a desert meadow, myself the same untied.
I have seen no boatman; this I can truly say;
And harm to none has happen'd by fault of mine to-day.

LXIV

Thereto the bold Burgundian Sir Gernot made reply,
" To-day deep care besets me; many a dear friend must die.
With not a boatman ready to put our people o'er,
'Twere hard to cross the river; this I must needs deplore."

LXV

Loud then shouted Hagan, "Lay down upon the grass
Our riding-gear, ye yeomen! I recollect I was
On Rhine the best of ferrymen that e'er took oar in hand.
Trust me, I'll put you over safe into Gelfrat's land."

XLVI

To make their passage quicker, the horses in a throng
They drove into the river; these swam so well and strong,
That by the forceful current the warriors lost not one;
A few down lower landed with weary toil foredone.

LXVII

Long and broad and massy was that huge ferry-boat.
Five hundred men and better it all at once could float
With their food and weapons from sounding shore to shore.
That day many a good warrior perforce strain'd at the oar.

LXVIII

Aboard then plac'd the heroes their gold and eke their weed.
The goal of dark destruction they sought with fatal speed.
Hagan was master-boatman; his luckless skill alone
Full many a gallant champion brought to that land unknown.

LXIX

Noble knights a thousand first he ferried o'er,
Thereto his own stout followers; behind still tarried more.
Nine thousand lusty varlets he after brought away.
The hand of him of Trony had little rest that day.

LXX

As the good knight thus deftly was putting o'er his freight,
He thought on the strange warning he had receiv'd so late
From those wise river-ladies with their prophetic breath;
It brought King Gunther's chaplain within a hair of death.

LXXI

By his holy things close seated he found the priest at rest,
With one hand gently leaning above a relique-chest;
But in the grasp of Hagan that help'd him not the least.
Sore wrong perforce he suffer'd, that heaven-forsaken priest.

LXXII

He caught and cast him over sooner than can be told.
Many a voice loud shouted, " Hold, hold, Sir Hagan, hold ! "
Wroth at the deed was Giselher, Dame Uta's youngest son,
But hold would not Sir Hagan till the mischief he had done.

LXXIII

Then the bold Burgundian the good Sir Gernot spake,
" What can it boot you, Hagan, the chaplain's life to take?
Had any other done it, he should have rued it straight.
What can thus have mov'd you the holy man to hate?"

LXXIV

Stoutly swam the chaplain; to 'scape ne'er doubted he,
Would any but assist him, but that was not to be ;
Stern Hagan, fierce and furious, as close he swam along,
Dash'd him to the bottom, wrong heaping still on wrong.

LXXV

None there but thought it outrage, yet none came to his aid,
Which when he saw, back turning for th' other bank he made ;
Though fail'd his strength o'erwearied, yet God's almighty
      hand
Back bore him through the billows, and brought him safe to
      land.

LXXVI

There stood the poor clerk shivering, and shook his dripping
      weed.
By this well knew Sir Hagan that their dark doom decreed,
As those wild mermaids warn'd him, 'twas all in vain to shun.
Thought he, " These hopeful champions must perish every
      one."

LXXVII

Soon as the bark was emptied, and all the goods it bore
By the three brethren's vassals were safely brought to shore,
Stern Hagan broke it piecemeal and down the current cast ;
The good knights star'd upon him, with wonder all aghast.

LXXVIII

" What are you doing, brother? " Dankwart sudden cried,
" How shall we cross the river, when back we have to ride
To the Rhine from Hungary our homes again to see? "
Thereafter Hagan told him, that that was ne'er to be.

LXXIX

Then said the Knight of Trony, " I do it to this end,
That, should a coward among us upon this journey wend,
Who would perchance desert us through heart-appalling fear,
A shameful death may meet him in the wild waters here."

LXXX

Then when the priest saw Hagan the bark in pieces break,
Far o'er the boiling billows to the stern knight he spake.
" What did I to you ever, base murderer," he began,
" That you this day attempted to drown a guiltless man? "

LXXXI

Then answer gave Sir Hagan, " Now of this no more;
I tell you on my honor, Sir Priest, it irks me sore
That thus you have escap'd me; I neither jest nor feign."
" For this God prais'd be ever! " said the poor chaplain.

LXXXII

" I fear you not, assure you, though brought to death so nigh.
Now on with you to Hungary; over the Rhine will I.
God grant you never thither come back, you knight untrue!
So hence with my worst wishes, for what you could not do! "

LXXXIII

With those undaunted squadrons from Burgundy there came
A bold quick-handed champion; Folker was his name.
Whate'er he thought, out-spake he with ready wit and light.
All that was done by Hagan, the minstrel held for right.

LXXXIV

Their steeds were ready saddled; their sumpters loaded too;
Not yet, throughout the journey, had one had cause to rue,
Save only the king's chaplain, the nearly drown'd divine;
He plod must weary homeward, and foot it to the Rhine.

TWENTY-SIXTH ADVENTURE

HOW DANKWART SLEW GELFRAT

I

WHEN now were all the warriors debark'd upon the strand,
The king began to question, " Who now can through the land
Direct us, lest we wander through wildering ways unknown?"
Then answer'd valiant Folker, "That task be mine alone."

II

" Now guard you well," said Hagan, "yeoman as well as
    knight,
And follow friendly counsel, for thus it seems me right;
News know I, sad to utter, and sad alike to learn;
Not one of us shall ever to Burgundy return.

III

" 'Twas told me by two mermaids this morn without disguise,
That back should we come never; now hear what I advise.
Take to your arms, ye heroes, and wend your wary way
(Since here we have stout foemen) in battailous array.

IV

" I thought to prove the mermaids, and catch them in a lie,
Who said that we in Hungary were surely doom'd to die,
And that alone the chaplain should come to Rhenish ground,
So him in yonder river I gladly would have drown'd."

V

The woe-denouncing tidings flew quick from rank to rank;
With ashen cheeks the warriors astonied sat and blank,
As on their death they ponder'd by dismal doom decreed,
From that disastrous journey; each shudder'd on his steed.

VI

'Twas near the town of Mœring that they the stream had
    cross'd;
'Twas there that Elsy's boatman his luckless life had lost.
Then thus bespake them Hagan, " This morning by the flood
I made me certain enemies, so look for wounds and blood.

VII

" I slew that self-same boatman at early dawn to-day;
By this, all know the story; so buckle to the fray;
If Gelfrat here and Elsy our onward journey cross,
Let it be, Burgundians, to their disgrace and loss.

VIII

" I know them for so valiant that they will ne'er abstain,
So let us pace our horses the slower o'er the plain,
That nobody may fancy we rather flee than ride."
" That counsel will I follow," young Giselher replied.

IX

" But who shall guide our party?   This country's strange and
    lone."
All shouted, " That shall Folker (for well to him are known
The highways and the byways), the hardy minstrel good."
They scarce had breath'd their wishes, when in his armor stood

X

The ever-ready gleeman; his helmet on he bound;
He donn'd in haste his hauberk that brightly flash'd around,
And to his spear-shaft fasten'd a pennon bloody red.
Soon with the kings his masters to a dismal doom he sped.

XI

By this, to valiant Gelfrat his boatman's death was known;
Swift-wing'd are evil tidings; the news as soon had flown
To the redoubted Elsy; sore griev'd thereat were both.
Straight summon'd they their vassals; all gather'd nothing
    loth;

XII

And I can well assure you, that scarce few hours were past,
Ere, to find the wrong-doers, were pricking fiery fast
A sturdy troop of warriors long prov'd in war before;
In aid of noble Gelfrat seven hundred came or more.

XIII

All for revenge were thirsting, all eager for th' attack,
Their warlike lords were foremost; too hotly in the track
They follow'd of those strangers, and learnt it to their cost.
Many a good friend soon after their valiant leaders lost.

XIV

Hagan the cautious Tronian their hasty counsels marr'd;
How could a warrior better his friends and kinsmen guard?
He took in charge the rearward, and there his men array'd
With his brave brother Dankwart; all with one soul obey'd.

XV

The day had sunk and vanish'd; 'twas gloom and darkness all.
He fear'd lest harm or danger his comrades should befall.
Well marshall'd through Bavaria beneath their shields went
          they;
Yet in short time their foemen assail'd them by the way.

XVI

On either side the highway, though nothing met their view,
Hoofs heard they frequent trample, and close behind them too.
Then out spoke fearless Dankwart, " Upon us is the foe;
Bind fast your helmets, warriors; prudence would have it so."

XVII

Upon their march they halted, for now they were so nigh,
That bucklers faintly glimmering they through the dark could
          spy,
Nor longer wish'd Sir Hagan in silence to abide.
" Who hunts us on the highway?" the deep-voiced warrior
          cried.

XVIII

The stern Bavarian Margrave Gelfrat gave answer back,
" We're seeking out our foemen, and close are on their track.
I know not who among you this morn my boatman slew;
He was a knight of prowess; his loss I surely rue."

XIX

Then answer'd he of Trony, " Was that same ferryman thine?
He would not put us over; the guilt, if guilt, is mine.
I slew him, I confess it, but what besides could I?
Myself first by his fury was all but done to die.

XX

" I offer'd gold and raiment for meed (what could I more?)
Into thy land, Sir Gelfrat, if he'd but put us o'er.
He flew into a fury, and caught me o'er the crown
With a heavy boat-pole, and knock'd me roughly down.

XXI

" I snatch'd my sword in anger; from his wrath I kept my life;
A mortal wound I gave him; this clos'd at once the strife.
Yet such amends I offer as you think just and right."
They hearken'd but to vengeance, burning with scorn and spite.

XXII

" I knew full well," said Gelfrat, " if Gunther pass'd along
This country with his meiny, that we should suffer wrong
At the hands of Hagan; 'scape shall he not to-day;
He did to death the ferryman, and for the deed shall pay."

XXIII

To smite above the bucklers they couch'd their lances straight.
Gelfrat and Hagan both clos'd with eager hate.
Elsy too and Dankwart each bore him like a knight;
Each prov'd the other's manhood; stern and stubborn was the
    fight.

XXIV

Who better could defend them who better could assail?
Borne was the stalwart Hagan clean o'er his horse's tail,
And on the grass lay floundering by Gelfrat's sturdy stroke.
In the shock asunder his charger's pöitral broke.

XXV

Then knew he what was fighting; all round the lances crash'd;
From the green Sir Hagan upstarted, unabash'd,
Or rather kindling courage from overthrow so rude.
He turn'd, I ween, on Gelfrat, not in the mildest mood.

XXVI

Who held them both their horses, is more than I can tell.
To the ground the champions were both brought down from
    selle.
They rush'd upon each other; they mingled sword and shield.
Their comrades to the rescue flock'd round from all the field.

XXVII

However fiercely Hagan on noble Gelfrat sprung,
A huge piece from his buckler (loud with the stroke it rung)
Was hewn by the stout margrave; fire forth in sparkles flew;
The ferryman like to follow was Gunther's liegeman true.

XXVIII

To the valiant Dankwart he shouted loud and high,
" Help, help me, dearest brother, I've just been like to die
By a stout-handed champion; he'll let me ne'er go free."
Thereto replied bold Dankwart, " Then I'll your umpire be."

XXIX

Close to them leapt the hero; nothing more he said;
Once his sword he lifted, down dropp'd Gelfrat dead.
Elsy had fain reveng'd him, but forc'd was he to yield.
He and his fear-struck comrades fled that disastrous field.

XXX

Slain was his valiant brother, himself was wounded sore,
Of his war-practis'd champions eighty the best, or more,
Lay with grim Death companion'd; what then beside could he
But from the men of Gunther with loss and anguish flee?

XXXI

Soon as they of Bavaria gave way through ghastly fear,
Behind them deadly sword-strokes loud ringing you might
        hear.
So the bold men of Trony held their foes in chase,
Who sought to 'scape the forfeit and ever fled apace.

XXXII

Then Dankwart thus behind them loud shouted o'er the plain,
" Forthwith must we be wending back on our steps again;
So let them fly unfollow'd, each bleeding as he flies,
While we rejoin our comrades; this I in truth advise."

XXXIII

When back had come the warriors to where the fight had been,
Thus spoke the Knight of Trony, " Chiefs, now 'twere fit, I
    ween,
To reckon up the missing, and learn whom we to-night
Have lost through Gelfrat's anger in this sharp sudden fight.

XXXIV

Four of their friends had perish'd, slight cause had they to
    plain,
For they had well aveng'd them; on th' other hand were slain
Of the repuls'd Bavarians a hundred men or more,
The shields of the stout Tronians were dimm'd and soak'd
    with gore.

XXXV

From the clouds a moment broke out the gleaming moon;
" We shall o'ertake," said Hagan, " our friends and comrades
    soon;
But none to my good masters speak of this hasty fray;
Let them without suspicion remain till dawn of day."

XXXVI

When those who fought the battle had now rejoin'd the rest,
They found them with long travail exhausted and oppress'd.
" How long have we to journey? " asked many a champion
    brave
" Here's neither host nor hostel," was th' answer Dankwart
    gave,

XXXVII

" You all must until morning ride on as best you can."
Next sent the nimble Folker, the leader of the van,
To ask the noble marshal, " Where shall we lodge the crew
To-night? Where rest the horses and our good masters too? "

XXXVIII

Then answer gave bold Dankwart, " That's more than I can
    say;
Rest must we ne'er a moment before the dawn of day,
And, wheresoe'er we meet it, lie down upon the green."
To most of those who heard him 'twas heavy news, I ween.

XXXIX

Long time remain'd unnotic'd the stains of bloody red,
Till the fair sun, up rising, his glittering radiance spread
At morn above the mountains; at once the king espied
That they had just been fighting, and full of anger cried,

XL

" How now, friend Hagan? so you, it seems, disdain'd
To have me for your comrade, when thus with blood was
　　stain'd
And dabbled all your hauberks; who put you in that plight? "
Said he, " 'Twas done by Elsy; he fell on us last night.

XLI

" To revenge his ferryman this fierce assault he plann'd
There slain was sturdy Gelfrat by my good brother's hand,
And Elsy scarce escap'd us; 'faith he was ill bestead.
We lost but four companions, and he a hundred dead."

XLII

We know not, where that morning the warriors laid them down,
Straight learn'd all the people in country and in town,
That noble Uta's children to court were on their road.
On them a hearty welcome was at Passau soon bestow'd.

XLIII

Well pleas'd was Bishop Pilgrin, the uncle of the queen.
That with so many champions, all cas'd in armor sheen,
His proud Burgundian nephews had come into the land.
Soon, what good will he bore them, he made them understand.

XLIV

Along the roads to lodge them their friends all did their best.
At Passau room was wanting to harbor every guest;
They cross'd perforce the water, where on an open ground
Were hasty tents erected, and rich pavilions pitch'd around.

XLV

They there were forc'd to tarry the space of one whole day,
And eke the night till morning; how well receiv'd were they!
Thence to the land of Rudeger they were to ride anew.
Swift to him the tidings of their coming flew.

XLVI

When the way-weary warriors had ta'en some needful rest,
And now were close approaching the country of their quest,
They found upon the border a man that sleeping lay;
Sir Hagan sprung upon him, and took his sword away.

XLVII

He was call'd Sir Eckewart, that sleep-oppressed knight;
Sore griev'd was he and downcast at his defenceless plight,
Stripp'd of so strong a weapon, and at a stranger's will.
They found the march of Rudeger watch'd and warded ill.

XLVIII

" Woe's me for this dishonor ! " the grief-struck warrior cried,
" Alas that the Burgundians e'er hither thought to ride !
Sure, since I lost Sir Siegfried, all joy is flown from me.
Oh, well away, Sir Rudeger, how have I injur'd thee ! "

XLIX

Sir Hagan scarcely waited to hear his sorrows through;
He gave him back his weapon, and six red armlets too.
" Take these, Sir Knight, as tokens that thou my friend wilt be:
Thou'rt a bold chief to slumber thus lonely on the lea."

L

" God quit you for your armlets ! " Sir Eckewart replied;
" Yet much, I own, it grieves me that to the Huns you ride.
You took the life of Siegfried, all hate you deadly here;
As your true friend I warn you; watch well, and wisely fear."

LI

" Now God watch well and ward us," Hagan gave answer back;
" No care have these good warriors, save for what now they
    lack,
Fit and convenient quarters; fain would we learn aright
Where we, both kings and subjects, may hope to lodge to-night.

LII

" Our steeds by this long journey are ruin'd past a doubt,"
Said the bold warrior Hagan, " our stores are all run out;
Naught's to be had for money; we need (or else we're sped),
Some host, who of his goodness to-night would give us bread."

LIII

Straight Eckewart made answer, " I'll show you such a host,
That scarcely could a better be found in any coast,
Than he, who here, assure ye, your coming fain will greet,
If you be pleas'd, bold strangers, Sir Rudeger to meet.

LIV

" He dwells fast by the highway, and never yet on earth
Was there a host more liberal; his heart gives virtues birth,
As meadows grass and flowerets in the sweet month of May,
To do good knights good service he waxes blithe and gay."

LV

Straight answer'd then King Gunther, " Will you a message
         take,
So ask my dear friend Rudeger, if he will for my sake
Me and my kinsmen shelter and all this numerous clan?
To serve him ever after I'll do the best I can."

LVI

" Fain will I do your bidding," Eckewart replied.
With good will off he started; well his spurs he plied,
And what he brought to Rudeger he told without delay.
To him no such glad tidings had come for many a day.

LVII

A knight toward Bechlaren spurr'd fast as fast might be;
Rudeger himself discern'd him; " On yonder road," said he,
" 'Tis Kriemhild's liegeman Eckewart, that rides so hot a pace."
He thought his foes had harm'd him, and held him still in chase.

LVIII

To the gate he hurried; the knight there saw he stand,
Who straight his sword ungirded, and laid it from his hand.
The news that he brought with him he car'd not to withhold
From the host and those about him, but straight his story told.

LIX

He thus bespake the margrave, " A message you I bring
From my good master Gunther, the stout Burgundian king,
And Giselher his brother and noble Gernot too;
Every one of the warriors sends you his service true.

LX

" The same does also Hagan and Folker bold, as well,
With firm entire devotion, and I beside must tell
What from the king's marshal I have too in command,
That need have the good yeomen of lodging at your hand."

LXI

Merrily laugh'd Sir Rudeger as thus he made reply,
" I joy to hear these tidings, that kings so great and high
Deign to request my service; my zeal they soon shall see;
If they my dwelling enter, right happy shall I be."

LXII

" Dankwart the marshal also by me the number sends
Of those, who seek your homestead with your Burgundian
    friends;
Sixty nimble champions, good knights a thousand too,
And yeomen full nine thousand." Right glad the margrave
    grew.

LXIII

" In truth I shall be happy," said noble Rudeger,
"·To see guests of such worship in my poor dwelling here,
To whom I have but rarely yet render'd service due.
Now ride ye forth to meet them, good friends and kinsmen
    true."

LXIV

With that in haste they mounted: forth flew squire and knight,
Whate'er their lord commanded, that pass'd with all for right;
The better thus their duties they did when need requir'd.
Yet nothing knew Dame Gotelind, who sat in power retir'd.

TWENTY-SEVENTH ADVENTURE

RUDEGER'S HOSPITALITY

I

THERE linger'd not the margrave, but straight the ladies
    sought,
His wife and his fair daughter, and what good news he brought,
By Eckewart deliver'd, told with exulting glee,
How their good lady's brethren their guests were soon to be.

II

" My dearest love and lady," his tale he thus 'gan tell,
" The noble kings approaching receive, as fits them, well,
Since hither they are passing to court with all their clan;
Accord, too, like fair greeting to Hagan, Gunther's man.

III

" With them besides on duty comes one that Dankwart hight;
And yet a third call'd Folker, a well-train'd courtly knight.
These six must you, Dame Gotelind, and you, fair daughter,
    kiss.
Nor at your hands let any of fitting kindness miss."

IV

That promis'd straight the ladies, and ready all things made.
Large store of goodly raiment forth from the chests they laid,
That they such noble warriors might meet in fit array;
Many a lovely lady bestirr'd herself that day.

V

How little spurious colors on their fresh cheeks were found!
Far-glittering golden fillets about their heads they wound,
And in such gorgeous bondage confin'd their radiant hair,
Lest the light frolic breezes should work disorder there.

VI

So let us leave the ladies in no unpleasing toil.
Meanwhile the friends of Rudeger swift scour'd the sounding soil,
Till, where they found the princes, they made a sudden stand.
The guests were warmly welcom'd to the good margrave's land.

VII

When to his home the margrave saw the Burgundians come,
Exulting thus bespoke he the strangers all and some,
" Welcome, ye lords! right welcome, you and your vassals too.
Here in my land full gladly I see such friends as you."

VIII

The brethren to his greeting their stately heads inclin'd,
To the loving love returning, and kindness to the kind.
Apart he greeted Hagan, whom he had known of old;
The same did he to Folker the minstrel blithe and bold.

IX

Last welcom'd he Sir Dankwart, who thus his host bespake,
" Since you will give us shelter, pray who in charge will take
The train we have brought hither, all in such weary plight? "
Then answer'd him the margrave, " Well will you rest to-night.

X

" My people shall keep safely all you have hither brought,
Silver and steeds and raiment; you need not think of aught.
Be sure, I'll take such order, that loss shall none occur.
You'll not miss all among you as much as half a spur.

XI

" So pitch your tents, ye yeomen, in the field apace;
Whatever here is missing, I'll willingly replace;
Off with bit and saddle—turn loose your weary steeds."
Such a host had rarely supplied the wanderer's needs.

XII

Well pleased were the Burgundians; when all was brought to
　　pass,
The lords rode on together; the yeomen on the grass
Laid them down in clusters; there to repose they fell;
I ween, in all their journey they ne'er had far'd so well.

XIII

And now from forth the castle the noble margravine
Had gone with her fair daughter; beside them there was seen
Many a lovely lady, and many a smiling maid,
All deck'd with store of bracelets, and in bright robes array'd.

XIV

Precious stones were sparkling ever and anon
About their gorgeous raiment; themselves yet brighter shone.
Thither rode up the strangers and lighted instantly.
Ah! what high bearing had they, those chiefs of Burgundy!

XV

Six and thirty maidens and thereto many a dame,
Each fair as wish could sigh for, or busy fancy fame,
Stepp'd forth to greet the strangers with warriors many a one;
Their task by those high ladies with comely grace was done.

XVI

The margravine went forward, and kiss'd the kings all three;
The like too did her daughter; Hagan, the next was he.
Her father bade her kiss him; a glance on him she cast,
And thought he look'd so dreadful, that him she fain had
　　pass'd.

XVII

At length perforce she did it, since so her father said,
Yet could not but change color, now waxing white, now red.
She kiss'd, too, noble Dankwart, and Folker last in place.
For his strength and valor the minstrel gain'd such grace.

XVIII

This done, with gentle gesture the damsel meek and mild
By the hand, yet trembling, took Giselher the child,
Her mother took King Gunther, the bold Burgundian lord.
So with the knights the ladies mov'd thence in blithe accord.

XIX

The host went with Sir Gernot into a spacious hall;
There both chiefs and ladies down sat together all.
Straight to his guests the margrave bade hand good wine
    around.
Better entertainment knights yet never found.

XX

There many a longing eye-glance from all sides might you see
Bent on the margrave's daughter, so fresh and fair was she.
Many a good knight was breathing for her the secret sigh;
In truth she well deserv'd it; her thoughts were pure and high.

XXI

They mus'd just as it pleas'd them, yet naught could thence
    befall.
Alike meanwhile were glances cast by the knights in hall
On other dames and damsels, whereof there sat good store.
Soon show'd the noble minstrel what love the host he bore.

XXII

And now at last they sever'd, as custom there requir'd;
Ladies and knights, as fitted, to separate rooms retir'd.
In the broad hall the tables in order straight were set;
There soon the noble strangers all lordly service met.

XXIII

To grace her guests, at table the noble hostess kind
Took place, but left her daughter, as fitted best, behind
Among her blooming maidens, with whom retir'd she sat.
The guests, who joy'd to see her, were little pleas'd with that.

XXIV

With meats and drinks abundant their fill had feasted all;
Then back the lovely ladies were usher'd to the hall;
Nor comely mirth there wanted, nor merriment, nor jest.
The gentle knight Sir Folker there shone above the rest.

XXV

Then out spake to Sir Rudeger that minstrel bold and true,
" High and puissant margrave, God sure has dealt with you
As one whom most He favors, since he so fair a wife
Has given you for a helpmate, and bless'd with joy your life.

XXVI

" If I were a monarch and if a crown I wore,"
Said the good knight, " no maiden should be my queen before
Your fair and gentle daughter; my heart's desire I tell;
Lovely is she to look on, high-born and nurtur'd well."

XXVII

Then spake the noble margrave, " What chance could ever
          bring
To woo my child beloved a proud and puissant king?
My wife and I are exiles, both worn with age and care,
And can give her nothing; what boots then all her fair?"

XXVIII

Thereat the courteous Gernot took up the word and spake,
" If I desir'd a helpmate after my heart to take
None would I ask more gladly than this same modest maid."
Thereupon Sir Hagan in courtly fashion said,

XXIX

" Now fits it my lord Giselher to take a bride, I ween,
And sure so high-descended is the young margravine,
That I and all his vassals would do her homage fain,
If crown'd we were to see her in our Burgundian reign."

XXX

Well pleas'd was good Sir Rudeger Sir Hagan's words to hear,
So, too, was Lady Gotelind; right joyous was her cheer.
Soon so the chiefs contriv'd it, that Giselher, nothing loth,
To wife took the fair maiden, as well beseem'd them both.

XXXI

When once a thing is settled, who further can gainsay?
Forthwith they bade the damsel to court to take her way.
Then for his wife to give him the lovely maid they swore,
Then he too vow'd to cherish and love her evermore.

XXXII

Next dower'd was the fair maiden with castles and with land;
With an oath assurance was giv'n by Gunther's hand,
As well as by Lord Gernot's, that so it should be done.
Then said the noble margrave, " Since castles I have none,

XXXIII

" With you will I forever a faithful friendship hold;
A hundred sumpters' burden of silver and of gold
(No unbefitting portion) I'll give the gentle bride,
So that the bridegroom's warriors may well be satisfied."

XXXIV

Then had the bride and bridegroom within a ring to stand,
For such was then the custom; a merry stripling band
Encircled the fair couple, and gaz'd on them their fill,
And thought the while as idly as think young people still.

XXXV

Now when was ask'd the damsel in homely phrase and plain,
If she would have the warrior, she felt a moment's pain;
Not that she was unwilling to take the stately one;
She blush'd but at the question, as many a maid has done.

XXXVI

Her father Rudeger told her at once to answer, " Yes,"
And that she fain would take him.   In a trice with tenderness
Young Giselher around her, the shrinking and the coy,
Lock'd his white hands together; alas! how fleeting was their
    joy!

XXXVII

Then spake again the margrave, " Ye rich and noble kings,
When you, as is the custom, after your revellings
Return by us to Rhineland, I'll give my child to you,
To take her in your party."   They promis'd so to do.

XXXVIII

The merry sound of revel was hush'd perforce at last.
With mincing step the maidens forth to their chambers pass'd,
And eke in rest the strangers slept on till break of day.
Then the first meal was ready; none better far'd than they.

XXXIX

Their fast they scarce had broken, when they at once would
    start
For the realm of Hungary; " You must not thus depart,"
Said the good host Sir Rudeger; " awhile here tarry yet,
Such guests and so beloved but seldom have I met."

XL

" That must not be," said Dankwart, "your ruin you design,
Where can you find provisions, bread as well as wine,
If day by day an army is eating up your store?"
Soon as the host had heard him, he said, " Talk thus no more.

XLI

" Nay, thus to refuse me, my dear lords, do not think;
For fourteen days together I'll find you meat and drink,
You and all those about you, your well-appointed train.
Full little of my substance has yet King Etzel ta'en."

XLII

Whate'er excuse they offer'd, there perforce they stay'd
Feasting till the fourth morning; then well their host display'd
His far-renowned bounty, and to his parting guests
Gave without stint for presents proud steeds and gorgeous
    vests.

XLIII

This now could last no longer; thence must they forward fare.
Little his custom'd bounty did then the margrave spare.
All then was had for asking; that morn denied was none;
All kindness and all honor to every guest was done.

XLIV

And now their noble meiny brought up before the gate
Store of good chargers saddled; thither to swell their state
Flock'd troops of foreign champions, all bearing shield in hand,
All with the Rhenish brethren bound to King Etzel's land.

XLV

The noble host in plenty proffer'd his gifts to all
Before the noble strangers came outside the hall.
With open hand liv'd Rudeger, stout heart, and honor clear;
He now his lovely daughter had given to Giselher.

XLVI

Then gave he valiant Gernot a sword full sharp and bright,
Which soon the bold Burgundian bore manfully in fight.
That so her husband gave it, well pleased the margrave's wife.
Alas! the fatal present cost Rudeger his life.

XLVII

Then to the great King Gunther he gave from out his store
A mailcoat, that with honor the sturdy champion wore.
But seldom could the monarch to take a present brook,
Yet at the hand of Rudeger this with warm thanks he took.

XLVIII

Then Gotelind, as was fitting, offer'd with fair accord
A parting gift to Hagan, that, like the king his lord,
He, too, not empty-handed, to Etzel court might ride,
But he declin'd the present, and to the dame replied,

XLIX

" I ne'er saw ought, fair lady, however rich and rare,
That it would more content me hence as my own to bear,
Than yonder well-form'd buckler that hangs on yonder wall.
To take that shield to Hungary would please me most of all."

L

Soon as the Lady Gotelind heard Hagan's accents deep,
They brought to mind her sorrow; she could not choose but
    weep.
Then thought she on bold Nudung, by mightier Wittich slain,
And to her wounded bosom the smart return'd again.

LI

Thus she bespake Sir Hagan, " That shield I freely give,
And would to God the warrior among us still did live,
Who bore it erst in battle; dead on the field he lay;
Him must I weep for ever, mourning my life away."

LII

Then from her seat she totter'd; her limbs with anguish shook;
The shield of her lamented in her white hands she took,
And carried it to Hagan; he grasp'd the gift she gave,
Giv'n and receiv'd in honor, and fitting well the brave.

LIII

A veil of glittering samite its varied hues conceal'd;
Never had the daylight shone on a better shield.
With precious stones far-beaming 'twas richly deck'd all o'er.
It could not have been purchas'd for a thousand marks or more.

LIV

So by command of Hagan the shield away was ta'en.
Then came to court Sir Dankwart among the parting train.
To him gave Rudeger's daughter robes richly broider'd o'er,
Which 'midst the Huns thereafter in joyous mood he wore.

LV

Of all the gifts that morning bestow'd on every guest,
Not one by those Burgundians had ever been possess'd,
But by the margrave's bounty, which so by proof they knew.
Soon they became such foemen, that they the giver slew.

LVI

And now the valiant Folker with high-bred courtly grace
Stepp'd forth before Dame Gotelind, and, standing there in
        place,
His sweetest tones attemper'd and sang his choicest lay,
Ere he from Bechlaren took leave and went his way.

LVII

With that the gentle hostess bade bring a casket near
(Of friendly gifts and bounty and kindness you must hear);
From this she took twelve bracelets, and drew them o'er his
        hand;
" These you must take, and with you bear hence to Etzel's land,

LVIII

" And for the sake of Gotelind the same at court must wear,
That I may learn, when hither again you all repair,
What service you have done me in yon assembly bright."
The lady's wish thereafter full well perform'd the knight.

LIX

Then the noble margrave his parting guests bespake,
" That you may ride the safer, myself the charge will take
To guide you, lest from robbers you suffer by the road."
With that upon his sumpters in haste was laid their load.

LX

The host he soon was ready with full five hundred men
Well horsed and well apparell'd ; them led he merrily then
To the proud feast of Etzel, and they him follow'd fain ;
Not one of them came living to Bechlaren back again.

LXI

The host from home departed with many a loving kiss :
The like did also Giselher ; his honor counsell'd this.
Each to his beating bosom his trembling lady press'd.
That parting planted sorrow in many a virgin breast.

LXII

All windows in Bechlaren now flew open wide.
Straight would to horse the margrave, and with his warriors
    ride
I ween, their hearts that moment their coming doom forbode.
Many a dame and many a damsel loud sobb'd as forth they
    rode.

LXIII

E'en for their best beloved in heart they sorrow'd sore,
For those, whom at Bechlaren they were to see no more.
Yet merrily the champions prick'd along the strand
Downward beside the Danube to reach the Hunnish land.

LXIV

Then thus to the Burgundians out spake the stately knight.
" Rudeger the noble, methinks, it were but right
We should announce we're coming e'en now to Hunnish
    ground ;
More pleasantly no tidings in Etzel's ear will sound."

LXV

Straight adown through Austria he bade a courier ride;
At once among the people 'twas publish'd far and wide,
That coming were the heroes from Worms beyond the Rhine.
Right glad were Etzel's vassals, and those of Etzel's line.

LXVI

With the news the couriers forth gallop'd hastily,
That the Nibelungers were now in Hungary.
"Well should'st thou receive them, Kriemhild, lady mine!
They come to do thee honor, these brethren dear of thine."

LXVII

Dame Kriemhild at a window was standing there to view;
She look'd out for her kinsmen as friend for friends will do.
From her native country saw she many a man.
The king too heard the tidings and for joy to laugh began.

LXVIII

"Now I at last am happy," exclaim'd th' exulting queen;
"Hither are come my kinsmen with many a mailcoat sheen,
And many a new-made buckler; who would for gold endeavor,
Let him my wrongs remember, and I'll befriend him ever.

LXIX

"Yes! I will so contrive it, to take revenge for all
At this same feast of Etzel's (whate'er thereafter fall)
On his abhorred body, who so the traitor play'd,
And all my joy so blasted.—I shall be now repaid."

TWENTY-EIGHTH ADVENTURE

HOW KRIEMHILD RECEIVED HAGAN

I

WHEN now the bold Burgundians had come into the land,
He of Bern soon heard it, the aged Hildebrand;
He told his lord the tidings; sore griev'd it the good knight;
He begged him the stout strangers receive as best they might.

II

Straight to bring up the horses quick Wolfhart order gave;
Then forward prick'd with Dietrich full many a champion
  brave.
Thence to the field to greet them; as friends to friends they went.
There had they pitch'd all ready full many a gorgeous tent.

III

Them riding thus at distance soon as Sir Hagan spied,
Thus he his courteous counsel unto his lords applied.
"Now every one, ye warriors, down instant from his seat,
And these, who'd bid you welcome, go forth yourselves to meet.

IV

"Well know I yon bright meiny, whom here we have at hand;
They are the choicest warriors; of th' Amelungers' land.
The Lord of Bern rides foremost; high-mettled chiefs are they,
So scorn not what fair service they proffer you to-day."

V

Then down from horse alighted, as fitting was and right,
With the redoubted Dietrich many a good squire and knight.
All to the noble strangers went forward hastily,
And courteously saluted the lords of Burgundy.

VI

Soon as discern'd Sir Dietrich how they to meet him came,
Now you would hear full gladly what words that chief of fame
Spoke to the sons of Uta; their journey griev'd him sore;
The truth, he thought, Sir Rudeger had known and told before.

VII

" Welcome, ye lords, right welcome, Gunther and Gernot true,
And Giselher and Hagan, the like to Folker too,
And ever-ready Dankwart. Do you not understand
That Kriemhild still mourns deeply the Chief of Niblung-
    land?"

VIII

" Why, she will weep forever," Sir Hagan made reply,
" 'Tis many a year, Sir Dietrich, since he was done to die.
She now has got King Etzel; of love she cannot lack;
Siegfried is dead and buried, and never can come back."

IX

" Just now let us, I prithee, leave Siegfried's wounds alone,"
The Lord of Bern, Sir Dietrich, replied in earnest tone,
" As long as lives Dame Kriemhild there's fear of mortal ill.
Trust of the Nibelungers! watch and be wary still."

X

" Why watch, and why be wary?" the lofty king replied.
" Etzel sent us envoys (what should I ask beside?)
To say, that with our visit he would be well content;
And by them many a message my sister Kriemhild sent."

XI

" To my advice," said Hagan, " I pray you, now give ear.
Entreat our friend Sir Dietrich and his good warriors here,
Of their suspicious tidings the utmost scope to show,
That we may come more fully Dame Kriemhild's mind to
    know."

XII

Then the three kings, retiring, to separate converse drew,
Gunther and Gernot and good Sir Dietrich, too.
" Now tell us, we beseech thee, right noble Knight of Bern,
How thou hast been able Queen Kriemhild's mind to learn."

XIII

The Lord of Bern thus answer'd, " What have I now to say?
I hear the wife of Etzel every break of day
To the great God of heaven sob out her dreary tale,
And for the loss of Siegfried yet ever weep and wail."

XIV

"What's done can ne'er be undone," spoke out the minstrel
    bold,
The death-defying Folker, "for all we've just been told.
So to court let's onward, and manfully abide
Whate'er may us stout champions among the Huns betide."

XV

So the bold Burgundians to court thence took their way
After their country's fashion in pomp and proud array.
Many a stout knight of Hungary among the gazers came
To look on Tronian Hagan, and mark his warrior frame.

XVI

Of him among the courtiers were rumors not a few,
That he it was who Siegfried, the Netherlander, slew,
The strongest of all champions, Dame Kriemhild's husband
    bold.
Hence much was there among them of Hagan ask'd and told.

XVII

Well grown and well compacted was that redoubted guest;
Long were his legs and sinewy, and deep and broad his chest.
His hair, that once was sable, with gray was dash'd of late,
And terrible his visage, and lordly was his gait.

XVIII

And now the bold Burgundians with shelter were supplied.
The knights were lodg'd together, the rest were sunder'd wide.
Through Kriemhild's hate to Gunther was plann'd this subtle
    train,
That easier in their quarters the yeomen might be slain.

XIX

Dankwart was the marshal, Hagan's brother brave;
The charge of the stout yeomen to him King Gunther gave,
That all might well be tended, and each might have his fill.
The Chief of the Burgundians bore all his train good will.

XX

Kriemhild the lovely with all her meiny went,
Where she the Nibelungers receiv'd with false intent.
She took her brother Giselher and took him by the hand.
That seeing drew Sir Hagan more tight his helmet's band.

XXI

"Sure after such a welcome," thus Hagan sternly spake,
"Methinks for men of action 'twere fitting, thought to take.
Greeting kings and subjects in such a different guise!—
I fear our journey hither will hardly pass for wise."

XXII

"To those who fain would see you," said Kriemhild, "welcome
  be;
Look not for friendly greeting for your own sake from me.
But tell me what you've brought me from Worms beyond the
  Rhine,
That you so warm a welcome should find from me or mine."

XXIII

"Why these words, my lady?" said Hagan, "what's their
  drift?"
That all these knights from Rhineland should bring you each
  a gift?
I knew you were so wealthy, and liv'd so royally,
I need not bring you presents as far as Hungary."

XXIV

"Then with this one plain question your memory I must goad.
The Nibelungers' treasure—where have you that bestow'd?
That was my own possession as well you understand.
'Twas that you should have brought me hither to Etzel's land."

XXV

"I' faith, my lady Kriemhild, 'tis now full ma y a day
Since in my power the treasure of the Nibelungers lay.
In the Rhine my lords bade sink it; I did their bidding fain,
And in the Rhine, I warrant, till doomsday 'twill remain."

XXVI

Then thus the queen made answer, "That was just what I
    thought.
Little of it, ay, little have you hither brought,
Though 'twas my own, unquestion'd to keep or give away.
I've had for it much sorrow and many a dreary day."

XXVII

"The devil a hoard I bring you," said Hagan, the stern knight;
"I've quite enough to carry in my mailcoat bright
And in my trusty buckler; my hand must wield the sword,
My head support the helmet;—how could I bring your hoard?"

XXVIII

"Think not I stir this matter because for gold I care;
To give have I such plenty, your gifts I well can spare.
One murder and two robberies! I have been beggar'd thrice
For these to the last farthing poor I demand the price."

XXIX

Then the Queen of Hungary bespake the warriors all;
"No weapons may be carried, ye knights, into the hall.
I'll have them kept in safety, so give them up to me."
"In truth," replied Sir Hagan, "that shall never be.

XXX

"I long not for the honor that a queen so great and fair
My shield and other armor should to my quarters bear.
Not so my father taught me; ever of old said he,
Let none but thou, son Hagan, thy armor-bearer be."

XXXI

"Oh! woe is me unhappy," burst Dame Kriemhild out,
"My brethren here and Hagan, why should they shrink and
    doubt?
Not trust me with their bucklers?—they have been warn'd, I
    see;
If I but knew who did it, death should be his fee."

XXXII

Thereto, inflam'd with anger, return'd Sir Dietrich brave,
" 'Twas I that the warning to the noble princes gave,
And to their liegeman Hagan, to whom such hate thou bear'st.
Now up, she-fiend! be doing, and harm me if thou dar'st!"

XXXIII

Deep blush'd the wife of Etzel for anger and for shame;
Much she fear'd Sir Dietrich, that vengeance-breathing dame;
Nor word she spake, but, turning, with many a sharp, quick
    glance
Ever as thence she parted glared on her foes askance.

XXXIV

Then two clasp'd hands as frankly as brother does with brother;
The one was good Sir Dietrich, Sir Hagan was the other.
Then spoke the lofty Berner with courteous words and true;
" In sooth your coming hither right bitterly I rue,

XXXV

" Through that which with such malice the vengeful queen let
    fall."
Straight answer'd he of Trony, " 'Faith, there's a cure for all."
Such words unto his fellow spoke either mighty man.
King Etzel had observ'd them, and thus to ask began.

XXXVI

" Fain would I learn," said Etzel, " if any here can tell,
Who is that champion yonder, whom Dietrich greets so well.
He is a man of mettle as I can guess by sight;
Whoever is his father, sure he's a peerless knight."

XXXVII

Then spake a man of Kriemhild's, " I'll tell you all I can.
That knight was born at Trony, his sire was Aldrian.
Though now he plays the courtier, he is a champion stern.
That I've not lied unto you, Sir King, you soon may learn."

XXXVIII

" That he's so stern a champion, how can I ever see? "
Of all the craft and cunning nothing yet knew he,
Wherewith about her kinsmen the queen her toils had wound,
That not a soul among them came back from Hunnish ground.

XXXIX

" Well knew I once good Aldrian; my man was he of yore.
With me much praise and honor obtain'd he heretofore;
'Twas I, a knight who dubb'd him, and gave him of my gold.
I could not but befriend him for true was he and bold.

XL

" So all that touches Hagan, I've known for many a year.
Of old two noble children my hostages were here,
He and the Spaniard Walter; here each grew up to man.
At last I sent home Hagan; Walter off with Hildgund ran."

XLI

So thought the king with pleasure on what had happ'd of yore.
His former friend of Trony he gladly saw once more,
Who with high deeds of knighthood in youth had serv'd his
     ends,
But in age spread wide destruction among his dearest friends.

TWENTY-NINTH ADVENTURE

HOW HAGAN REFUSED TO RISE TO KRIEMHILD

I

THEN parted the bold couple, both hardy knights and stern,
Hagan the chief of Trony, and Dietrich lord of Bern.
Then, looking o'er his shoulder, King Gunther's liegeman eyed
The crowd to find a comrade, whom in a trice he spied.

II

Folker, the skilful minstrel, he saw by Giselher stand,
And pray'd him to come with him apart from all the band,
For well he knew his fierceness and danger-daring mood.
He was a knight in all things of dauntless hardihood.

III

They left the lords assembled where in the court they stood;
Alone retir'd this couple of hardy knights and good,
And cross'd the court far distant, and reach'd a palace fair.
Of hostile spite or outrage naught reck'd the peerless pair.

IV

Before the house down sat they upon a bench hard by,
Facing a hall of Kriemhild's; a fairer ne'er met eye.
Bright from their stately persons their glittering armor shone.
Each knight would fain have known them of all who there
    look'd on.

V

As on wild beasts, grim rangers of wood or dreary wold,
The whispering Huns at distance gaz'd on the champions bold.
Queen Kriemhild from a window espied them thus apart,
And a frown o'ercast her beauty, and passion shook her heart.

VI

She thought on all her sorrows, and straight began to weep.
There many a man of Etzel's stood lost in wonder deep.
All ask'd, what so disturb'd her, and chang'd her cheer anew.
" Hagan," she answer'd, " Hagan, ye warriors bold and true! "

VII

Thus they bespake their lady, " How can this have been?
But now we saw you merry and blithe of mood, fair queen.
How bold soe'er the warrior who has wrong'd King Etzel's
    wife,
Give but the word of vengeance and cost shall it his life."

VIII

" Thanks, warriors, thanks for ever! on him who wreaks my
    woe,
All that he can ask for straight will I bestow.
At your feet I throw me," sobbing thus she spake,
" Revenge me on this Hagan, and slay him for my sake."

IX

Straight ready made for mischief sixty men of might;
Instant would they have hasten'd in fair Kriemhild's right
To take the life of Hagan, that redoubted one,
And of the fearless gleeman; with forethought all was done.

X

But when the queen survey'd them, and found the band so few,
Thus she, amidst her fury, bespake her friends anew.
" Be still awhile, ye warriors! your martial mood restrain;
Ne'er can a troop so scanty stern Hagan's might sustain.

XI

" Strong is the Knight of Trony, and oft in battle tried,
But stronger yet the warrior who sits him there beside,
Folker, the valiant gleeman; he is a dangerous man.
Attack them not so rashly; first muster all you can,"

XII

They hearken'd to her warning; then many more came on,
Till round her knights four hundred in burnish'd armor shone.
The furious queen was longing her rage on both to sate;
Thence came the chiefs soon after to stand in deadly strait.

XIII

When so she saw her meiny each in his harness stand,
Thus she sternly smiling bespake th' impatient band.
" Wait yet, my friends, a moment, ere with yon pair you close;
My crown upon my temples will I confront my foes.

XIV

" First hear, and from the doer, whose hand my heart has torn,
The wrongs, that I from Hagan, my brother's man, have borne,
I know him for so haughty, that out he'll speak them all;
And I too care as little what thence on him may fall."

XV

When that redoubted minstrel, who kept good watch, I ween,
Descending swift a staircase beheld the noble queen,
And thence beyond the threshold—when he this espied
In a trice bespake he his comrade by his side.

XVI

" Look there! look there! friend Hagan! how hither there she
　　hies,
Who to this land has drawn us with friendly seeming lies!
Queen yet saw I never begirt with such a band,
Each marching as to battle with naked sword in hand.

XVII

" Know you that here, friend Hagan, you're hated bitterly?
So keep you all the better from force or treachery;
Look to your life and honor; this is what I advise;
They're coming on in anger if rightly I surmise.

XVIII

" And many there are among them so broad across the chest—
If we are to defend us, 'tis time to do our best.
Each about his body a shining mailcoat wears,
But whom therewith they threaten, not a tongue declares."

XIX

Thereto in wrath Sir Hagan gave answer stern and proud,
" Well know I wherefore musters yon armor-bearing crowd;
'Gainst me they gird the hauberk and wave the sword on high,
Yet back again to Rhineland in spite of them will I.

XX

" Tell me now, friend Folker, will you stand me by,
If these men of Kriemhild's would my mettle try?
Show me, if you love me, faithful friend and true!
And when you need my service I'll do as much for you."

XXI

" To death will I stand by you," the minstrel answer made,
" Though came the king against us with all his knights to aid.
As long as life is in me, to fight I will not slack,
Nor from your side for terror one foot will I give back."

XXII

" Now God in heaven requite you, good friend in danger tried!
Let them come on, and welcome; what can I need beside!
If Folker is my second, as I rejoice to hear.
Yon knights, methinks, will ponder before they venture near."

XXIII

" To rise would now become us," the gleeman straight replied,
" She is a king's companion, and nobly born beside.
As a queen and a lady, such honor is her due.
By fitly doing honor we both shall gain it too."

XXIV

" Nay, as you love me, Folker," said Hagan, " do not so.
Were we to rise an instant in face of yonder foe,
They'd fancy we were flinching, and that through fear 'twere
 done.
Here will I sit before them, and rise will I for none.

XXV

" Sure it becomes us better here as we are to wait.
How can I ever honor who bears me deadly hate?
That will I do never as long as I have life.
I care not, I, a tittle for the wrath of Etzel's wife."

XXVI

Across his legs his broadsword o'erweening Hagan laid,
A keen well-temper'd weapon; on the pummel fair display'd
A beaming precious jasper, greener than grass, it bore.
At a glance did Kriemhild know it for that which Siegfried
 wore.

XXVII

At the sight she started; nigh her senses fled;
Golden was the handle, the scabbard trimm'd with red;
It brought back all her sorrow; her tears began to flow.
For that, I ween, had Hagan laid out the weapon so.

XXVIII

On the bench beside him Folker the swift and strong
A fiddlestick grasp'd closer, massy and broad and long,
As sharp as any razor, much like a battle-blade.
There sat the lofty couple unmov'd and undismay'd.

XXIX

So proud they felt together that pair of champions bold,
That rise would they never for one of mortal mould.
Straight up to them went Kriemhild, scarce deigning to bestow
The stern contemptuous greeting that foe accords to foe.

XXX

Said she, " Now say, Sir Hagan, who has sent for you,
That you have dar'd hither to come with yonder crew?
And yet you must remember all you have done to me.
Had you been in your senses, you'd sure have let it be."

XXXI

" 'Tis true," straight answer'd Hagan, " no one sent for me.
To this land were invited royal brethren three;
My lords are those three brethren, and their man am I,
And courts they seldom visit but Hagan must be by."

XXXII

Said she, " Now tell me further, why did you that ill deed,
That my undying hatred has won you, fitting meed?
'Twas you that did Sir Siegfried, my noble husband, slay,
For whom must I for ever weep to my dying day."

XXXIII

Said he, " Why question further? That were a waste of breath.
In a word, I am e'en Hagan, who Siegfried did to death.
How dearly paid the warrior, the best good knights among,
For all fair Brunhild suffer'd from Lady Kriemhild's tongue!

XXXIV

" What I have done, proud princess, I never will deny.
The cause of all the mischief, the wrong, the loss, am I.
So now, or man, or woman, revenge it who so will;
I scorn to speak a falsehood, I've done you grievous ill."

XXXV

Said she, " You hear it, warriors, how he confesses all,
All the wrong he did me; what thence may him befall,
To me it nothing matters, ye knights, King Etzel's best!"
The haughty Huns stood doubting, and each look'd on the rest.

XXXVI

Whate'er had then befallen, had once the strife begun,
Sure had those two companions the palm of knighthood won;
Well had they prov'd their valor in many a field before.
The Huns their high adventure perforce through fear gave
    o'er.

XXXVII

Thus spake one of the warriors, " Why look ye so on me?
From this foolish promise at once I'll set me free.
No gifts shall ever move me to lose my precious life.
The queen misleads us merely; trust not King Etzel's wife."

XXXVIII

" Ay, friend! " rejoin'd another, " I'm in the self-same case;
Yonder large-lim'b minstrel never would I face,
No, not if one would give me whole towers of good red gold.
Mark his sharp, quick glances; he's wary as he's bold.

XXXIX

" Well know I, too, Sir Hagan, e'en from his youthful days,
And so can well give credence when others speak his praise.
In two and twenty battles I've seen him sway the strife;
That arm of his, believe me, has widow'd many a wife.

XL

" He and the valiant Spaniard many an adventure sought
While here they dwelt with Etzel, and many a battle fought
To the king's boot and glory; full oft they prov'd their might;
All tongues must so much honor yield Hagan as his right.

XLI

" Yet then the hardy warrior in years was but a child;
Now are they grave and grizzled who then were raw and wild.
Now is he proved in counsel, a champion stern and strong,
And eke wears trusty Balmung, which erst he gain'd by
      wrong."

XLII

Thus 'twas at once decided, and struck was not a blow.
Sore irk'd it angry Kriemhild; her heart was wrung with woe.
Thence back the knights departed, each fearing to be sped
By that redoubted couple; good cause had they for dread.

XLIII

Then spoke the valiant gleeman, " We now have seen too clear,
As we were told by Dietrich, that foes beset us here.
Best to court hence hurry, and with the kings unite;
Then none against our masters will dare provoke the fight."

XLIV

How oft does the faint waverer let slip the lucky hour,
While friend by friend firm standing confronts the deadliest
store.
Be they but bold and ready! no charm 'gainst sword and dart
Like that which smith ne'er temper'd, wise head and fearless
heart.

XLV

"Lead on then," answer'd Hagan, "I'll follow close behind."
They went, where yet the warriors they were in time to find
In the court still waiting, girt by a glittering crowd.
Thereat the dauntless Folker cried to his lords aloud,

XLVI

"Noble Burgundian princes! how long here will you stay
In all this crowd and pressure? better to court away,
And learn the mind of Etzel from his own proper tongue."
Then each chose his companion the well-prov'd knights
among.

XLVII

The Prince of Bern, Sir Dietrich, took friendly by the hand
Gunther the puissant ruler of Burgundy's fair land,
Irnfried went pair'd with Gernot the knight devoid of fear,
And to court strode Rudeger with youthful Giselher.

XLVIII

Howe'er the rest were coupled, as mov'd to court the train,
Folker and Hagan they parted ne'er again,
Save in one mortal struggle, e'en to their dying hour.
That strife high dames lamented each in her widow'd bower.

XLIX

So on to court mov'd slowly the kings in royal state,
Their train a thousand nobles proud on such lords to wait;
With them were sixty champions, the flower of all confest,
Whom in his land Sir Hagan had chosen for the best.

L

Hawart and Iring, of knighthood each the pride,
With the royal brethren mov'd softly side by side;
Dankwart and Wolfhart, a valiant hardy knight,
Display'd their courteous bearing in each beholder's sight.

LI

Soon as the Lord of Rhineland had come within the door,
The mighty monarch Etzel could keep his seat no more.
At the first glimpse of Gunther up you might see him spring,
And welcome him as warmly as king did ever king.

LII

"Sir Gunther, welcome hither! welcome Sir Gernot too,
And your fair brother Giselher; my faithful service true
I sent you, as befitted, to Worms beyond the Rhine.
Your friends, too, all are welcome alike to me and mine.

LIII

"And you, bold pair, trice welcome, whom I together view,
Danger-defying Folker, and peerless Hagan too,
To me and to my lady; she'll see you nothing loath.
She many a friendly message to Rhine has sent for both."

LIV

Then said the Knight of Trony, "Such oft have reach'd my ear
And, had I not come hither to serve my lieges dear,
I fain, to do you honor, had ridd'n into this land."
His guests then noble Etzel took friendly by the hand.

LV

Straight to the seat he led them where he had just been sitting;
Then to the guests were handed with grave and zeal befitting
Mead, morat, wine, successive, in golden goblets bright,
And each the noble strangers welcom'd as best he might.

LVI

Then thus resum'd King Etzel, "I will confess to all,
That in this world could nothing so to my wish befall
As your arrival hither; besides, this happy day
Has to my queen giv'n comfort, and charm'd her griefs away.

LVII

"Before, I own, I wonder'd what wrong I could have wrought,
That, while in crowds my table guests of high lineage sought,
You ne'er had ridden hither, as though from some annoy,
But now that here I see you my wonder's lost in joy."

LVIII

The lofty-minded Rudeger thereto this answer gave,
" Well may you joy to see them ; they're good and true as brave.
The kinsmen of my lady all honor's lore are taught ;
They many a stately warrior have to your dwelling brought."

LIX

'Twas an eve of fair midsummer when the lords of Rhineland
    came
To the court of mighty Etzel, and seldom chiefs of fame
Met so warm a welcome as was on these bestow'd.
'Twas now the hour of revel : the king with them to table
    strode.

LX

Host with guest together ne'er merrier took his seat.
They gave them in abundance alike of drink and meat.
Whate'er they wish'd or fancied was brought in plenteous store.
Great wonders of the warriors had oft been told before.

LXI

Etzel, the mighty monarch, had on th' Hungarian soil
Uprais'd a spacious fabric with mickle cost and toil,
Palaces and turrets within a fortress wide,
And chambers without number, and a splendid hall beside.

LXII

Long, high and wide had Etzel uprear'd this gorgeous frame,
For that to him such numbers of trooping champions came ;
Beside his other courtiers, twelve kings that sceptres bore ;
And crowds of worthy warriors had he at all times more

LXIII

Than king had e'er assembled, as I for truth have found.
He lived in mirth and honor with his kin and men around.
The shouting and the pressing of knights from far and wide
Had the good prince ever about him ; he thus the world defied.

THIRTIETH ADVENTURE
HOW THE KNIGHTS KEPT WATCH

I

THE day it now was ended, the night was near at hand;
Deep care was now besetting the travel-tainted band,
When they should take their slumber; for rest they sorely
  yearn'd.
That question put Sir Hagan, and answer soon return'd.

II

To th' host thus spake King Gunther, " God grant, you long
  may live!
Fain would we now repose us; such leave, I pray you, give.
If so you wish, to-morrow we'll come at break of day."
The host dismiss'd them gladly, and all went each his way.

III

Sore throng'd were then the strangers, such crowds to see
  them ran;
Thereat the valiant Folker thus to the Huns began.
" How dare you crowd and press us, ill-train'd, unnurtur'd
  crew?
Give place, or you'll discover 'twill be the worse for you.

IV

" My fiddlestick's no feather; on whom I let it fall,
If he has friends that love him, 'twill set them weeping all.
Make way then for us warriors, for so it seems me right.
We're equals all in knighthood, not so in mood and might."

V

While thus in wrath the minstrel reprov'd the jostling crowd,
Hagan, who had gone forward, look'd back and cried aloud,
" List to the valiant gleeman; he gives you good advice;
To your quarters, knights of Kriemhild! Let us not warn you
  twice.

VI

"Your malice lacks performance; e'en now, methinks, you
　　doubt;
So, if you would aught with us, by daylight seek us out,
And, for this night, to slumber leave us wayfarers free.
Never, I ween, did warriors so long for it as we."

VII

Then led were the bold strangers thence to a spacious hall.
For rest as for convenience they found it furnish'd all
With beds, long, broad and sumptuous, arrang'd throughout
　　the room,
Dame Kriemhild still was plotting their bale and deadly doom.

VIII

Many a fine quilt from Arras you might see glittering there
Of stuff most rich and precious, and many a tester fair
Of silk from far Arabia the best that could be found,
And thereupon were borders that bright shone wide around.

IX

And coverlets in order were laid of ermine white,
And others of dark sable, whereunder every knight
Should pass the hours in slumber e'en to the dawning day.
A king with his attendants ne'er in such splendor lay.

X

"Alas for these night quarters!" the youthful Giselher cried!
"Alas for our good comrades who 'midst the Huns abide!
However kind the message that from my sister sped,
I fear, through her devices we all shall soon lie dead."

XI

"Now think not of such danger," the dauntless Hagan spake,
"Myself this night about you the sentry's charge will take.
I'll keep you safe, believe me, e'en to the dawn of day.
For so long fear for nothing; then turn his doom who may."

XII

They bow'd to the good champion, and thank'd him, as was
    due,
Then to the beds betook them, nor many moments flew
Ere stretch'd upon his pallet was every mighty man.
Hagan the wakeful sentry to don his arms began.

XIII

Thereat the good Knight Folker, the valiant minstrel, spake,
" If you'll not scorn it, Hagan, I'd fain your watch partake
This night, till early morning bring us both relief."
Right cordially Sir Hagan thus thank'd the friendly chief:

XIV

" Now God in heaven reward you, Folker, dear friend and true.
For ne'er another comrade I long, but only you,
What strait soe'er beset me; I'm yours to my last breath,
And well will I requite you, if hinder'd not by death."

XV

With that his glittering hauberk each girt his waist about,
Each grasp'd in hand his buckler, and straight, with courage
    stout
From the house forth issuing, took post outside the door,
And there with faith and manhood still watch'd their comrades
    o'er.

XVI

The swift-footed minstrel scarce had he left the hall,
Ere he his good buckler set down against the wall,
And back hurried thither; his viol he took in hand,
And with it as became him charm'd the way-wearied band.

XVII

Upon the stone he sat him beneath the palace door;
Minstrel more undaunted viol ne'er struck before;
He struck the strings so sweetly ever as he play'd,
That the meed of thanks to Folker each haughty stranger paid.

XVIII

The house it all re-echoed, he struck so loud and shrill;
The minstrel's strength was matchless, nor less the minstrel's
skill.
Sweeter anon and softer when he to play began,
On the beds he steep'd in slumber many a care-harrow'd man.

XIX

When they in sleep were buried, and this by proof he knew,
Once more in hand his buckler grasp'd the champion true,
And, from the room forth stalking, before the tower he stepp'd,
And so the slumbering strangers from the men of Kriemhild
kept.

XX

'Twas of the night the middle, or something earlier yet,
When the bright gleam of helmets the glance of Folker met
At distance through the darkness; 'twas Kriemhild's street-
clad train,
To do the guests a mischief all hastening on amain.

XXI

Ere thither had Queen Kriemhild these warriors darkling sent,
She said, " For heaven's sake listen to this my fix'd intent.
Harm none of yonder sleepers, but one whom I detest,
The faithless murderer Hagan; slay him and spare the rest."

XXII

Then spake the fearless gleeman, " Friend Hagan, we must
bear
(As fits us) like true comrades the wakeful warder's care.
Before the house discern I a band of men in mail,
Who, as I think, will instant our wary watch assail."

XXIII

" Hush, hush," quick answer'd Hagan, " let them yet nearer
steal;
Before they can espy us, they shall our weapons feel.
Our hands thus many a headpiece shall sudden split in twain,
And send them hence with sorrow to Kriemhild back again."

XXIV

One of the Hunnish champions in a trice espied
That the door was guarded; how at once he cried,
" This plan of ours, my comrades, we must straight give o'er;
I see the minstrel standing on guard the hall before.

XXV

" Look how his helmet glitters! 'tis not more bright than stout,
To dint of steel impassive, and temper'd well throughout;
His mail like fire is glowing; by him stands Hagan too;
The guests may sleep in safety with guards so stout and ruet."

XXVI

Back at once they hasted; when Folker this espied,
To his valiant partner in sudden wrath he cried,
" Now let me hence, friend Hagan, after yonder crew.
Fain would I to the skulkers a question put or two."

XXVII

" No! for my sake," said Hagan, " 'twould to our loss redound;
If but this post you quitted, they all would flock you round,
And bring you to such peril if once they hemm'd you in,
That I should fly to help you; then ill would fare my kin;

XXVIII

" For while we two were fighting, and both in dubious case,
Three or four of yonder cowards might in a moment's space
Rush into the chamber, and on the sleepers set,
And do them all such mischief as we could ne'er forget."

XXIX

" Yet this at least allow me," the minstrel-knight replied,
" Let's show the men of Kriemhild, we have their steps espied,
That this to-morrow morning may be denied by none,
That they a shameful treason would willingly have done."

XXX

With that behind them Folker sent forth a lusty shout,
" How now, ye men of Kriemhild? Why walk ye, arm'd,
       about?
For murder or for robbery is it that ye ride?
My friend and I would help you, come take us on your side."

XXXI

Not a tongue gave answer; wroth was the good knight;
" Fie! Ye bloody dastards! " he cried with all his might.
" So you would us have murder'd, sleeping, every one!
On such good knights has rarely so foul a deed been done."

XXXII

Full soon unto Queen Kriemhild the sorry tidings came,
That her men had compass'd nothing; it set her heart on flame.
Another course she ventur'd, festering with fell despite,
That brought death and destruction on many a hapless knight.

THIRTY-FIRST ADVENTURE

HOW THE KNIGHTS WENT TO CHURCH

I

" So cold I feel my hauberk," the minstrel said at last,
" The night, I ween, friend Hagan, must needs be waning fast.
The nipping air assures me that close at hand is day."
Then wak'd they of their comrades who yet in slumber lay.

II

Then broke the gleam of morning on those within the hall.
Straight began Sir Hagan to rouse the warriors all,
If they would to the minster the early mass to hear.
Meanwhile in Christian fashion the bells were ringing clear.

III

The chants were so discordant, thereby you well might see,
That Christian men and heathen together ill agree.
The valiant men of Gunther would thence to church away.
From their beds they started; little linger'd they.

IV

With that at once they laced them all in such gorgeous vests,
That into no king's country had ever knightly guests
Brought weed more fair and costly; ill did it Hagan please;
" Here," said he, " are fitting for other clothes than these.

V

" My friends, what toils beset us, you all well understand;
So for the rose, ye warriors, take the good sword in hand,
And for the cap of jewels the morion beaming bright.
Remember what fell Kriemhild devis'd but yesternight.

VI

" To-day must we do battle, so I bid you well beware;
For the soft silken tunic the clashing hauberk wear,
And for the sumptuous mantle the buckler stout and wide,
That, when they rage against ye, the brunt you well may bide.

VII

" Give ear, my dearest masters, my kin and comrades too,
Go to the church, and welcome, it fits you so to do,
And wail to God in heaven your need, while you have breath,
And know ye this for certain, that at our heels is death.

VIII

" Forget not then, moreover, if aught ye ill have done,
And fervently for pardon pray, every mother's son;
For this I warn you, warriors, nor hold these words for vain,
Ne'er, but God show you mercy, mass will ye hear again."

IX

Then went they to the minster, the princes and their band.
Just at the holy churchyard bold Hagan bade them stand,
And keep all well together, and thus bespake the crew.
" Who knows, to us Burgundians what yonder Huns may do?

X

" Take heed, my friends, your bucklers bring down before your
    feet,
And, if a soul our party in hostile guise should greet,
Requite him with a death-stroke; so seems to Hagan right,
So doing, will each among us be found as fits a knight."

XI

Folker then and Hagan both together went
And stood before the minster; 'twas done with this intent,
That they might see if Kriemhild would stir the slumbering
    feud
Passing contemptuous by them; right stern were both of mood.

XII

And now came on King Etzel and eke his lady fair,
Both, as their state befitted, in garments rich and rare,
With crowds of knights all ready to do their high commands.
Uprose the dust to heaven from Kriemhild's trampling bands;

XIII

When the king, advancing, so arm'd to point espied
The kings and their bold vassals, how quick to them he cried,
" What's this? my friends in armor marching thus along?
In sooth, 'twould sore afflict me if they have suffer'd wrong.

XIV

" Amends I'll make, and gladly, as shall to them seem right;
If any have put on them affront or foul despite,
I'll show them, that such outrage I also inly rue,
And all that they demand me, I ready am to do."

XV

Then Hagan thus made answer, " Naught has to us been done;
But my lords have a custom, till three whole days be run,
When royal feasts they visit, their warlike arms to wear;
All wrong that may be done us, to Etzel we'll declare."

XVI

Right well heard Lady Kriemhild what Trony's knight replied.
How bitterly the warrior under her lids she eyed!
Yet, though the truth well knowing as a Burgundian dame,
She would not to her husband her country's use proclaim.

XVII

How deep soe'er and deadly the hate she bore her kin
Still, had the truth by any disclos'd to Etzel been,
He had at once prevented what afterward befell.
Through proud contemptuous courage they scorn'd their
    wrongs to tell.

XVIII

Then on went haughty Kriemhild girt with a mighty crowd,
Yet swerve would not before her that pair of champions proud
So much as e'en two hands'-breadth; that gall'd th'
    Hungarians sore.
Perforce they press'd and jostled with the warriors through
    the door.

XIX

The chamberlains of Etzel therewith were ill content;
They had straight the haughty strangers defied as in they
    went;
But that they fear'd to do so their monarch's eyes before;
Pressing enough and jostling there was, but nothing more.

XX

When serv'd was God as fitted, and thence would every one,
Straight into the saddle leapt many a warlike Hun;
The while around fair Kriemhild many a bright maid was seen,
And full seven thousand champions begirt the stately queen.

XXI

Queen Kriemhild and her ladies now at the windows sat
With the wide-ruling Etzel; well pleas'd was he with that.
They would survey the tourney where knights their prowess
    show'd
Ah! what stranger warriors in the court before them rode!

XXII

Thither too the marshal was with the yeomen come;
The redoubted Dankwart had muster'd, all and some,
The followers of his master, the flower of Rhenish ground.
For the bold Nibelungers well-saddled steeds were found.

XXIII

Thither the kings came riding and with them many a man,
When the good minstrel Folker to counsel this began,
That they should joust together each in his country's mode.
Thereafter in the tourney the chiefs full knightly rode.

XXIV

What so the warrior counsell'd gave all who heard content.
A mighty press and clatter uprose incontinent.
Into the court's broad circuit prick'd many a mighty man.
King Etzel and Queen Kriemhild now to look on began.

XXV

There came into the tourney six hundred warriors fleet,
Retainers of Sir Dietrich, the stranger knights to meet.
With the bold Burgundians they long'd a course to run.
Had Dietrich but permitted fain would they so have done.

XXVI

Ah! what good knights among them rein'd the proud battle-
    steed!
To their good lord Sir Dietrich the news was brought with
    speed
With Gunther's knights forbade he his knights a lance to cross,
Naught from such game forboding but grief and deadly loss.

XXVII

When now from out the tilt-yard the men of Bern were gone,
Sir Rudeger's retainers before the hall came on,
Five hundred from Bechlaren with shields and armor gay.
Well had it pleas'd the margrave had they been far away.

XXVIII

Then he rode in his wisdom up to the muster'd band,
And earnestly bespake them, and gave to understand,
That Gunther's men were sullen and all on mischief bent;
If they would quit the tourney, 'twould give him much content.

XXIX

When thence were now departed the margrave's warriors bold,
Then came the men of Thüringen, as has to us been told,
And from the realm of Denmark a thousand proud and high.
Then from the crashing lances were seen the shivers fly.

XXX

Irnfried then and Hawart into the tourney rode.
Proudly the bold Burgundians their sturdy brunt abode.
The noble knights of Thüringen they met in many a joust,
And many a glittering buckler pierc'd through with many a
    thrust.

XXXI

Sir Blœdel with three thousand rode forward frank and free;
By Etzel and by Kriemhild full well observ'd was he;
Before them both, his tilting perform'd each gallant knight;
Through hate to the Burgundians it gave the queen delight.

XXXII

She ponder'd thus in secret (as nigh to pass it came),
"Should they by chance hurt any, at once this gentle game
Would turn to bloody earnest; then I on these my foes
Should be reveng'd for ever, and quit of all my woes."

XXXIII

Schrutan and stout Gibek into the tourney rode,
And Ramung and swift Hornbog after the Hunnish mode.
Against the bold Burgundians they knightly bore them all;
High flew the whizzing splinters o'er the king's mighty hall.

XXXIV

And yet all their performance was but an empty sound.
Hall might you hear and palace with clashing shields resound,
Where rode the men of Gunther: by them proud deeds were
    done.
His train of that fair tourney the highest honors won.

XXXV

So great was then the pastime when front to front they met,
That through the reeking foot-cloths forth burst the frothy
    sweat
From the high-mettled coursers which the good knights
    bestrode,
As 'gainst the lords of Hungary in haughty wise they rode.

XXXVI

Then spake the noble minstrel Folker with scornful glance,
" These knights, methinks, will never confront us lance to
    lance.
I hear it loudly rumor'd they bear us mortal spite;
Surely can they never find better time to fight.

XXXVII

" So let us to our quarters," the fearless warrior cried,
" Send hence our weary horses; back we can hither ride,
If there be time, toward evening; 'twere fitter then than now;
What if to us Burgundians the queen should praise allow? "

XXXVIII

Just then there rode so proudly into the lists a Hun,
That so no knight among them the general gaze had won.
Perchance e'en then in secret for some fair maid he sigh'd.
He wore as rich apparel as any noble bride.

XXXIX

At once outspake Sir Folker, " I needs must spoil his cheer;
Yonder ladies' darling must feel a push of spear.
No one shall prevent it—let him guard his life.
I reck not, though it kindle the wrath of Etzel's wife."

XL

" No! as you love me, Folker," straight the king 'gan say,
" The people all will blame us if we commence the fray.
Let the Huns begin it: 'twere better so, I ween."
Still was King Etzel sitting beside his moody queen.

XLI

" I'll join you in the tourney," fierce Hagan sternly cried;
" Let's show both knights and ladies how we Burgundians ride.
'Twere well, by proof they knew it; they'd rate us higher then.
Now they deny all credit to good King Gunther's men."

XLII

Back into the tourney swift Folker hotly spurr'd;
Thereby was many a lady to grievous sorrow stirr'd.
Right through that proud Hun's body he drove the griding
    spear.
That stroke both dames and damsels cost many a bitter tear.

XLIII

That saw at once Sir Hagan, nor dallying there abode;
With sixty of his champions, all thundering as they rode,
'Gainst th' Huns he hotly hurtled fast by the gleeman's side.
King Etzel and Queen Kriemhild the tourney closely eyed.

XLIV

Nor would the three kings basely in dastard sloth repose,
And leave the minstrel aidless among unnumber'd foes,
With them came to the rescue a thousand warriors good;
Haughty and overweening they did whate'er they would.

XLV

Soon as by Sir Folker the wealthy Hun was slain,
You might hear his kinsmen cry out and loudly plain.
All in a breath were asking, " Who has this outrage done?"
" Folker the bold minstrel," gave answer many a one.

XLVI

Straight for swords and bucklers were calling all the band
Akin to the young margrave of the Hunnish land;
The fearless minstrel Folker they thought at once to slay.
The host down from a window took in haste his way.

XLVII

From the Huns on all sides a cry arose amain.
Before the hall alighted the kings and all their train.
Every bold Burgundian sent his steed away;
Up in haste came Etzel and parted straight the fray.

XLVIII

He found one of the kinsmen with his sword drawn in his hand;
From him in an instant he snatch'd the naked brand,
And beat the brawlers backward, chafing and raging sore.
" In sooth with these good warriors my favor all were o'er,"

XLIX

Said Etzel, " If among us this minstrel here ye slew;
'Twas by mere misadventure he ran your kinsman through.
I had my eye upon him just as he struck the blow.
It was his steed that stumbled; 'twas heaven would have it so.

L

" Then leave my friends in quiet, and from the tilt-yard speed."
Himself then gave them escort; meanwhile each battle-steed
Was led thence to their quarters, for those Burgurdian guests
Had many a zealous varlet to tend their high behests.

LI

Then with his friends King Etzel into his palace went;
He bade all cease from anger, and calm'd their fierce intent.
Ready were set the tables; for all was water brought.
The lives of the Burgundians many a stout foeman sought.

LII

However irk'd it Etzel, still many an armed knight
Press'd close behind the princes, e'en in the king's despite,
Lowering with hateful glances as they to table went,
Each to revenge his kinsman on those proud strangers bent.

LIII

" 'Tis an ill use," said Etzel, " and one I scarce can bear,
At the feastful table the weeds of war to wear.
But whosoe'er his vengeance on these my guests shall wreak,
His head shall pay the forfeit; this to you Huns I speak."

LIV

'Twas long before was seated every lordly guest.
Fell care and deep disquiet wrung Kriemhild's laboring breast.
" Prince of Bern," she murmur'd, " thy counsel, aid and grace
I seek in sore affliction; pity my mournful case."

LV

Then answer'd her Sir Hildebrand, a warrior frank and free,
" Who'd slay the Nibelungers shall have no help from me,
No, not for countless treasure; th' attempt he well may rue;
The good knights ne'er were conquer'd, with whom he'll have
    to do."

LVI

Said she, " Yet surely Hagan has done me cruel wrong;
He murder'd my beloved, the strongest of the strong.
Who'd lure him from the others, should have my gold for meed.
'Twould inly discontent me should one but Hagan bleed."

LVII

Then answer'd Master Hildebrand, " How can that ever be?
Slay him among his fellows? Why surely you must see,
That, if we strike at Hagan, to battle straight will all,
And rich and poor together must in one slaughter fall."

LVIII

Then in his courteous fashion thereto Sir Dietrich spake,
" Great queen, this talk give over, and better counsel take.
Me never wrong'd your kinsmen, nor is there cause that I
Should warriors, whom I value, to mortal strife defy.

LIX

" It does you little honor, the simple truth to say,
Against your trusting kinsmen such deadly plots to lay.
'Twas under a safe-conduct they enter'd Etzel's land.
Revenge for Siegfried never expect from Dietrich's hand."

LX

When she no spark of treason found in the Berner brave,
Of a wide march to Blœdel the promise straight she gave.
It once belong'd to Nudung; a gift 'twas for a queen;
Yet a stroke of Dankwart's made him forget it quite and clean.

LXI

" To give me help, Sir Blœdel," said she, " the task be thine;
Harbor'd within this palace are mortal foes of mine,
The same, who my dear husband Sir Siegfried did to die;
Who helps me to revenge it, to him for ever bound am I."

LXII

Thus answer'd her Sir Blœdel, " Lady, to truth give ear;
I dare not wreak your vengeance, for Etzel's wrath I fear.
He's glad to see your kinsmen and all their vassals throng,
And never would forgive me if I should do them wrong."

LXIII

" Nay, say not so, Sir Blœdel, I'll stand thy friend at need;
Silver and gold in plenty I'll give thee for thy meed,
Besides a beauteous damsel, whom Nudung had to wife.
Lapp'd in her soft caresses thou'lt lead a loving life.

LXIV

" The lands and eke the castles to thee I'll freely give;
So may'st thou, noble warrior, with joy for ever live,
If thou but win the lordships where Nudung once held sway.
I'll truly keep the promise I've given you here to-day."

LXV

No sooner heard Sir Blœdel of such a guerdon tell,
Beside that for her beauty the lady pleas'd him well,
Than he resolv'd by battle to win the lovely bride.
He miss'd, alas! the damsel, and lost his life besides.

LXVI

He thus bespake Queen Kriemhild, " To th' hall back haste
　　　away;
Ere one can take precaution, I'll stir a bloody fray.
Hagan, who sow'd in murder, shall reap a harvest meet.
I'll bring the man of Gunther in fetters to your feet.

LXVII

" Now arm ye straight," said Blœdel, " my merry men one and
　　　all!
Hence to the strangers' quarters upon our foes to fall.
So wills our royal lady, King Etzel's noble wife.
Ye heroes! at her bidding each boldly risk his life."

LXVIII

When Kriemhild thus found Blœdel to work her will intent,
And eager to do battle, to table straight she went
With the redoubted Etzel and eke with all his train,
Against the guests from Rhineland fell counsel had she ta'en.

LXIX

How they went all to table, I now at full must say.
First went the king attended, crown'd and in rich array;
Many a proud prince behind them, many a good knight was
    seen,
And all display'd their courtship before the noble queen.

LXX

The good host at the tables found place for every guest;
He seated close beside him the highest and the best.
The Christian knights and heathen there feasted nothing loath.
Their food indeed was different, but there was store for both.

LXXI

The yeomen in their quarters the time in feasting spent.
Servers were by good King Etzel to do their bidding sent,
Who gave them all they ask'd for, and serv'd both high and low.
Their merriment and revel were soon outweigh'd by woe.

LXXII

Still her old grudge lay rankling in Kriemhild's poison'd heart;
When else 'twere hard a quarrel to stir on either part,
To table 'mid the feasters she sent for Etzel's son.
When for revenge by woman was deed so fearful done?

LXXIII

With that four men of Etzel's went out at her command;
They brought the young King Ortlieb and led him by the hand
Up to the princes' table, where sat fierce Hagan by,
Doom'd all too soon, poor infant! by his fell hate to die.

LXXIV

Soon as the proud King Etzel his little son espied,
Graciously his wife's kinsmen bespake he at his side,
" See, friends, my boy and Kriemhild's, our only son and heir.
To you may henceforth profit come from this child so fair.

LXXV

" If he grow up like his kinsmen, he'll prove a man of might,
Of noble mind and lineage, a strong and fearless knight.
Should I live some time longer, I'll give him twelve broad
    lands,
So look for useful service at this fair infant's hands.

LXXVI

" Now therefore I beseech you, ye dearest friends of mine,
When hence you make your journey back to your native Rhine,
To take with you this infant, your loving sister's son,
And treat him well and kindly as should by kin be done;

LXXVII

" And bring him up in honor, till to a man he grow,
And, should your land be harried by force of any foe,
He'll help you to avenge it, when he his arms can wield."
All this was heard by Kriemhild; her lips stern silence seal'd.

LXXVIII

" He well may help these warriors," Sir Hagan straight began,
" If ever by good fortune he come to be a man;
Yet seems the young king's aspect no long life to foreshow.
Methinks I shall have seldom to Ortlieb's court to go."

LXXIX

Sore irk'd the speech King Etzel; the knight he sternly eyed
Though not a word in answer the haughty prince replied,
Down it weigh'd his spirits, and overcast his heart.
Unfit was Hagan's nature in joy to bear a part.

LXXX

Woe was the low'ring monarch, and all his chiefs as well,
When such dark words from Hagan on that fair infant fell.
That they should bear it longer, deep murmur'd all the crew.
Little thought the warriors what he was yet to do.

LXXXI

Many, who there had heard him, and bore him mortal hate,
Had gladly set upon him; the king had done it straight
But for his word of honor; then ill had Hagan sped;
Soon worse did he to Ortlieb; in Etzel's sight he struck him
    dead.

THIRTY-SECOND ADVENTURE

HOW BLŒDEL WAS SLAIN

I

ALL the knights of Blœdel were ready in array;
With a thousand hauberks to the hall they took their way,
Where Dankwart at the table sat with the yeomen tall.
Straight among the warriors uprose a deadly brawl.

II

At once up to the tables Sir Blœdel fiercely strode,
When Dankwart this fair greeting on the stern knight
    bestow'd.
" Welcome, my lord, Sir Blœdel, you here are gladly seen.
We look'd not for your presence; what may this meeting
    mean?"

III

" Greet me not," said Blœdel, " 'tis a waste of breath;
Know, my coming hither to thee must needs be death.
Thank thy brother Hagan who noble Siegfried slew.
Thou now shalt pay the Huns for it, thou and many another
    too."

IV

" Nay, say not so, Lord Blœdel," Sir Dankwart answer made,
" So should we rue this visit in faith and honor paid.
I was a little infant when Siegfrid lost his life;
How could I have offended King Etzel's moody wife?"

V

" I know not, and I care not, if this be false or true.
'Twas done by your base kinsmen, Gunther and Hagan too.
So ward ye well, ye strangers! 'tis all in vain to fly;
Your lives are pledg'd to Kriemhild, and take them now will I."

VI

" So you are fix'd," said Dankwart, " for murder all prepar'd!
Would I had ne'er besought you! that had been better spar'd."
Upstarted from the table the warrior swift and strong;
Out he drew a broadsword heavy and sharp and long.

VII

Straight at luckless Blœdel he struck a blow so fleet,
That his head in an instant lay before his feet.
" Take that, thou thriving wooer!" victorious Dankwart cried,
" For a marriage-morning's present to Nudung's mincing
       bride.

VIII

" Another mate to-morrow may wed the widow'd dame;
I'll pay him with like measure, should he the dowry claim."
(A faithful Hun that morning had told him underhand,
That deadly fraud against them the vengeful queen had
       plann'd.)

IX

When Blœdel's men their master saw dead upon the floor,
Such loss from the fierce strangers they could endure no more.
On squires at once and yeomen with high rais'd swords they
       flew
In deadly wrath; full many that hour had cause to rue.

X

To his train shouted Dankwart, loud o'er the crash and din,
" Ye see, bold squires and yeomen, what danger hems us in.
Fight for your lives, ye friendless! in sooth we're foully shent,
For all the loving greetings that fraudful Kriemhild sent."

XI

They, who had not their broadswords, benches asunder tore,
Or many a chair and footstool snatch'd up from the floor.
The bold Burgundians stay'd not, but all for weapons used;
Heads with heavy settles were pummel'd sore and bruis'd.

XII

How fiercely the lorn strangers themselves defended there!
Out they drove their foemen all weapon'd as they were;
Yet, within, five hundred were lifeless left or more.
Dankwart's men pursued them dripping red with gore.

XIII

Straight the sorry tidings to every Hunnish chief
Were borne by hasty rumor (it gave them mortal grief)
That slaughter'd with his warriors was Blœdel good at need,
That Dankwart and the yeomen had done the bloody deed.

XIV

Before King Etzel knew it, inflam'd with deadly hate
Two thousand Huns or better donn'd their armor straight.
They march'd against the yeomen to deal them mortal dole,
And living of the party let not escape a soul.

XV

Before the house they muster'd, an army deep and dense;
Though succorless, the strangers stood well on their defence;
Yet what avail'd their valor?   Dead perforce they lay.
Thence arose soon after a yet more horrid fray.

XVI

Now you must hear a wonder as never yet was told,
Within the hall lay lifeless nine thousands yeomen bold,
Thereto of Dankwart's followers twelve hardy knights and
    good,
And now among his foemen alone the warrior stood.

XVII

Hush'd was the din of battle, laid was the wild uproar;
He sternly o'er his shoulder survey'd the horrid floor,
And spake, " Alas, brave comrades! what? not a dying groan?
Then stand, must Dankwart aidless among his foes alone."

XVIII

Upon his single person fell thund'ring sword-strokes rife,
Yet cause gave he for weeping to many a hero's wife.
He rais'd his buckler higher and lower brought the thong.
Blood stream'd beneath his buffets through many a hauberk
    strong.

XIX

"Woe's me! I'm faint and stifled," the son of Aldrian cried;
"Now, ye knights of Hungary! stand a little wide;
Let the air refresh me—I'm wearied with the fight."
Then manfully among them stepp'd forth the stately knight.

XX

As faint and exhausted from the house he sprang,
What redoubled sword-strokes on his morion rang!
Those, who had not yet witness'd what wonders wrought his
    hand,
Forward leapt upon him, the knight from Gunther's land.

XXI

"Now would to God," said Dankwart, "a messenger would go
To let my brother Hagan my fearful peril know,
Among this band of traitors how sore beset am I!
He'd come and hence would help me, or by my side would die."

XXII

"Nay, do thyself thy message," the fierce Hungarians said,
"When we unto thy brother bring thee cold and dead
Then shall the man of Gunther the smart of sorrow know.
Thou here hast wrought King Etzel such grievous loss and
    woe."

XXIII

Said he, "Your threats give over, stand from me farther yet,
Or I will make your hauberks with blood all dripping wet.
Myself the heavy tidings will bring to yonder court,
And to my lords with wailing our deadly wrongs report."

XXIV

So much the knights of Etzel his matchless strength dismay'd,
That not a man amongst them durst meet him blade to blade,
But darts into his buckler they shot so thick around,
That, by the weight o'ermaster'd he dropp'd it on the ground.

XXV

Seeing him thus unshielded, they fiercer forward drove;
How then with deadly gashes the shields and helms he clove!
Down perforce before him stoop'd many a lofty knight.
What praise was then Sir Dankwart's, alone to sway the fight!

XXVI

They rush'd at him from both sides; none then would keep
  aloof;
But, match'd with him, found many most speed was least
  behoof.
Right through his foes the champion made his red passage
  good
As through the dogs the wild-boar amidst the echoing wood.

XXVII

Ever the ground beneath him with smoking gore was wet.
When better fought a champion with countless foes beset?
So to court before them, along his bloody road,
Unconquer'd still and stately fierce Hagan's brother strode.

XXVIII

Cupbearers and servers heard sword-strokes clashing nigh.
Dainty drinks and dishes they threw in hurry by,
The which they in were bringing upon the board to set.
A crowd of sturdy foemen e'en on the stairs he met.

XXIX

"How now, ye servers?" said Dankwart with bloody toil
  oppress'd,
" 'Tis your's to feed the hungry, and cheer the thirsty guest,
And store of savory viands to feasting knights to bear;
Give place, for I would something to my good lords declare."

XXX

All, who dar'd confront him as up the stairs he flew,
Met with such fearful slashes, that soon at distance due
From that weighty broadsword stood trembling every one.
Such surpassing wonders by Dankwart's strength were done.

THIRTY-THIRD ADVENTURE

HOW THE BURGUNDIANS FOUGHT WITH THE HUNS

I

Soon as the fearless warrior beneath the lintel hied,
He bade the men of Etzel keep distance yet more wide.
The blood from that fierce combat down all his armor pour'd,
And in his hand uplifted he held his naked sword.

II

Just at the very moment that in burst Dankwart so,
It chanc'd the young Prince Ortlieb was carried to and fro
From table unto table; the news of that fell strife,
So sudden brought among them, cost the fair child his life.

III

To a good knight then Dankwart shouted loud and strong,
" Be stirring, brother Hagan, you're sitting all too long.
To you and God in heaven our deadly strait I plain;
Yeomen and knights together lie in their quarters slain."

IV

" Tell me who has done it? " Hagan fiercely cried.
" Sir Blœdel and his meiny," Dankwart straight replied,
" And paid too has he dearly; he's dead among the dead;
This hand from off his shoulders smote at a stroke his head."

V

" Small is the loss," said Hagan, " whenever one can tell
That a vanquish'd hero by hands heroic fell.
Thus it still befitteth a knight to yield his breath;
So much the less fair ladies should sorrow for his death.

VI

" Now tell me, brother Dankwart, why are you so red?
Your wounds, methinks, oppress you; they must have sorely
    bled.
If he's yet in this country who has harm'd you thus in strife,
But the foul fiend aid him, it shall cost his life."

VII

" You see me whole and hearty; my weed with blood is wet,
But 'tis from wounds of others whom sword to sword I met,
Of whom I slew so many, though furious all and fell,
That, if I had to swear it, th' amount I ne'er could tell."

VIII

Said th' other, " Brother Dankwart, keep guard upon the door;
Let not one Hungarian step the threshold o'er.
Straight, as need impels us, converse with them will I.
Our friends by their devices were guiltless done to die."

IX

" Since I'm to be door-keeper," replied the champion true
"(And well to such great monarchs such service I can do),
As fits me, 'gainst all comers the staircase I'll maintain."
Naught could be more distasteful to Kriemhild's knightly train.

X

" In sooth," resum'd Sir Hagan, " I can't but wonder here,
What now these Huns are whisp'ring each in his fellow's ear.
I ween, they well could spare him, who keeps the door so bold,
Him, who to us Burgundians his courtly tale has told.

XI

" Long have I heard and often of moody Kriemhild tell,
That still her heart's deep sorrow she harbors fierce and fell;
Now then let's drink to friendship! king's wine shall quench
    our thirst,
And the young Prince of Hungary himself shall pledge us
    first."

XII

With that the good Knight Hagan smote Ortlieb the young
    child;
The gushing blood, down flowing, both sword and hand defil'd;
Into the lap of Kriemhild bounded the ghastly head.
At once among the warriors a fearful butchery spread.

XIII

Then with both hands uplifted he dealt a stroke at large
'Gainst the grave-visag'd tutor, who had the child in charge;
His sever'd head down falling, before the table lay.
For all his learned lessons t' faith 'twas sorry pay.

XIV

Just then at Etzel's table a minstrel met his view;
Upon him in an instant in wrath Sir Hagan flew.
His right hand on his viol off lopp'd he suddenly;
"Take that for the kind message thou brought'st to
    Burgundy."

XV

"Alas! my hands!" cried Werbel frantic with pain and woe,
"What have I done, Sir Hagan, that you should serve me so?
I came in faith and honor into your master's land.
How can I now make music since I have lost my hand?"

XVI

Little reck'd Sir Hagan if ne'er he fiddled more;
Then round his death-strokes dealing he stretch'd upon the
    floor
Many a good knight of Etzel's, and wide the slaughter spread,
Turning to bale the banquet, and heap'd the hall with dead.

XVII

Up the ready Folker leapt from table quick;
In his hand loud clatter'd his deadly fiddlestick.
Harsh crashing notes discordant King Gunther's minstrel
    play'd.
Ah! what a host of foemen among the Huns he made!

XVIII

Up, too, leapt from table the royal brethren three;
They thought to part the battle ere mischief more should be.
But lost was all their labor, vain was all help of man;
When Folker and stern Hagan once so to rage began.

XIX

When saw the Lord of Rhineland no power could stint the
    strife,
He too dealt dole about him with wounds that let out life,
Through the shining hauberks cutting deadly way.
A prowest knight was Gunther, as clear he show'd that day.

XX

At once into the battle the sturdy Gernot flew;
Thick as they flock'd around him the clustering Huns he slew
With his sword, the gift of Rudeger, the which he wielded so,
That many a knight of Etzel's he laid for ever low.

XXI

The third too of the brethren rush'd into the fray;
Through th' helms of Etzel's warriors his swords made bloody
    way;
Death follow'd every buffet; right wondrous deeds were done
That hour by youthful Giselher, Dame Uta's youngest son.

XXII

Well fought that day the brethren, well too their men of might,
But ever valiant Folker stood foremost in the fight,
Against his foes so knightly himself the warrior bore.
Many brought he among them to wallow in their gore.

XXIII

On their defence, too, stoutly stood Etzel's champions all.
Then might you see the strangers through the kingly hall
With their glittering broadswords slashing and hewing go.
Loud thrill'd throughout the palace wild screams of wail and
    woe.

XXIV

Then those without in hurried to aid their friends within,
But found upon the staircase more was to lose than win;
Out fain would rush the others, and through the doorway fare.
To none gave Dankwart passage, nor up nor down the stair.

XXV

To force the guarded portal throng'd the Huns amain.
With the clattering sword-strokes the morions rang again.
Then stood the valiant Dankwart in deadly peril there;
Of that his loving brother took heed with timely care.

XXVI

Straight to dauntless Folker, Hagan shouted loud,
" See you there my brother beset by yonder crowd,
Batter'd by blades unnumber'd, by countless bucklers cross'd?
Up, and save him, comrade! or the good knight is lost."

XXVII

" Fear not," replied the minstrel, " I'll do your bidding soon."
Straight strode he through the palace playing his harshest tune.
Oft clash'd the keen-edg'd broadsword that in his hand he bore.
The noble chiefs of Rhineland thank'd him o'er and o'er.

XXVIII

Then to the fearless Dankwart the minstrel-knight 'gan say,
" You must have surely suffer'd sore press and toil to-day.
Sent hither by your brother to aid you I have been.
If you'll without be warder, I'll keep the door within."

XXIX

Firm the nimble Dankwart stood outside the door;
All who the stairs were mounting down drove he evermore;
In the grasp of the warriors their swords clash'd fearfully.
The like within did stoutly Folker of Burgundy.

XXX

Loud the valiant minstrel shouted o'er the throng,
" The hall is shut, friend Hagan! the locks are firm and strong.
The hands of two stout warriors King Etzel's door secure;
A thousand bolts, believe me, would not be half so sure."

XXXI

When Hagan saw the portal secur'd against attack,
By the thong his buckler the fiery chief threw back,
And whirl'd his sword for vengeance with huge two-handed
    sway;
No hope had then his foemen with life to come away.

XXXII

When good Sir Dietrich noted how with each swashing stroke
The furious Lord of Trony a Hunnish morion broke,
On to a bench straight leapt he, to see the knights of Rhine.
Said he, " Sure Hagan's serving the very worst of wine."

XXXIII

The host was sore bewilder'd with horror and surprise;
What crowds of friends and subjects were slain before his eyes!
Scarce 'midst the bloody turmoil himself from danger free,
He sat in mortal anguish; what boot was his a king to be?

XXXIV

Proud Kriemhild cried to Dietrich in ghastly drear affright,
" Help me with thy valor, good and noble knight
By the worth of all the princes of th' Amelungers' land.
If Hagan only reach me, Death have I close at hand."

XXXV

" Fair queen," replied Sir Dietrich, " how can I help you here?
Or how protect another when for myself I fear?
So wroth are these Burgundians, so high their passions run,
That I in such a moment can promise peace to none."

XXXVI

" Nay, say not so, Sir Dietrich, renown'd and noble knight!
Show forth this day amongst us thy high heroic might
To bring me hence in safety; else, I shall surely die.
Dole and dismay beset me; in mortal strait am I."

XXXVII

" At least I'll make the trial, if boot you yet I can,
For ne'er before beheld I many a mighty man,
To sudden wrath enkindl'd, so fierce to battle rush.
Blood see I through the helmets at every sword-stroke gush."

XXXVIII

So the fair queen's entreaty he would no longer scorn;
Up his voice he lifted like a blast on a buffalo's horn,
That all the echoing castle rung through its breadth and length;
So loud the voice of Dietrich, so wondrous was his strength!

XXXIX

Soon as heard King Gunther the voice of such a man
Peal o'er the clash and tumult, to listen he began.
Said he, " The voice of Dietrich sounds in my ears amain;
I fear our eager champions some friend of his have slain.

XL

" I see him on the table beckoning with his hand.—
Loving friends and kinsmen of Burgundy's fair land,
Hold a little season! let us hear and see
What we have done to Dietrich, or what his wish may be."

XLI

Soon as thus King Gunther begg'd and commanded too,
In th' heat of that dire struggle back their swords they drew;
Yet more his power effected, that still they stood and stern;
Then thus the King of Rhineland bespake the Lord of Bern.

XLII

Said he, " Right noble Dietrich, has any of my friends
Done you here an injury? I'll make you full amends.
Be sure, the satisfaction shall with the fault along.
In sooth, 'twould inly grieve me, were you to suffer wrong.

XLIII

Him answer'd good Sir Dietrich, " No cause have I to grieve;
Let me with your safe-conduct this hall of Etzel's leave,
And quit this bloody banquet with those who follow me,
And for this grave for ever I'll at your service be."

XLIV

" Why beg instead of bidding? " fierce Wolfhart interpos'd,
" The door, methinks, yon minstrel has not so firmly clos'd,
But we can set it open, and go where'er we will."
" Silence! " return'd Sir Dietrich, " the devil prompts thee ill."

XLV

" I give you full permission," thus noble Gunther spake,
" Hence whom you will, Sir Dietrich, or few or many, take,
Except my mortal foeman; in Hungary have they
Done deadly wrong to Gunther, and here behind must stay."

XLVI

Then lingered not the Berner; under his arm he took
The noble queen all trembling; fear-stricken was her look.
On the other side King Etzel away with him he led,
Eke many a stately champion forth with Sir Dietrich sped.

XLVII

The noble Margrave Rudeger then cried, " If any more
May quit this house uninjur'd, and pass yon reeking door,
Tell us, who ever lov'd you, and now would serve your ends,
So peace will last for ever with true and faithful friends."

XLVIII

Thereto made answer Giselher, the knight of Burgundy,
" Let there be peace betwixt us and constant amity,
For you were ever faithful, you and your warriors tried,
So part ye hence in safety, and all your friends besides."

XLIX

Soon as the good Sir Rudeger left the blood-reeking hall,
There follow'd him stout champions five hundred or more in all.
In this the lords of Rhineland did faithfully and well,
Yet ruin and destruction King Gunther thence befell.

L

Just then a knight of Hungary, who saw King Etzel take
His way beside Sir Dietrich, came nigh for safety's sake,
When him the furious minstrel with such a sword-stroke sped,
That at the feet of Etzel straight lay his sever'd head.

LI

Soon as the Lord of Hungary from th' house had come at last,
He turn'd, and on fierce Folker as fierce a glance he cast.
" Woe's me for these fell strangers! Oh, grievous strait," he
     said,
" That all my faithful warriors should lie before them dead!

LII

" Ah! woe for this sad meeting! woe for this festal-fight!
There spreads, within, destruction one that Folker hight;
Like a wild boar he rages, yet but a minstrel he.
Thank heaven! 'tis well in safety from such a fiend to be.

LIII

" In sooth, ill sound his measures; his strokes are bloody red;
His oft-repeated quavers lay many a hero dead.
I know not why this gleeman should spite us o'er the rest;
Never had I for certain so troublesome a guest."

LIV

Thereat straight to their quarters the noble knights withdrew,
The lord of Bern, Sir Dietrich, and the good margrave too.
To mix in that fierce struggle neither had desire,
And from it, too, their followers they bade in peace retire.

LV

But had the bold Burgundians foreseen the deadly woe
That they from those two champions were soon to undergo,
Ne'er from the hall had either so quietly been sent,
But at their hands had suffer'd a bloody chastisement.

LVI

They, whom they pleas'd, permitted to leave that hall of ill;
Then rose within, redoubled, the death-cry wild and shrill.
The guests 'gainst their wrong-doers for deadly vengeance
      strove;
Folker the valiant minstrel, ah! how the helms he clove!

LVII

At the clash King Gunther turn'd, and to Hagan cried,
" Hear you what a measure Folker, the door beside,
Plays with each poor Hungarian who down the stairs
      would go;
See! what a deep vermilion has dyed his fiddle-bow!"

LVIII

" I own, it much repents me," Hagan straight replied,
" That I sat here at table from the good knight so wide.
We still were constant comrades, not wont before to sever.
If we again see Rhineland, no chance shall part us ever.

LIX

" Now see, great king! right loyal to thee is Folker bold;
Well deserves the warrior thy silver and thy gold.
His fiddlestick, sharp-cutting, can hardest steel divide,
And at a stroke can shiver the morion's beamy pride.

LX

" Never yet saw I minstrel so high and lordly stand,
As did to-day Sir Folker among the hostile band.
On helms and clattering bucklers his lays make music rare.
Ride should he good war-horses, and gorgeous raiment wear."

LXI

Of all the fierce Hungarians that at the board had been,
Now not a single champion remain'd alive within.
Then first was hush'd the tumult, when none was left to fight.
Then down his sword laid reeking each bold Burgundian
knight.

THIRTY-FOURTH ADVENTURE

HOW THEY THREW DOWN THE DEAD

I

THEN after all their labor the lords sat down at last.
Before the hall together Folker and Hagan pass'd.
The pair of haughty champions upon their bucklers leant,
And each the time with th' other in gentle converse spent.

II

Then the youthful Giselher thus his mind express'd,
" Ye must not yet, dear comrades, think of ease or rest;
From out the house first hasten to bear the dead away.
Once more shall we do battle; that I can truly say.

III

Beneath our feet 'twere better they should no longer lie.
Ere these proud Huns subdue us, and we o'ermaster'd die,
Hewn will be many a hauberk, and blood in torrents flow;
No sight can please me better than a bleeding foe."

IV

" I'm proud of such a master," cried Hagan with delight;
" Who could e'er give such counsel save a redoubted knight?
When words so wise and valiant from our young lord you hear,
Needs must ye, bold Burgundians! be all of lively cheer."

V

The counsel straight they follow'd, and carried through the
    door,
And cast out from among them, seven thousand dead or more.
Adown the stairs they tumbled and lay in heaps below.
Then burst forth from their kinsmen a thrilling scream of woe.

VI

'Mongst these was many a warrior, though wounded and in
    pain,
Who yet with milder treatment might have wax'd whole again.
Crush'd by the fall they perish'd, who half had 'scap'd the sword.
Their friends with moans of sorrow their fatal doom deplor'd.

VII

Then spake the minstrel Folker, the warrior void of fear,
" I oft have heard reported, and now behold I clear,
That Huns are vile and worthless; they like weak women wail,
When they should tend the wounded, and soothe their dreary
    bale."

VIII

Then ween'd a Hunnish margrave, he thus through kindness
    spake;
He saw a luckless kinsman fall'n in a bloody lake;
So threw his arms about him, and hoped away to bear.
Him shot to death the minstrel; down fell he dying there.

IX

When this was seen by th' others, they took at once to flight;
That same redoubted gleeman all curs'd with all their might.
He brandish'd high a javelin, well-temper'd, bright, and keen,
Which by a Hun against him before had darted been.

X

This through the echoing castle he sent with mastering main
Far o'er the crowd of tremblers; that shot to Etzel's train
Gave another station more distant from the hall.
The matchless strength of Folker dismay'd their leaders all.

XI

Before the house assembled were many thousand men;
Sir Folker and Sir Hagan both together then
Began unto King Etzel all their mind to tell,
Whence grievous ill thereafter both the good knights befell.

XII

" The trembling crowd to hearten," said Hagan, " sure 'tis right
That kings and leaders ever be foremost in the fight;
E'en so do here among us my own redoubted lords,
And, when they cleave the morions, blood spouts beneath their
    swords."

XIII

A valiant knight was Etzel; his shield in hand he took.
" Be wary," cried Dame Kriemhild: " to your good liegemen
    look;
Fill shields with gold, to move them yon stranger to defy.
Death must be needs your neighbor if Hagan comes you nigh."

XIV

The king he was so fearless, he would not budge an inch;
Seldom are such great princes so disinclin'd to flinch.
By his shield's thong his warriors then drew him back perforce.
Hagan went on to mock him in accents loud and coarse.

XV

" I' faith the kin was distant," he cried with scornful sound,
" That Etzel and Sir Siegfried in one alliance bound.
He cheer'd fair Lady Kriemhild long ere she look'd on thee.
Dishonor'd king and worthless! why knit thy brow at me?"

XVI

His proud disdainful mockery the wrath of Kriemhild stirr'd;
To be revil'd of Hagan, while Etzel's warriors heard,
And jeer'd before the many, was more than she could brook,
So now yet deadlier counsel against the guests she took.

XVII

" Who Hagan, Lord of Trony, shall slay," she fiercely said,
" And bring unto me hither his abhorred head,
For him the shields of Etzel I'll heap with ruddy gold,
And give him, too, for guerdon lands and castles manifold."

XVIII

" I know not," said the minstrel, " what now can keep them
   back ;
Sure never saw I warriors so heartless stand and slack,
When a fair dame had promis'd such rich and ample pay.
Etzel can trust them never if they should flinch to-day.

XIX

" Those who the bread of Etzel have eaten many a year,
And, when his need is greatest, like cowards fail him here,
These see I stand fear-troubled ; they dare not move a jot,
And yet would pass for warriors ! shame ever be their lot ! "

XX

Thus with distress and sorrow was Etzel ill bestead,
Right bitterly bewailing his kin and subjects dead.
Good knights of many a country stood round, a mournful ring,
And for that bloody banquet wept with their weeping king.

XXI

Then thought the best among them, " Sure Folker tells us
   true."
But none so inly sorrow'd of all that wavering crew,
As the bold Margrave Iring, the fearless Danish knight ;
This soon he prov'd before them by deeds of manly might.

THIRTY-FIFTH ADVENTURE
HOW IRING WAS SLAIN.

I

THEN loudly shouted Iring the Danish margrave strong,
" I've shap'd my course in honor, and aim'd at glory long,
And ever have in battle borne me like a knight,
So bring me now my harness, and I'll with Hagan fight."

II

" That I scarce would counsel," in scorn Sir Hagan cried.
" Bid the knights of Hungary stand farther yet aside,
Let two or three together then leap into the hall,
Back wounded down the staircase I'll dash them one and all."

III

" I'll not renounce my challenge," Iring stern replied,
" Ere now have I, and often, such hard adventures tried.
Now sword to sword I'll meet thee; let ruth aside be flung!
What boots thy haughty passion, and valor of the tongue?"

IV

Then at once Sir Iring arm'd him for the fight,
And Irnfried or Thüringia, a young and lusty knight,
And the large-limb'd Hawart with a thousand in his train;
All sought to vouch the quarrel of that redoubted Dane.

V

Soon as the dauntless minstrel so huge a troop espied
Forth all in armor coming on the fierce margrave's side,
Each with his glittering helmet laced ready for the fray,
Somewhat the wrath of Folker kindled at their array.

VI

" See you now, friend Hagan, how comes Sir Iring nigh?
Sure I must condemn him—ill fits a knight to lie.
To stand against thee singly he promis'd just before,
And now he brings in armor a thousand chiefs or more."

VII

" Call me not a liar," Hawart's liegeman cried.
" Yes! I have givèn a promise; I'd fain my words abide.
I'll ne'er renounce th' adventure; fear is to me unknown;
How fierce soe'er be Hagan, I'll meet him here alone."

VIII

He begg'd his friends and kinsmen, down falling at their feet,
That they would let him singly the stern Burgundian meet.
Fain would they have denied him, for all too well they knew
How stout a knight was Hagan, and how remorseless too.

IX

So long he still entreated, at last they gave consent;
When him on that fierce battle they saw so wildly bent
And so athirst for honor, with grief they let him go.
A deadly strife then follow'd 'twixt either frowning foe.

X

The valiant knight of Denmark bore high his quivering spear,
And crouch'd beneath his buckler through caution, not through
    fear,
Then, to the hall swift mounting, with Hagan sought to close.
From the death-doing champions a deafening din arose.

XI

Each cast his spear at th' other with such o'ermastering might,
Piercing through the strong bucklers e'en to the harness bright,
That the shafts, high whirling, to a distance flew;
Their swords then, sternly frowning, the rival champions drew.

XII

Huge was the strength of Hagan, his heart and hand were
    stout,
Yet on him smote Sir Iring, that rang the hall throughout.
Wall and tower re-echoed at every thundering blow.
Still could not he his purpose work on his burly foe.

XIII

So Iring there let Hagan as yet unwounded stand,
And on the warlike minstrel, turn'd at once his hand;
He thought to bring him under with buffets fierce and fell,
But the long-practis'd gleeman his blows all warded well.

XIV

Then Folker, kindling passion, smote Iring's buckler so,
That the steel plates which bound it flew off at every blow.
Then turn'd he from the minstrel (he struck too boisterously),
And fell at once on Gunther the King of Burgundy.

XV

Then 'twixt the valiant couple a furious strife arose;
King Gunther and Sir Iring, like hail they bandied blows.
Yet the red blood could neither with all his buffets draw,
So goodly was their harness without a fault or flaw.

XVI

With that he left King Gunther, and straight at Gernot ran;
The fire from out his mailcoat to hammer he began.
But then to him King Gernot made such a fierce reply,
That the redoubted Iring he all but did to die.

XVII

From the prince he bounded; swift the warrior flew;
Four of the Burgundians in a trice he slew,
All high-descended courtiers from Worms across the Rhine;
Well might the youthful Giselher at such a loss repine.

XVIII

" Now by heaven, Sir Iring ! " in his wrath he said,
" Thy life shall pay the forfeit for those who here lie dead
Through thy remorseless fury."—He ran at him full fleet,
And smote the Dane so sternly, he could not keep his feet.

XIX

Down he dropp'd before him grovelling in the gore;
Sure then ween'd each beholder that he never more
Blow would give or parry on a battle-day;
Yet Iring all unwounded before his foeman lay.

XX

So deep his morion sounded, so loud the sword-stroke clash'd,
His senses were confounded as to the ground he dash'd,
And like a corpse, though living, he lay unconscious there;
So wondrous was the prowess of strong-arm'd Giselher!

XXI

When from his brain bewilder'd the swoon had parted slow,
Which had his wits confounded from that o'er mastering blow,
Thought he, " I yet am living, and all unwounded, too.
Now know I Giselher's manhood, and feel what he can do."

XXII

He heard his foes about him as there he lay o'erthrown;
Worse would he have to suffer if once the truth were known
Well, too, the youthful Giselher perceiv'd he standing by.
Then thought he, from amongst them, by what device to fly.

XXIII

From the blood he started; pressing was his need;
Sure for his good fortune he might thank his speed.
From the house he darted just where Hagan stood,
And struck at him in passing with all the force he could.

XXIV

Then thought the Knight of Trony, " Thou'rt in the clutch of
    death;
Sure, but the devil guard thee, thou canst not 'scape with
    ` breath."
Yet with a wound through th' head-piece he straight Sir
    Hagan paid;
That did the knight with Wasky, his sharp and peerless blade.

XXV

Soon as fierce Sir Hagan felt the gash and pain,
With his sword uplifted he rush'd upon the Dane.
No more against his fury could Hawart's man make head;
Swift down the stairs Sir Hagan pursued him as he fled.

XXVI

Above his head bold Iring held up his buckler strong;
Had that same scanty staircase been full trice as long,
No time had Hagan left him to strike a single stroke.
Ah! what a shower of sparkles red from his morion broke!

XXVII

Yet safe and sound Sir Iring came to his friends again.
Soon then were told to Kriemhild th' achievements of the Dane,
And what he unto Hagan had done with his good blade.
Thus unto the warrior her fervent thanks she paid.

XXVIII

" Now God reward thee, Iring! a noble knight thou art;
Thou hast reviv'd my courage and comforted my heart.
On Hagan's blood-stain'd armor, through thy bold deed, I
    look."
With her own hand then from him his shield for joy she took.

XXIX

" Your thanks you'd better husband," said Hagan stern and
    high,
" 'Twould well befit a warrior his chance once more to try.
If then he came back scathless, he'd be indeed a knight.
This scratch will boot you little; so e'en a child could smite.

XXX

" The blood you see so gladly, which streaks my mail with red,
It but the more provokes me to heap this land with dead.
My strength is undiminish'd, my wrath is now begun;
You'll feel how little mischief to me has Iring done."

XXXI

Iring the Knight of Denmark there stood against the breeze,
Cooling him in his mailcoat, with helm unlaced for ease.
Loud said those about him how bold he was and brave.
Their praise to the good champion the loftiest courage gave.

XXXII

Then thus outspoke Sir Iring, " Friends! this for certain know;
Arm me, and delay not; once more I'll prove my foe.
His fierce and haughty bearing I can no longer brook."
His shield was hewn and shatter'd; a better straight he took.

XXXIII

Soon was arm'd the warrior, and better than before;
He shook in wrath and fury the weighty spear he bore;
With this against his foeman with sturdy strides he went.
Hate-sparkling eyes upon him the fierce Sir Hagan bent.

XXXIV

Th' attack of bold Sir Iring he would not there await;
Down the stairs he bounded, and ran upon him straight,
Now darting, and now smiting; his wrath was at the height;
Little then his prowess avail'd the Danish knight.

XXXV

The champions smote so fiercely, that fire-red blasts began
To burn from either buckler; then Hawart's luckless man
So grievously was wounded by Hagan's monstrous main
Through sever'd shield and morion, he ne'er was whole again.

XXXVI

That wound dash'd Iring's courage; he felt him ill bestead;
He rais'd his shield yet higher to guard his bleeding head;
He deem'd it grievous mischief, the wound it was so sore;
Yet at the hand of Hagan had he to suffer more.

XXXVII

A spear the man of Gunther found lying at his feet;
This at the head of Iring he darted sure and fleet,
So that the shaft outjutted, quivering, from his brow.
A fatal end has Hagan made of his foeman now!

XXXVIII

Back to his Danes Sir Iring recoil'd with faltering pace;
Ere from his head his comrades the helmet could unlace,
They broke from it the javelin; then close was death at hand.
His kindred wept around him, a sorrow-laden band.

XXXIX

'Anon the queen came thither; she o'er the dying bent,
Bewailing dauntless Iring with ghastly dreariment,
And for his wounds sore weeping, and mourning for his sake.
Then thus among his kinsmen the hero faintly spake.

XL

" Fair and noble lady! cease for me to grieve.
What avails your weeping? my life I needs must leave;
Yes! the wounds are mortal that thus have pierc'd me through.
Death will not leave me longer to Etzel and to you."

XLI

Then thus to each Thüringian he spake, and every Dane,
" Hope not for gifts from Kriemhild, nor count her gold for
    gain,
For here, my friends! I warn you, e'en with my latest breath,
If once you fight with Hagan, you needs must look on death."

XLII

His lively hue was faded; the stamp of death he bore;
For the redoubted Iring his comrades sorrow'd sore.
Never could recover stout Hawart's vassal true.
Perforce each man of Denmark took to his sword anew.

XLIII

Irnfried at once and Hawart both hurried toward the hall
With a thousand warriors; from amongst them all
Loud peal'd the shout of battle; fierce was their wrath and hot.
Ah! what a sleet of javelins at those of Rhine they shot!

XLIV

Upon the valiant gleeman bold Irnfried rush'd amain,
But at his hand destruction was all that he could gain.
A stern man was the minstrel as e'er in field met foe.
Through th' helm he smote the landgrave a deep and deadly
    blow.

XLV

Sir Irnfried on Sir Folker dealt too a sturdy stroke,
That of his temper'd hauberk the links asunder broke,
And with the dint his harness all sparkled fiery red.
Then straight before the minstrel down dropp'd the landgrave
    dead.

XLVI

Sir Hawart and Sir Hagan clos'd too in deadly fight;
Their strife to each beholder was sure a wondrous sight.
Huge strokes from their keen weapons fell thick on either side,
Till by the stern Burgundian perforce Sir Hawart died.

XLVII

When Danes now and Thüringians saw both their leaders slain,
Against the house yet fiercer rush'd on the shouting train.
Loud round the sounding portal the din of battle peal'd,
And many a helm was cloven, and shatter'd many a shield.

XLVIII

" Fall back, my friends ! " said Folker, " E'en let them enter in,
Yield for a while the passage they so desire to win.
Full soon they'll fall together within our bloody hold,
And reap with death and ruin Dame Kriemhild's fatal gold."

XLIX

Those overweening champions the hall had enter'd now;
Many a proud head among them was sudden taught to bow
Beneath the deadly sword-strokes of the fierce warriors there.
Well fought the valiant Gernot, well, too, young Giselher.

L

A thousand and four together had come into the hall;
You might see the broadswords flashing rise and fall;
Soon the bold intruders all dead together lay;
Of those renown'd Burgundians strange marvels one might say.

LI

Thereafter reigned deep silence ; the din of war was hush'd ;
Through every creak and cranny the blood on all sides gush'd
From that huge hill of slaughter ; red did the gutters run.
So much was through their prowess by those of Rhineland
    done !

LII

With that the bold Burgundians sat down awhile to rest.
His bloody sword and buckler down laid each panting guest.
Still stood th' unwearied minstrel on guard the house before,
To watch if any foeman should seek to force the door.

LIII

Sore wail'd the royal Etzel, sore too his lady wept,
And sobbing dames and damsels like mournful concert kept.
Fell Death, I ween, had taken his oath to do them ill.
Alas! by those fierce strangers more were to perish still.

THIRTY-SIXTH ADVENTURE

HOW THE QUEEN GAVE ORDERS TO BURN DOWN THE HALL

I

" So now unlace your helmets," undaunted Hagan cried,
" I and my comrade o'er you will watch lest harm betide,
And should the men of Etzel again to fight come on,
Be sure I will not dally, but warn my lords anon."

II

Then many a prowest champion disarm'd his lofty head;
Down sat they on the corpses, that wide the floor bespread,
And lay in blood before them as by their hands they died;
Close still by Hate and Vengeance the noble guests were spied.

III

Not yet come on had evening, when the fierce king anew
And vengeance-breathing Kriemhild to fight together drew
The mighty men of Hungary; before him muster'd stood
Better than twenty thousand prepar'd for blows and blood.

IV

Once more 'gainst the Burgundians a fearful strife arose;
Dankwart before the portal among the clustering foes
From his lords undaunted leapt forth with a light bound.
'Twas thought he long had perish'd; out stepp'd he safe and sound.

V

The deadly struggle lasted till it was stopp'd by night;
The guests themselves defended 'gainst Etzel's men of might,
As well became good warriors, all through a summer's day.
Ah! what redoubted champions dead before them lay!

VI

'Twas e'en on a midsummer befell that murderous fight,
When on her nearest kinsmen and many a noble knight
Dame Kriemhild wreak'd the anguish that long in heart she
bore,
Whence inly griev'd King Etzel, nor joy knew ever more.

VII

Yet on such sweeping slaughter at first she had not thought;
She only had for vengeance on one transgressor sought.
She wish'd that but on Hagan the stroke of death might fall;
'Twas the foul fiend's contriving, that they should perish all.

VIII

And now the day was ended; ill were they then bestead.
They thought, 'twere surely better that they at once were dead,
Than in slow torture lingering unhopeful of release.
Those high and haughty warriors, ah! how they yearn'd for
peace!

IX

They begg'd the Huns, King Etzel to bring before the hall;
Themselves then, blood-bedabbled and harness-stain'd withal,
With the three royal brethren from th' house mov'd faint and
slow.
To whom to plain, they knew not, in their o'ermastering woe.

X

So near them both Etzel and Kriemhild drew;
To them belong'd the country; their host thus greater grew.
He thus bespake the strangers, " Now what would you with
me?
Hope you for peace and friendship? that sure can hardly be.

XI

" After the deadly mischief that you to me have done,
The slaughter of my kinsmen, the murder of my son,
Cause shall you have to rue it as long as I have life; —
So peace and truce expect not, but war and mortal strife."

XII

" Our grievous need compell'd us," in answer Gunther said,
" My train before your warriors fell in their quarters dead;
How had I e'er deserved it, or they, that bloody end?
I came in faith to see thee, I ween'd thou wert my friend."

XIII

Then spake the bold Burgundian, the youthful Giselher,
" Ye noble knights of Etzel, who yet are living here,
In what have I offended? or how incurr'd your blame?
In kind and simple friendship into this land I came."

XIV

" Ah!" said they, " to our sorrow this castle and realm beside
Are both full of thy kindness; would you had never hied,
Thou and thy bloody brethren, from Worms across the Rhine!
You've fill'd our land with orphans;—so much for thee and
    thine!"

XV

Thereto in angry accents Sir Gunther made reply,
" If you would turn to friendship, and this wild hate lay by
'Gainst us home-distant warriors, 'twere well for us and you.
Your king will strike the guiltless if otherwise he do."

XVI

Then to the guests said Etzel, " No equal loss, I trow,
Have you and I encounter'd; the toil, the pain, the woe,
The shame as well as damage that I have borne to-day—
For this, not one among you shall living hence away."

XVII

Then to the king said Gernot, the death-defying knight,
" At least may God work with you in this to do us right.
If you are resolv'd to slay us, to th' open space and free
Let us come down to meet you; 'twill to your honor be.

XVIII

" Whate'er is to befall us, let it quick be done;
'Gainst such a host of warriors hope can we cherish none.
Scarce can we fight o'erwearied, much less attempt to fly.
How long will you compel us to pant and struggle ere we
    die?"

XIX

Then would the knights of Etzel their wish have granted
    straight,
And let come out the strangers before the palace gate.
Wroth thereat was Kriemhild; she had heard it soon.
Quickly to the strangers was denied the boon.

XX

" No! no! Hungarian heroes! My counsel take for true,
And grant them not their longing; beware of what you do;
Ne'er let those bloody murderers come out from yonder hall,
Or surely must your kinsmen endure a deadly fall.

XXI

" Were none of them yet living but Uta's children there,
My high-descended brothers, if once they got fresh air
To cool their heated harness, you'd one and all be lost;
The world has no such warriors; you'd learn it to your cost."

XXII

Then spake the youthful Giselher, " Fairest sister mine,
I little ween'd thy summons call'd me o'er the Rhine,
In this net of treason and mortal strait to lie.
How here of these Hungarians have I deserved to die?

XXIII

" To thee true was I ever; I never did thee wrong;
Loving and confiding I hither came along,
For thou, I thought, dear sister, didst bear like love to me.
Oh! look on us with kindness! what else should we expect
    from thee?"

XXIV

" Talk not to me of kindness! Unkind is all my thought.
Against me he of Trony such grievous wrong has wrought,
Never can I forgive it as long as I have life;
For that you all must suffer," said Etzel's furious wife.

XXV

" Yet would you to me Hagan up for a prisoner give,
No longer I'd refuse you, but fain would let you live,
For you're indeed my brethren, all of one mother sprung;
Then of the fit atonement I'd speak these lords among."

XXVI

" Now God in heaven forbid it ! " Sir Gernot proudly said;
" Were there a thousand of us, we'd rather all lie dead,
All thy noble kinsmen, than e'er that only one
Give up to thee a captive; no! that can ne'er be done."

XXVII

" So we must die," said Giselher, " 'scape can we never hence;
Still valiantly and knightly we'll stand on our defence,
Let him then, who would prove us, do now his worst endeavor;
I never friend abandoned, nor will abandon ever."

XXVIII

Then, scorning longer silence, cried Dankwart void of fear,
" Ay! my good brother Hagan stands not lonely here.
They who peace deny us, shall soon their anger rue.
We'll teach you bitter knowledge; take these my words for
true."

XXIX

Then spake the queen, " Brave warriors, this hour to you
belongs;
Up! closer to the staircase! take vengeance for my wrongs!
What thrift requites good service, I'll show you well to-day.
The insolence of Hagan I will in full repay.

XXX

" Let not a soul forth sally; their courage soon we'll tame;
I'll straight at the four corners bid set the hall on flame,
And thus will I revenge me at once for all my woes."
Quick Etzel's knights made ready, and fell upon her foes.

XXXI

Who yet without were standing, they instant drove within
By dint of darts and broadsword; deafening rose the din;
Yet naught their valiant followers could from the princes part;
Close link'd they stood together with fix'd and faithful heart.

XXXII

With that, the wife of Etzel bade set the hall on fire.
How sore then were they tortur'd in burning anguish dire!
At once, as the wind freshened, the house was in a glow.
Never, I ween, were mortals in such extremes of woe.

XXXIII

"We all are lost together," each to his neighbor cried,
"It had been far better we had in battle died.
Now God have mercy on us! woe for this fiery pain!
Ah! what a monstrous vengeance the bloody queen has ta'en!"

XXXIV

Then faintly said another, "Needs must we here fall dead!
What boots us now the greeting, to us by Etzel sped?
Ah me! I'm so tormented by thirst from burning heat,
That in this horrid anguish my life must quickly fleet."

XXXV

Thereat outspake Sir Hagan, the noble knight and good,
"Let each, by thirst torment'd, take here a draught of blood.
In such a heat, believe me, 'tis better far than wine.
Naught's for the time so fitting; such counsel, friends, is mine."

XXXVI

With that straight went a warrior, where a warm corpse he
    found.
On the dead down knelt he; his helmet he unbound;
Then greedily began he to drink the flowing blood.
However unaccustom'd, it seem'd him passing good.

XXXVII

"Now God requite thee, Hagan," the weary warrior cried,
"For such refreshing beverage by your advice supplied.
It has been my lot but seldom to drink of better wine.
For life am I thy servant for this fair hint of thine."

XXXVIII

When th' others heard and witness'd with what delight he quaff'd,
Yet many more among them drank too the bloody draught,
It strung again their sinews, and failing strength renew'd.
This in her lover's person many a fair lady rued.

XXXIX

Into the hall upon them the fire-flakes thickly fell;
These with their shields they warded warily and well.
With smoke and heat together they were tormented sore.
Never, I ween, good warriors such burning anguish bore.

XL

Through smoke and flame cried Hagan, " Stand close against the wall;
Let not the burning ashes on your helm-laces fall;
Into the blood yet deeper tread every fiery flake.
In sooth, this feast of Kriemhild's is ghastly merry-make."

XLI

'Twas well for the Burgundians that vaulted was the roof;
This was, in all their danger, the more to their behoof.
Only about the windows from fire they suffer'd sore.
Still, as their spirit impell'd them, themselves they bravely bore.

XLII

In such extremes of anguish pass'd off the dreary night.
Before the hall yet sleepless stood the gleeman wight,
And leaning on his buckler, with Hagan by his side,
Look'd out, what further mischief might from the Huns betide.

XLIII

Then thus bespoke he Hagan, " Let's back into the hall;
These Huns will then imagine that we have perish'd all
In the fiery torment they kindled to our ill.
They'll see yet some among us who'll do them battle still."

XLIV

Then the youthful Giselher, the bold Burgundian, spake,
"Methinks the breeze is fresh'ning, the day begins to break.
Better times may wait us—grant it God in heaven!
To us my sister Kriemhild a fatal feast has given."

XLV

With that outspake a warrior, "Ay! now I see the day.
Since we can hope no better in this our hard assay,
Let each don straight the harness, and think upon his life;
For soon will be upon us King Etzel's murderous wife."

XLVI

The host he little doubted but all the guests were dead,
By toil and fiery torture alike so ill bestead.
But yet within were living six hundred fearless wights;
Crowned king about him ne'er had better knights.

XLVII

The scouts who watched the strangers, had now the truth
    descried,
That, spite of all the travail and torment that had tried
The strength of lords and liegemen, they had survived it all,
And safe and sound as ever stalk'd up and down the hall.

XLVIII

'Twas told the queen that many unharm'd were yet to see;
"No! no!" made Kriemhild answer, "Sure it can never be
That such a fiery tempest has spared a single head.
Far sooner will I credit that one and all are dead."

XLIX

Still long'd both lords and liegemen for mercy and for grace,
If they might look for either from any there in place;
But neither grace nor mercy found they in Hunnish land,
So vengeance for their ruin they took with eager hand.

L

And now by early morning a deafening hostile din
Greeted the weary warriors; sore peril hemm'd them in.
From all sides round, against them a shower of missiles flew;
The dauntless band full knightly stood on defence anew.

LI

The mighty men of Etzel came on embolden'd more,
For that they hoped from Kriemhild to win her precious store;
And others, too, would frankly their king's command obey;
Thus had full many among them to look on death that day.

LII

Of promises and presents strange marvels might be told.
She bade bring bucklers forward heap'd high with ruddy gold;
She gave to all who'd take it; none empty went away.
Never were spent such treasures to work a foe's decay.

LIII

The best part of the champions came on in warlike gear.
Then cried the valiant Folker, " We're still to be found here.
Warriors advance to battle ne'er saw I yet so fain,
As those, who to destroy us, King Etzel's gold have ta'en."

LIV

Then from within cried many, " Nearer, ye warriors, still!
What's to be done, do quickly, whether for good or ill.
Here's not a man among us but is resolv'd to die."
Darts straight fill'd all their bucklers, so quick the Huns let fly.

LV

What can I tell you further? twelve hundred men or more
To force the fatal entrance attempted o'er and o'er.
But with sharp wounds the strangers soon cool'd their fiery
    mood.
None the stern strife could sever; flow might you see the blood

LVI

From gashes deep and deadly; full many there were slain,
Comrade there for comrade wept and wail'd in vain,
Till all in death together sank Etzel's valiants low.
Sore mourn'd for them their kinsmen in wild but bootless woe.

THIRTY-SEVENTH ADVENTURE

HOW MARGRAVE RUDEGER WAS SLAIN

I

THAT morn had fought the strangers as fitted well their fame;
Meanwhile fair Gotelind's husband into the courtyard came.
Naught saw he there on all sides but woe and doleful drear.
At the sight wept inly the faithful Rudeger.

II

" Woe's me," began the margrave, " That ever I was born,
That none can stay the sorrows of this disastrous morn!
Howe'er I long for concord, the king will ne'er agree;
Woes sees he wax around him, and more has yet to see."

III

With that, the faithful margrave to good Sir Dietrich sent,
That they might seek together to turn the king's intent.
Thereto sent answer Dietrich, " The mischief who can stay?
To none will now King Etzel give leave to part the fray."

IV

Just then a Hunnish warrior observ'd the margrave true
With tearful eyes there standing, as he was wont to do.
The same thus said to Kriemhild, " See how he stands to-day,
Whom Etzel o'er his fellows hath rais'd to power and sway,

V

" He who from all has service, from liegemen and from land!
O'er what a crowd of castles has Rudeger command!
How much the royal Etzel has giv'n him, well we know,
Yet ne'er in all this battle has he struck one knightly blow.

VI

" Methinks, of what befalls us he takes but little care,
While of broad fiefs at pleasure he holds an ample share.
'Tis said, in skill and courage the margrave stands alone,
But ill, I'm sure, have either here in our need been shown.

VII

In angry mood this slander the faithful warrior took;
He turn'd and on the murmurer cast a withering look.
Thought he, "Thou sure shalt pay for it; thou say'st that I
am cow'd;
I'll show how much I fear thee: thy tale was told too loud."

VIII

At once his fist he doubled, and fiercely on him ran.
Such a fearful buffet he dealt the Hunnish man,
As needed not a second; dead at his feet he lay.
This wrung the heart of Etzel and heighten'd his dismay.

IX

"Away with thee, base babbler!" (thus the good margrave
spake)
"Here have I pain and trouble enough my heart to break,
And thou, too, must revile me, as here I would not fight!
These guests I should with reason have held in high despite,

X

"And plagued them to my utmost alike in act and thought,
But that I the warriors myself had hither brought.
I was their guide and conduct into my master's land;
Against them ne'er can Rudeger uplift his wanderer's hand."

XI

Then unto the margrave spake Etzel standing near,
"How have you this day help'd us, right noble Rudeger!
When dead in such abundance our bleeding country fill,
More we nothing needed; you've done us grievous ill."

XII

The noble knight made answer, "I own he stirr'd my mood,
Twitting me with the favors (brawler coarse and rude!)
That thy free hand so largely has shower'd upon me here;
But his malicious tattle hath cost the liar dear."

XIII

Then came the fair Queen Kriemhild; she too had seen full well
What from the hero's anger the luckless Hun befell;
And she too mourn'd it deeply; with tears her eyes were wet.
Thus she spake to Rudeger, " How have we ever yet

XIV

" Deserv'd, that you, good Rudeger, should make our anguish
    more;
Now sure to me and Etzel you've promis'd o'er and o'er,
That you both life and honor would risk to do us right.
That you're the flower of knighthood, is own'd by every knight.

XV

" Now think upon the homage that once to me you swore,
When to the Rhine, good warrior, King Etzel's suit you bore,
That you would serve me ever to either's dying day.
Ne'er can I need so deeply, that you that vow should pay."

XVI

" 'Tis true, right noble lady; in this we're not at strife;
I pledg'd, to do you service, my honor and my life,
But my soul to hazard never did I vow.
I brought the princes hither, and must not harm them now."

XVII

Said she, " Remember, Rudeger, the promise thou didst make,
Thy word, thy oath remember that thou would'st vengeance
    take
On whosoever wrong'd me, and wrong with wrong repay."
Thereto replied the margrave, " I've never said you nay."

XVIII

With that, to beg and pray him the king began as well;
King and queen together both at his feet they fell.
Then might you the good margrave have seen full ill bestead,
And thus in bitterest anguish the faithful hero said.

XIX

" Woe's me the heaven-abandon'd, that I have liv'd to this!
Farewell to all my honors! woe for my first amiss!
My truth — my God-giv'n innocence — must they be both
    forgot?
Woe's me, O God in heaven! that death relieves me not!

XX

" Which part soe'er I foster, and whichsoe'er I shun,
In either case forsaken is good, and evil done;
But should I side with neither, all would the waverer blame.
Ah! would He deign to guide me, from whom my being came!"

XXI

Still went they on imploring, the king and eke his wife,
Whence many a valiant warrior soon came to lose his life
By the strong hand of Rudeger, and he, too, lastly fell.
So all his tale of sorrow you now shall hear me tell.

XXII

He nothing thence expected but loss and mortal teen.
Fain had he giv'n denial alike to king and queen.
Much fear'd the gentle margrave, if in the stern debate
He slew but one Burgundian, the world would bear him hate.

XXIII

With that, unto King Etzel thus spake the warrior bold,
" Sir king! take back, I pray you, all that of you I hold,
My fiefs, both lands and castles; let none with me remain.
To distant realms, a wanderer, I'll foot it forth again.

XXIV

" Thus stripp'd of all possessions I'll leave at once your land.
Rather my wife and daughter I'll take in either hand,
Than faithless and dishonor'd in hateful strife lie dead.
Ah! to my own destruction I've ta'en your gold so red."

XXV

Thereto replied King Etzel, " Who then will succor me?
My land as well as liegemen, all will I give to thee,
If thou'lt revenge me, Rudeger, and smite my foemen down.
High shalt thou rule with Etzel, and share his kingly crown."

XXVI

Then spake the blameless margrave, " How shall I begin?
To my house I bade them, as guests I took them in,
Set meat and drink before them, they at my table fed,
And my best gifts I gave them;—how can I strike them dead?

XXVII

" The folk ween in their folly that out of fear I shrink.
No! no! on former favors, on ancient bonds I think.
I serv'd the noble princes, I serv'd their followers too,
And knit with them the friendship, I now so deeply rue.

XXVIII

" I to the youthful Giselher my daughter gave of late;
In all the world the maiden could find no fitter mate,
True, faithful, brave, well-nurtur'd, rich, and of high degree;
Young prince yet saw I never so virtue-fraught as he."

XXIX

Then thus bespake him Kriemhild, " Right noble Rudeger
Take pity on our anguish! thou see'st us kneeling here,
The king and me, before thee; both clasp thy honor'd knees.
Sure never host yet feasted such fatal guests as these."

XXX

With that, the noble margrave thus to the queen 'gan say,
" Sure must the life of Rudeger for all the kindness pay,
That you to me, my lady, and my lord the king have done.
For this I'm doom'd to perish, and that ere set of sun.

XXXI

" Full well I know, this morning, my castles and my land
Both will to you fall vacant by stroke of foeman's hand,
And so my wife and daughter I to your grace commend,
And all at Bechlaren, each trusty homeless friend."

XXXII

" Now God," replied King Etzel, " reward thee, Rudeger ! "
He and his queen together resum'd their lively cheer.
" From us shall all thy people receive whate'er they need;
Thou too, I trust, this morning thyself wilt fairly speed."

XXXIII

So body and soul to hazard put the blameless man.
Meanwhile the wife of Etzel sorely to weep began.
Said he, " My word I gave you, I'll keep it well to-day.
Woe for my friends, whom Rudeger in his own despite must
    slay."

XXXIV

With that, straight from King Etzel he went with many a sigh.
Soon his band of heroes found he muster'd nigh.
Said he, " Up now, my warriors ! don all your armor bright.
I 'gainst the bold Burgundians must to my sorrow fight."

XXXV

Quick his valiant followers bade their arms be brought.
In a trice th' attendants shields and helms up caught,
And all their glittering harness bore to their masters bold.
Soon to the haughty strangers the sorry news were told.

XXXVI

Arm'd were to see with Rudeger five hundred men of might;
Twelve besides went with him, each a prowest knight,
Who hoped to win them worship on that fierce Rhenish band.
Little thought the warriors, how close was Death at hand.

XXXVII

So to war the margrave under helmet strode;
Sharpest swords his meiny brandish'd as they rode;
Each in hand, bright-flashing, held his shield before.
That saw the dauntless minstrel and seeing sorrow'd sore.

XXXVIII

Then too was by young Giselher his lady's father seen
With helm laced as for battle; " What," thought he, " can he
    mean?
But naught can mean the margrave but what is just and right."
At the thought full joyous wax'd the youthful knight.

XXXIX

" Well's me with friends so faithful," Sir Giselher 'gan say,
" These, whom by happy fortune we gain'd upon the way.
My late-espoused lady will stand us in good stead.
In sooth it much contents me, that e'er I came to wed."

XL

" I know not what you trust in ;" thus the stern minstrel spake ;
" Where saw you warriors ever for reconcilement's sake
With helmets laced advancing, and naked swords in hand?
On us will earn Sir Rudeger his castles and his land."

XLI

Scarcely the valiant minstrel his words had utter'd all,
When the noble Rudeger was close before the hall.
His shield, well prov'd in battle, before his feet he laid,
But neither proferr'd service, nor friendly greeting made.

XLII

To those within he shouted, " Look not for succor hence ;
Ye valiant Nibelungers, now stand on your defence.
I'd fain have been your comrade ; your foe I now must be.
We once were friends together ; now from that bond I'm free."

XLIII

The hard-beset Burgundians to hear his words were woe.
Was not a man among them, but sorrow'd, high and low,
That thus a friend and comrade would 'gainst them mingle
        blows,
When they so much already had suffer'd from their foes.

XLIV

" Now God forbid," said Gunther, " that such a knight as you
To the faith, wherein we trusted, should ever prove untrue,
And turn upon his comrades in such an hour as this.
Ne'er can I think that Rudeger can do so much amiss."

XLV

" I can't go back," said Rudeger, " the deadly die is cast ;
I must with you do battle ; to that my word is past.
So each of you defend him as he loves his life.
I must perform my promise, so wills King Etzel's wife."

XLVI

Said Gunther, " This renouncement comes all too late to-day.
May God, right noble Rudeger, you for the favors pay
Which you so oft have done us, if e'en unto the end
To those, who ever lov'd you, you show yourself a friend.

XLVII

"Ever shall we be your servants for all you've deign'd to give,
Both I and my good kinsmen, if by your aid we live.
Your precious gifts, fair tokens of love and friendship dear,
Given when you brought us hither, now think of them, good
    Rudeger!"

XLVIII

" How fain that would I grant you!" the noble knight replied;
" Would that my gifts forever might in your hands abide,
I'd fain in all assist you, that life concerns or fame,
But that I fear, so doing, to get reproach and shame."

XLIX

"Think not of that, good Rudeger," said Gernot, "in such
    need.
Sure host ne'er guests entreated so well in word or deed,
As you did us, your comrades, when late with you we stay'd.
If hence alive you bring us, 'twill be in full repaid."

L

" Now would to God! Sir Gernot," said Rudeger ill bestead,
" That you were safe in Rhineland, and I with honor dead!
Now must I fight against you to serve your sister's ends.
Sure never yet were strangers entreated worse by friends."

LI

" Sir Rudeger," answer'd Gernot, " God's blessing wait on you
For all your gorgeous presents! your death I sore should rue,
Should that pure virtue perish, which ill the world can spare.
Your sword, which late you gave me, here by my side I wear.

LII

" It never once has failed me in all this bloody fray;
Lifeless beneath its edges many a good champion lay.
Most perfect is its temper; 'tis sharp and strong as bright;
Knight sure a gift so goodly will give no more to knight.

LIII

" Yet, should you not go backward, but turn our foe to-day,
If of the friends around me in hostile mood you slay,
With your own sword, good Rudeger, I need must take your
    life,
Though you (heaven knows) I pity, and your good and noble
    wife."

LIV

" Ah! would to heaven, Sir Gernot, that it might e'en be so!
That e'en as you would wish it this matter all might go,
And your good friends 'scape harmless from this abhorréd
    strife!
Then sure should trust in Gernot my daughter and my wife."

LV

With that, the bold Burgundian, fair Uta's youngest, cried,
" Why do you thus, Sir Rudeger? my friends here by my side
All love you, e'en as I do; why kindle strife so wild?
'Tis ill so soon to widow your late-betrothed child.

LVI

" Should you now and your followers wage war upon me here,
How cruel and unfriendly 'twill to the world appear!
For more than on all others on you I still relied,
And took, through such affiance, your daughter for my bride."

LVII

" Fair king! thy troth remember," the blameless knight 'gan
    say,
" Should God be pleas'd in safety to send thee hence away.
Let not the maiden suffer for aught that I do ill.
By your own princely virtue vouchsafe her favor still."

LVIII

" That will I do and gladly," the youthful knight replied,
" But should my high-born kinsmen, who here within abide,
Once die by thee, no longer could I thy friend be styl'd;
My constant love 'twould sever from thee and from thy child."

LIX

"Then God have mercy on us!" the valiant margrave said.
At once their shields they lifted, and forward fiercely sped
In the hall of Kriemhild to force the stranger crowd.
Thereat down from the stair-head Sir Hagan shouted loud,

LX

"Tarry yet a little, right noble Rudeger!
I and my lords a moment would yet with you confer;
Thereto hard need compels us, and danger gathering nigh;
What boot were it for Etzel though here forlorn we die?

LXI

"I'm now," pursued Sir Hagan, "beset with grievous care;
The shield that Lady Gotelind gave me late to bear,
Is hewn and all-to broken by many a Hunnish brand.
I brought it fair and friendly hither to Etzel's land.

LXII

"Ah! that to me this favor heaven would be pleas'd to yield
That I might to defend me bear so well-prov'd a shield,
As that, right noble Rudeger, before thee now display'd!
No more should I in battle need then the hauberk's aid."

LXIII

"Fain with the same I'd serve thee to th' height of thy desire,
But that I fear, such proffer might waken Kriemhild's ire.
Still, take it to thee, Hagan, and wield it well in hand.
Ah! might'st thou bring it with thee to thy Burgundian land!"

LXIV

While thus with words so courteous so fair a gift he sped,
The eyes of many a champion with scalding tears were red.
'Twas the last gift, that buckler, e'er given to comrade dear
By the Lord of Bechlaren, the blameless Rudeger.

LXV

However stern was Hagan, and of unyielding mood,
Still at the gift he melted, which one so great and good
Gave in his last few moments, e'en on the eve of fight,
And with the stubborn warrior mourn'd many a noble knight.

LXVI

" Now God in heaven, good Rudeger, thy recompenser be!
Your like on earth, I'm certain, we never more shall see,
Who gifts so good and gorgeous to homeless wanderers give.
May God protect your virtue, that it may ever live!

LXVII

" Alas! this bloody business!" Sir Hagan then went on,
" We have had to bear much sorrow, and more shall have anon.
Must friend with friend do battle, nor heaven the conflict part?"
The noble margrave answer'd, "That wounds my inmost
　　　heart."

LXVIII

" Now for thy gift I'll quit thee, right noble Rudeger!
Whate'er may chance between thee and my bold comrades here,
My hand shall touch thee never amidst the heady fight,
Not e'en if thou should'st slaughter every Burgundian knight."

LXIX

For that to him bow'd courteous the blameless Rudeger.
Then all around were weeping for grief and doleful drear,
Since none th' approaching mischief had hope to turn aside.
The father of all virtue in that good margrave died.

LXX

Then from the house call'd Folker, the minstrel good at need,
" Now that my comrade Hagan has to this truce agreed,
From my hand too, Sir Rudeger, take firm and sure the same.
You've ever well deserv'd it since to this land we came.

LXXI

" For me, most noble margrave! you must a message bear;
These bracelets red were given me late by your lady fair,
To wear at this high festal before the royal Hun.
View them thyself, and tell her that I've her bidding done."

LXXII

" Ah! might it please th' Almighty," Sir Rudeger replied,
" That the margravine hereafter should give you more beside!
Yet doubt not, noble Folker, I'll bear this message fain
To my true love and lady, if e'er we meet again."

LXXIII

So promis'd gentle Rudeger, nor longer dallied yet;
Up his shield he lifted, and forward fiercely set.
He leapt on the Burgundians like a prowest knight;
Many a swift stroke among them he struck to left and right.

LXXIV

Sir Folker and Sir Hagan both from him further stepp'd
According to their promise which faithfully they kept,
But at the stairs were standing warriors so bold and stout,
That Rudeger the battle began with anxious doubt.

LXXV

King Gunther and Sir Gernot in let him force his way
To take his life the surer; stern knights and fierce were they.
Young Giselher kept his distance; e'en yet he look'd for life,
So spar'd, though half unwilling, the father of his wife.

LXXVI

Forward the margrave's warriors leapt with fierce intent;
In their master's footsteps manfully they went.
Sharp-cutting blades they brandish'd as in close fight they
    strove,
And shiver'd many a buckler, and many a morion clove.

LXXVII

The guests, though faint and weary, dealt many a storm-swift
    blow
At those of Bechlaren, that deep and smooth did go
To flesh and bone and inward through links of iron weed.
They wrought in that stern struggle full many a doughty deed.

LXXVIII

The noble train of Rudeger now in had enter'd all.
Folker at once and Hagan leapt on them in the hall,
Nor quarter gave to any, but to that single man.
The blood beneath their broadswords down through the
    helmets ran.

LXXIX

What a fearful clatter of clashing blades there rang!
From shields beneath the buffets how the plates they sprang,
And precious stones unnumber'd rain'd down into the gore!
They fought so fell and furious as man will never more.

LXXX

The Lord of Bechlaren went slashing here and there,
As one who well in battle knew how himself to bear.
Well prov'd the noble Rudeger in that day's bloody fight,
That never handled weapon a more redoubted knight.

LXXXI

On the other side the slaughter Gunther and Gernot led;
They smote in that grim conflict full many a hero dead;
Giselher and Dankwart, little of aught reck'd they;
Full many a prowest champion they brought to his last day.

LXXXII

Well prov'd the fiery margrave his strength and courage too,
His weapon and his harness;—ah! what a host he slew!
That saw a bold Burgundian; his passion mounted high.
Alas for noble Rudeger! e'en then his death drew nigh.

LXXXIII

Loud o'er the din of battle stout Gernot shouted then,
" How now, right noble Rudeger? not one of all my men
Thou'lt leave me here unwounded; in sooth it grieves me sore
To see my friends thus slaughter'd; bear it can I no more.

LXXXIV

" Now must thy gift too surely the giver harm to-day,
Since of my friends so many thy strength has swept away.
So turn about, and face me, thou bold and high-born man!
Thy goodly gift to merit, I'll do the best I can."

LXXXV

Ere through the press the margrave could come Sir Gernot
    nigh,
Full many a glittering mailcoat was stain'd a bloody die.
Then those fame-greedy champions each fierce on th' other
    leapt,
And deadly wounds at distance with wary ward they kept.

LXXXVI

So sharp were both their broadswords, resistless was their dint;
Sudden the good Sir Rudeger through th' helmet hard as flint
So struck the noble Gernot, that forth the blood it broke;
With death the stern Burgundian repaid the deadly stroke.

LXXXVII

He heav'd the gift of Rudeger with both his hands on high,
And, to the death though wounded, a stroke at him let fly
Right through both shield and morion; deep was the gash and
    wide.
At once the lord of Gotelind beneath the swordcut died.

LXXXVIII

In sooth a gift so goodly was worse requited ne'er,
Down dead dropp'd both together, Gernot and Rudeger,
Each slain by th' other's manhood, then prov'd, alas! too well.
Thereat first Sir Hagan furious wax'd and fell.

LXXXIX

Then cried the knight of Trony, " Sure we with ill are cross'd;
Their country and their people in both these chiefs have lost
More than they'll e'er recover;—woe worth this fatal day!
We have here the margrave's meiny, and they for all shall pay."

XC

All struck at one another, none would a foeman spare.
Full many a one, unwounded, down was smitten there,
Who else might have 'scap'd harmless, but now, though whole
    and sound,
In the thick press was trampled, or in the blood was drown'd.

XCI

" Alas! my luckless brother who here in death lies low!
How every hour I'm living brings some fresh tale of woe!
And ever must I sorrow for the good margrave too.
On both sides dire destruction and mortal ills we rue."

XCII

Soon as the youthful Giselher beheld his brother dead,
Who yet within were lingering by sudden doom were sped.
Death, his pale meiny choosing, dealt each his dreary dole.
Of those of Bechlaren 'scap'd not one living soul.

XCIII

King Gunther and young Giselher, and fearless Hagan, too,
Dankwart as well as Folker, the noble knights and true,
Went where they found together out-stretch'd the valiant twain.
There wept th' assembled warriors in anguish o'er the slain.

XCIV

" Death fearfully despoils us," said youthful Giselher,
" But now give over wailing, and haste to th' open air
To cool our heated hauberks, faint as we are with strife.
God, methinks, no longer will here vouchsafe us life."

XCV

This sitting, that reclining, was seen full many a knight;
They took repose in quiet; around (a fearful sight!)
Lay Rudeger's dead comrades; all was hush'd and still;
From that long dreary silence King Etzel augur'd ill.

XCVI

"Alas for this half friendship!" thus Kriemhild frowning spake,
" If it were true and steadfast, Sir Rudeger would take
Vengeance wide and sweeping on yonder murderous band;
Now back he'll bring them safely to their Burgundian land.

XCVII

" What boot our gifts, King Etzel? Was it, my lord, for this
We gave him all he ask'd us? The chief has done amiss.
He who should have reveng'd us will now a treaty make."
Thereto in answer Folker, the gallant minstrel, spake.

XCVIII

" Not so the truth is, lady ! the more the pity, too !
If one the lie might venture to give a dame like you,
Most foully 'gainst the margrave you've lied, right noble queen !
Sore trick'd in that same treaty he and his men have been.

XCIX

" With such good-will the margrave his king's commands
    obey'd,
That he and all his meiny dead on this floor are laid.
Now look about you, Kriemhild ! for servants seek anew ;
Well were you serv'd by Rudeger ; he to the death was true.

C

" The fact, if still you're doubting, before your eyes we'll bring."
'Twas done e'en of set purpose her heart the more to wring.
They brought the mangled margrave, where Etzel saw him well.
Th' assembled knights of Hungary such utter anguish ne'er
    befell.

CI

When thus held high before them they saw the margrave dead,
Sure by the choicest writer could ne'er be penn'd nor said
The woful burst of wailing from woman and eke from man,
That from the heart's deep sorrow to strike all ears began.

CII

Above his weeping people King Etzel sorrow'd sore ;
His deep-voiced wail resounded loud as the lion's roar
In the night-shaded desert ; the like did Kriemhild too ;
They mourn'd in heart for Rudeger, the valiant and the true.

THIRTY-EIGHTH ADVENTURE

HOW SIR DIETRICH'S MEN WERE ALL SLAIN

I

THE cry of lamentation now spread so far around
That tower and hall and palace rang with the rueful sound.
A certain Berner heard it, the noble Dietrich's man.
To tell the bloody tidings, how swift away he ran!

II

Then thus the prince bespake he, " Sir Dietrich, hear my tale;
Surely heard I never such wild and woful wail,
As in my ears is ringing, through all the life I've past.
The king himself, I doubt not, has join'd the feast at last.

III

" Why else should such loud sorrow through all the people
    spread?
The king, or Lady Kriemhild, or both of them are dead,
By those redoubted strangers laid low through fell despite;
So weeping and so wailing is many a courtly knight."

IV

Then outspake the Berner, " My merrymen every one,
Now be not over-hasty; what has e'en now been done
By those home-distant champions, through hard constraint be-
    fell.
I proffer'd them my service, now let it boot them well."

V

Quick then spake Sir Wolfhart, " Straight I'll thither run,
And inquire the tidings, what the guests have done,
Then, my good lord, will tell you, when I there have been
And of the truth possess'd me, what all this wail may mean."

VI

Thereto replied Sir Dietrich, " When the heart is gall,
Should reckless, rough inquiries just then perchance befall,
Wrath's yet glowing embers flame up with ease anew.
I would not have the question, good Wolfhart, ask'd by you."

VII

Then turn'd he to Sir Helfrich, and bade him speed his best,
And either from Hungarian or from stranger guest
Learn what had really happen'd, that so their grief had stirr'd.
Ne'er had in any country so wild a wail been heard.

VIII

The messenger 'gan question, "Why what has here been
    done?"
"Oh! we are lost forever!" straight replied a Hun.
"All joy's forever vanish'd, that cheer'd King Etzel's reign.
Here lies the noble Rudeger, by yon Burgundians slain.

IX

"Of those who enter'd with him return'd no living soul."
At the words stood Helfrich struck dumb with mortal dole.
Tale of such deep horror never met his ear.
The messenger to Dietrich went back with many a tear.

X

"What are the news you bring us?" cried Dietrich at the
    sight,
"Why do you weep so bitterly, Sir Helfrich, noble knight?"
"Alas!" exclaim'd the champion, "well may I weep and plain;
The hands of yon Burgundians good Rudeger have slain."

XI

"Now God forbid!" cried Dietrich, "that could I ne'er have
    ween'd;
Sure 'twere a fearful vengeance, and sport for the foul fiend.
How at their hands had Rudeger deserv'd so sad an end?
Full well I know, those strangers had ne'er so firm a friend."

XII

Then answer made Sir Wolfhart, "If they this deed have done,
Their lives shall pay the forfeit; die shall they every one.
'Twould be to our dishonor, should we such outrage bear.
Oft we have had good service from noble Rudeger."

XIII

The lord of th' Amelungers yet more to know was bent.
Down sat he at a window anxious and ill content;
Then Hildebrand straight bade he haste to the strangers bold,
And what had really happen'd from their own lips be told.

XIV

A well-approved warrior was master Hildebrand,
Yet took he, on his message, nor shield nor sword in hand,
For all in peaceful fashion to seek the guests he meant.
His sister's son beheld it with angry discontent.

XV

Then sternly spake grim Wolfhart, "If thus unarm'd you go,
Naught but reproach and insult can hap from such a foe.
With outrage and dishonor needs must you hither back;
But if you're seen in harness, you'll find the foremost slack."

XVI

So th' old and wise took counsel of the foolish and the young.
Ere he could don his armor, theirs on in haste had flung
All the knights of Dietrich; each shook his naked blade.
Sore it irk'd the warrior; full fain had he renounced such aid.

XVII

Whither would they, inquir'd he—" Thither, good knight with
          you;
What if o'erweening Hagan, to his ill habit true,
So much the worse upon you his spite and scorn should vent."
When this was told the champion, he could not but consent.

XVIII

Soon as the valiant Folker saw sheath'd in armor bright
The flower of Bern advancing, Sir Dietrich's men of might,
Bucklers all uplifting, girded all with swords,
Ready notice gave he to his Burgundian lords.

XIX

Thus spake the fearless minstrel, "On this, my lords, advise;
There see I Dietrich's Berners come on in hostile guise,
All helmeted and harnessed;—they'll fight us, well I know.
With us forlorn and friendless ill now, I ween, 'twill go."

XX

Scarce had he done speaking, when Hildebrand came on.
Before his feet the warrior set down his shield anon,
And thus began his question to put to Gunther's crew;
" Alas! ye valiant heroes, what has Rudeger done to you?

XXI

I come from my lord Dietrich, from you the truth to gain,
If any here among you with bloody hand has slain
The good and noble margrave, as some to us declare.
Such weight of mortal sorrow were more than we could bear."

XXII

" The woful news," said Hagan, " cannot be denied;
Would for the sake of Rudeger your messenger had lied,
And yet the chief were living! 'tis all too true a tale;
For the good knight must ever both man and woman wail."

XXIII

Soon as the knights of Dietrich heard he indeed was dead,
As love and truth impell'd them, they wailed drearihead.
Bitter tears forth gushing beard and chin ran o'er;
Such deep remorse for Rudeger in their inmost hearts they
    bore.

XXIV

A duke of Bern, Sir Siegstab, sighing then began,
" So comes to end the kindness, wherewith this blameless man,
After our days of sorrow, reliev'd our woe and pain.
Here the poor exile's comfort lies by you heroes slain."

XXV

Next him, the Amelunger, the good Sir Wolfwine, said,
" If I saw to-day my father before me lying dead,
More I could not sorrow e'en for such a life.
Alas! who now can comfort the gentle margrave's wife?"

XXVI

Then spake in storm of passion Wolfhart the moody knight,
" Who now will harnessed warriors lead to so many a fight,
As oft has done the margrave, and to our foemen's cost,
Alas! right noble Rudeger, that thee we thus have lost!"

XXVII

Sir Wolfbrand and Sir Helfrich and eke Sir Helmnot shed
True tears, with all their comrades, for him who there lay dead.
Old Hildebrand through sobbing could not inquire the rest;
Said he, " Go to, ye warriors, perform my lord's request.

XXVIII

" Give us the corpse of Rudeger from out yon reeking hall;
So pale and dead lies with him the comfort of us all;
And let us now requite him for all he e'er has done
To us of his great kindness, and besides to many a one.

XXIX

" We ourselves are exiles like blameless Rudeger.
Wherefore would you delay us?   Him hence then let us bear,
And pay him every honor now that he dead is laid.
Such unto the living we gladlier would have paid."

XXX

Thereto replied King Gunther, " Service so good is none,
As after death, Sir Hildebrand, to friend by friend is done.
That, whosoe'er performs it, firm steadfast faith I call.
You pay him as is fitting, for well he serv'd you all."

XXXI

" How long must we be waiting? " cried Wolfhart proud and
        high;
" Since our choicest comfort you have done to die,
And we no more can have him amongst us safe and sound,
Let us take him forthwith hence to the burial ground."

XXXII

" None here will fetch him to you," the minstrel answer gave;
" Enter the hall and take him, where lifeless lies the brave,
Deep gash'd with gaping death-wounds, as in the blood he fell.
'Tis all you can do for him, and thus you'll serve him well."

XXXIII

"Sir gleeman," said fierce Wolfhart; "you've done us grievous
  ill.
God knows, that you had better not move us further still.
But for my lord's injunctions, you'd be in evil plight;
Now we must pass it over; forbidd'n are we to fight."

XXXIV

Then spake the fiery minstrel, "His courage is but small,
Who, soon as one forbids him, would fain pass over all.
Such can I never reckon the mood of a true knight."
His comrade's words Sir Hagan approv'd as just and right.

XXXV

"Persist not to provoke me," said Wolfhart, "or full soon
Your strings, without your leave too, I'll put so out of tune,
You'll have enough to talk of on your journey hence.
No longer I with honor will bear your insolence."

XXXVI

Straight replied the minstrel, "Sir knight, howe'er you may
Put my strings out of order and spoil my viol's play,
This hand shall first dim sadly our helmets brilliancy,
However chance may bring me back to fair Burgundy."

XXXVII

With that the furious Wolfhart had leapt upon him fain,
But Hildebrand, his uncle, still held him back amain.
"Thy silly rage would drive thee, I ween, to draw the sword,
And so thou'dst lose forever the favor of my lord."

XXXVIII

"Let loose the lion, master, that storms so fierce and proud.
If I can only reach him," the minstrel shouted loud,
"Though all the world together his prowess may have slain,
I'll strike him such a swordstroke, he'll ne'er reply again."

XXXIX

By this the Berner's fury was kindled to the height.
His shield at once before him held Wolfhart the swift knight.
Forward, like a wild lion, he darted to th' attack.
A crowd of nimble followers cluster'd at his back.

XL

But swift as was the warrior, and swift as was his band,
First at the foot of the staircase was aged Hildebrand.
None would he have before him where'er a field was fought.
Soon among the strangers found they what they sought.

XLI

Straight upon Sir Hagan leapt Master Hildebrand;
The sword you might hear clatter in either champion's hand.
Well might you note their fury by many a sturdy stroke.
From their clashing broadswords a fire-red blast there broke.

XLII

Soon were they swept asunder by th' heady stream of fight;
'Twas done by the fierce Berners hurtling in their might.
So from grim Sir Hagan turn'd off that aged man.
Wolfhart meanwhile in fury at valiant Folker ran.

XLIII

On the good helm the minstrel he smote with fell intent,
So that the edge, descending, e'en to the beaver went.
That stroke the forceful gleeman repaid with such a blow,
As sent the sturdy Wolfhart tottering to and fro.

XLIV

They clash'd, that from the hauberks sparks were seen to start.
Either bore the other deadly hate at heart.
A Berner then, Sir Wolfwine, parted that stormy fight.
Who on such deed could venture, was sure a prowest knight.

XLV

The noble king, Sir Gunther, with frank and willing hand
Met the renowned champions of th' Amelungers' land.
Then, too, the good Sir Giselher himself so knightly bore,
That he made the polish'd morions red and wet with gore.

XLVI

Dankwart, Hagan's brother, was a champion grim.
Whate'er on Etzel's meiny had late been wrought by him,
A puff was to the tempest that now to rise began;
So furiously did battle the son of Aldrian.

XLVII

Ritschart as well as Gerbart, Helfrich and Wichart, too,
Spared themselves but seldom with bloody work to do;
This in the fierce hurly to Gunther's men they show'd.
Into the strife Sir Wolfbrand like a noble warrior strode.

XLVIII

Then, as though he were frantic, fought aged Hildebrand.
Many a good knight, o'ermaster'd by Wolfhart's stalwart hand
Into the blood, death-stricken, beneath his broadsword fell.
Thus the bold knights of Dietrich reveng'd the margrave well.

XLIX

Then, as his courage mov'd him, the good Sir Siegstab strove;
Ah! how the glittering morions of his stern foes he clove
In that tempestuous conflict, Sir Dietrich's sister's son!
Amidst the storm of battle ne'er had he better done.

L

The valiant minstrel Folker, soon as he espied
A bloody brook forth gushing as Siegstab fiercely plied
His sword upon the hauberks, in a storm of rage was tossed;
Furious he leapt upon him; at once Sir Siegstab lost

LI

His life by that stern minstrel, who, to the warrior's ill,
Proof gave him so resistless of his surpassing skill,
That at a stroke before him down fell dead the knight.
Him straight revenged Sir Hildebrand, as well beseem'd his
      might.

LII

" Ah, my dear lord! " in anguish cried Master Hildebrand,
"Dost thou then here lie lifeless by Folker's bloody hand?
But hence, be sure, shall never this minstrel scathless go."
However could noble Hildebrand rush fiercer on a foe?

LIII

At once so smote he Folker with weapon sharp and true,
That to the walls on all sides a shower of shivers flew
From helm and eke from buckler like chaff before the blast.
Thereby the sturdy Folker came to his end at last.

LIV

At that, the men of Dietrich rush'd on from every side.
They slash'd, that links of hauberk went whirling far and wide,
And the snapp'd sword-points flicker'd with momentary
    gleam;
They drew from out the morions the smoking bloody stream.

LV

Soon Hagan spied Sir Folker dead on the reeking floor;
Ne'er had he felt such anguish throughout the feast before
For kinsman lost or liegeman, as then his bosom shook.
Alas! for his slain comrade what dire revenge he took!

LVI

" Ne'er from me shall scathless go aged Hildebrand.
My helpmate lies before me, slain by the hero's hand.
Never had I comrade so valiant and so true."
He rais'd his shield, and forward slashing and hewing flew.

LVII

Just then the stalwart Helfrich slew Dankwart the good
    knight;
Gunther as well as Giselher, woe were they at the sight,
When down he fell, and, writhing, out panted his last breath.
He with his sword beforehand had well reveng'd his death.

LVIII

What crowds soe'er had thither muster'd from many a land,
Beneath right puissant princes against their little band,
Weren't not that Christian people conspir'd to work their fall,
Their prowess well had kept them against the heathens all.

LIX

Meanwhile redoubted Wolfhart rush'd fiercely to and fro,
King Gunther's men down hewing with oft-repeated blow.
Thrice through that place of slaughter he cut his bloody way.
Before, behind, around him the dead and dying lay.

LX

With that, the young Sir Giselher to the stern warrior cried,
" Woe's me that I should ever so fierce a foe abide!
Noble knight and fearless, turn thee now to me.
I'll help to end this matter; it must no longer be."

LXI

Wolfhart turn'd on Giselher soon as thus defied;
Each in that grim battle wounds cut gaping wide.
Upon the king fierce rushing so forcefully he sped,
The blood beneath his trampling flew high above his head.

LXII

The bold son of fair Uta with many a rapid blow
Received the furious onset of his redoubted foe;
Huge as was Wolfhart's puissance, boot it none could bring.
Ne'er was so brave a battle fought by so young a king.

LXIII

At last through the good hauberk he smote Sir Dietrich's man,
That the blood, out-spurting, down in a torrent ran.
So to the death he wounded that high o'erweening one.
'Twas sure a peerless champion who such a deed had done.

LXIV

Soon as fearless Wolfhart felt the deadly pain,
Down he dropp'd his buckler; with fierce hand amain
His huge sharp-cutting broadsword higher he heav'd in air;
Through helm at once and hauberk then smote he Giselher.

LXV

So they one another both of their lives bereft.
Now of all Dietrich's liegemen not a soul was left.
Hildebrand, the aged, dead saw Wolfhart fall;
Among his long life's sorrows that was the worst of all.

LXVI

There in that hall of slaughter dead lay King Gunther's train,
Dead too the men of Dietrich. Sir Hildebrand amain
Ran where redoubted Wolfhart fall'n in the blood he found,
And cast his arms about him to lift him from the ground.

LXVII

He drove his dying nephew forth from the house to bear,
But found his weight too mighty; he needs must leave him
    there.
Then from the blood the wounded a clouded glance upcast;
He saw that fain his uncle had help'd him at the last.

LXVIII

Then spake the fainting warrior, " Dear uncle, kind and true,
No more can it avail me whatever you can do.
But Oh! beware of Hagan; this seems me good to tell.
Heart had never champion so furious and so fell.

LXIX

" And if my loving kinsmen would sorrow o'er my clay,
This to the best and nearest, dear uncle, of me say,
That I need no lamenting, that tears were better dried,
That 'twas a king that slew me, and gloriously I died.

LXX

" Besides, in this wild slaughter I've sold my life so dear,
That many a knight's pale lady 'twill cost full many a tear.
If any ask the question, straight let the truth be shown.
Here lie at least a hundred slain by this hand alone."

LXXI

Just then redoubted Hagan upon the gleeman thought,
Whom the good knight Sir Hildebrand so late to death had
    brought.
Thus he bespake the conqueror, " You for my grief shall pay;
Of many a valiant champion you've robb'd us here to-day."

LXXII

So struck he then at Hildebrand, that all at once might hear
'Twas Balmung there was sounding, the sword that he whilere
Had ta'en from noble Siegfried when he the hero slew.
Well was his onset warded by the graybeard stout and true.

LXXIII

Sir Dietrich's aged liegeman the tearful stroke repaid
With one that show'd, that he, too, wielded a griding blade;
Still from the man of Gunther no drop of blood he drew.
Sir Hagan with a second cut his good hauberk through.

LXXIV

Soon as aged Hildebrand felt the sharp gash aright,
He look'd for worse, by waiting, from Hagan's stormy might;
So o'er his back his buckler straight threw Sir Dietrich's man,
And swift, though sorely wounded, away from Hagan ran.

LXXV

Now not a man was living of that Burgundian train
Gunther except, and Hagan, these the sole breathing twain.
Old Hildebrand thence hasted, with blood all dabbled o'er,
And to the noble Dietrich his sorry tidings bore.

LXXVI

Apart he found him sitting, solemn and sad of cheer;
What more might move his sorrow the prince had yet to hear.
Straight Hildebrand beheld he clad in his bloody mail;
He ask'd him of his tidings, yet fear'd to hear his tale.

LXXVII

" Now tell me, Master Hildebrand, what brings you here so
    wet
With life-blood? Who has done it? What mischief have you
    met?
I fear, you have been fighting in th' hall with yonder guests;
I earnestly forbade it; you should have kept your lord's
    behests."

LXXVIII

Straight his lord he answer'd, " 'Twas Hagan did it all;
This wound, that so is bleeding, he gave me in the hall,
As from the knight I turn'd me, and would have left the strife.
Scarce from that very devil have I escaped with life."

LXXIX

Him thus the Berner answer'd, "This mishap's your due;
You heard me promise friendship to yonder knightly crew,
And yet the peace I gave them you have presum'd to break.
Were it not beneath me, your life for it I'd take."

LXXX

"Nay, my good Lord Dietrich, be not so wroth of mood;
To me and mine already has too much loss accrued.
We wish'd the noble Rudeger to take from where he died;
We ask'd the men of Gunther, and proudly were denied."

LXXXI

"Woe's me for this misfortune! Is Rudeger then dead?
Him must I wail forever; now I indeed am sped.
Woe for the Lady Gotelind! My cousin's child is she.
Woe, too, for the poor orphans that at Bechlaren be!"

LXXXII

The margrave's death impress'd him with pity and ruth so
deep,
He could refrain no longer, but straight began to weep.
"Alas! My faithful comrade! Such loss I needs must rue.
Ne'er can I cease bewailing King Etzel's liegeman true.

LXXXIII

"Come now, Master Hildebrand, the truth discover plain,
Tell me, who's the champion, who has the margrave slain."
Said he, "'Twas noble Gernot whose strength the margrave
sped;
He by the hand of Rudeger in turn was stricken dead."

LXXXIV

Then thus replied Sir Dietrich, "Thither will I anon;
So go and tell my warriors their armor straight to don,
And bid my glittering hauberk be brought me instantly;
I myself will question yon knights of Burgundy."

LXXXV

Then spake Master Hildebrand, "Whom would you have me
    call?
Of those who yet are living you see before you all;
I'm now your only soldier, the others they are dead."
Sore shudder'd then Sir Dietrich for dole and drearihead.

LXXXVI

In all the world such ruin did ne'er the knight befall.
Said he, " If they have slaughtered my liegemen one and all,
Then I'm of God forgotten. Poor Dietrich! Lost am I,
Who was a king but lately so haughty and so high."

LXXXVII

Then further spake the champion, " But how could this have
    passed?
How could such puissant warriors have perish'd to the last
By battle-wearied foemen, fainting and need-beset?
Sure, but through my ill-fortune they had been living yet.

LXXXVIII

" Since my hard fate condemns me to suffer every ill,
Tell me, of those grim strangers if one be living still."
Then answer'd Master Hildebrand, " God knows, their lives
    not one,
Save Hagan and King Gunther; the rest their course have run."

LXXXIX

" Ah! woe is me, dear Wolfhart; since thou from me art torn,
Well may it repent me that ever I was born.
Siegstab, Wolfwine, and Wolfbrand, my true and trusty band!
Who back can ever help me to th' Amelungers' land?

XC

" The danger-daring Helfrich, his doom has he too met?
Gerbart and valiant Wichart, how can I these forget?
My friends are dead together; who so bereft as I?
Ah! woe is me, that wretches of grief can never die."

THIRTY-NINTH ADVENTURE

HOW GUNTHER AND HAGAN AND KRIEMHILD
WERE SLAIN

I

THEN took the good Sir Dietrich himself his mail in hand;
His ready aid to arm him gave aged Hildebrand.
Such piteous moan then made he the while, that mighty man,
That with his voice of thunder the house to ring began.

II

Yet soon did he recover his high heroic mood.
In wrath he donn'd his harness, and ready now he stood.
A shield of prov'd allowance he grasp'd in his strong hand,
And thence in haste forth sallied with Master Hildebrand.

III

Then spake the Knight of Trony, "I yonder see come on
With sturdy strides Sir Dietrich; he'll fight with us anon
To venge his slaughter'd kinsmen whom we have done to die.
To-day shall all bear witness, who best his sword can ply.

IV

" Howe'er himself may value the haughty Lord of Bern,
Though ne'er so stout of body, of mood though ne'er so stern,
If us for our late doings he now attempt to quit,
He'll find in me," said Hagan, " an equal opposite."

V

Dietrich as well as Hildebrand the words of Hagan caught;
He came, and close together the twain, whom here he sought,
Outside the house and leaning against the wall he found.
Sir Dietrich straight his buckler set down upon the ground.

VI

With anguish deep impassion'd the warrior thus began,
" Why have you thus entreated a wandering banish'd man?
What have I done, King Gunther, that you should serve me so?
I'm reft of all my comfort, all at a single blow.

VII

" It seem'd you all too little, that to our loss and pain
By your hands our comrade, good Rudeger, was slain;
And now you have bereft me my warriors every one.
I, sure, to you, ye heroes, such wrong would ne'er have don.

VIII

" Think of yourselves, your sorrow, your long disastrous toil,
The death of your brave comrades in this abhorréd broil,
If to the dust with anguish it bows your lofty cheer.
Ah! how my heart is bleeding for the death of Rudeger!

IX

" In all the world before us such horror ne'er befell.
On me you've brought destruction and on yourselves as well.
All joys I had whatever, by you they all lie slain;
Ne'er for his slaughter'd kinsmen can Dietrich cease to plain."

X

" Nay," replied Sir Hagan, " we're not so much to blame;
To this house in harness your eager warriors came,
In one broad band advancing, embattled fierce and bold.
The truth, methinks, Sir Dietrich, you've not been fairly told."

XI

" How can I doubt the story? I heard from Hildebrand,
That, when my trusty comrades of th' Amelungers' land
Begg'd that the corpse of Rudeger you'd give them from the hall,
They met with proud denial and mannerless scoffs withal."

XII

The Lord of Rhine then answer'd, " They sought to carry out
The corpse of noble Rudeger; I, not from wish to flout
Them, but in scorn of Etzel, what they desired, denied;
Then in a moment Wolfhart began to chafe and chide."

XIII

Thereto replied the Berner, " Well then! so must it be.
Now by thy gentle breeding, King Gunther, list to me;
For all the harm thou'st done me such satisfaction make
As thou may'st give with honor, and I with honor take.

XIV

" Yield thee to me a captive, thou and thy valiant man,
And surely I'll defend thee with all the strength I can
From whatso'er against thee the vengeful Huns may do,
And never shalt thou find me but faithful, kind, and true."

XV

" Now God in Heaven forbid it!" redoubted Hagan cried;
" Never to thee shall yield them two knights of mettle tried,
Who yet in their good harness unfetter'd stand and free,
Ready to bid defiance to their foes, whoe'er they be."

XVI

" You ought not to deny me," Sir Dietrich answer made,
" King Gunther and Sir Hagan; on my heart and soul you've
    laid
Such overwhelming sorrow as you can ne'er requite,
And, if amends you make me, you yield me but my right.

XVII

" My faith, besides, I'll give you, and my assuring hand,
That back I will ride with you to your Burgundian land,
And bring you thither safely, or die with you along,
And for your sakes forever forget my grievous wrong."

XVIII

" Demand of us no further," return'd Sir Hagan bold;
" Ill would it become us, if it ever should be told,
That two knights of such worship yielded at once to thee;
For at thy side, save Hildebrand, there's not a soul to see."

XIX

Then spake Master Hildebrand, " God, Sir Hagan, knows,
My lord's your true well-wisher; he treats you not as foes.
E'en now the hour is coming, his terms you'll gladly take.
Th' amends, that he proposes, you'd better frankly make.

XX

" So would I do far sooner," Sir Hagan made reply,
" Than ever from a palace so like a coward fly,
As you did, Master Hildebrand, but lately here in place.
I thought, i' faith, you better an opposite could face."

XXI

To him made answer Hildebrand, " Why twit you me with
    that ?
Who was 't that by the Waskstone upon a buckler sat,
While of his kin so many the Spaniard Walter slew ?
Look to your own shortcomings ; you'll have enough to do."

XXII

Then spake the good Sir Dietrich, " Ill fits it warriors bold
Like two testy beldams to squabble and to scold.
I charge you, Master Hildebrand, urge this discourse no more.
I'm now a lonely wanderer ; my sorrow whelms me o'er.

XXIII

" Now let me know, Sir Hagan," he thus pursued his speech,
" What your two active champions were saying each to each,
When thus equipp'd for battle you mark'd me drawing nigh.
Was it not, that you against me alone your strength would
    try ? "

XXIV

" Neither of us denies it," thus Hagan sternly spoke,
" I'd fain straight make the trial with many a sturdy stroke,
Unless this my good weapon, the sword of Nibelung, break.
I'm wroth that you of both of us expect a prize to make."

XXV

Soon as heard Sir Dietrich what grim Hagan thought,
Up to him his buckler quick the warrior caught.
How swift against him Hagan down the staircase dash'd !
Loud on the mail of Dietrich the sword of Nibelung clash'd.

XXVI

Well knew the noble Dietrich how fierce and fell a knight
Was standing now against him ; so warily the fight
'Gainst those tempestuous sword-strokes wag'd the good lord
    of Bern,
The strength and skill of Hagan he had not now to learn.

XXVII

He fear'd, too, mighty Balmung as down it swept amain;
Yet at times Sir Dietrich with craft would strike again,
Till that to sink before him he brought his foeman strong;
A fearful wound he gave him that was both deep and long.

XXVIII

Sir Dietrich then bethought him, "Thou'rt faint and ill bestead;
I should win little worship, were I to strike thee dead.
I'll make a different trial, if thou can'st now be won
By main force for a pris'ner." With wary heed 'twas done.

XXIX

Down he threw his buckler; wondrous was his might;
He his arms resistless threw round Trony's knight.
So was by his stronger the man of strength subdued.
Thereat the noble Gunther remain'd in mournful mood.

XXX

His vanquish'd foe Sir Dietrich bound in a mighty band,
And led him thence to Kriemhild, and gave into her hand
The best and boldest champion that broadsword ever bore.
She after all her anguish felt comfort all the more.

XXXI

For joy the queen inclin'd her before the welcome guest;
"Sir Knight! in mind and body heaven keep thee ever blessed!
By thee all my long sorrows are shut up in delight.
Ever, if death prevent not, thy service I'll requite."

XXXII

"Fair and noble Kriemhild," thus Sir Dietrich spake,
"Spare this captive warrior, who full amends will make
For all his past transgressions; him here in bonds you see;
Revenge not on the fetter'd th' offences of the free."

XXXIII

With that she had Sir Hagan to durance led away,
Where no one could behold him, where under lock he lay.
Meanwhile the fierce King Gunther shouted loud and strong,
"Whither is gone the Berner? he hath done me grievous
  wrong."

XXXIV

Straight, at the call, to meet him Sir Dietrich swiftly went.
Huge was the strength of Gunther, and deadly his intent.
There he no longer dallied; from th' hall he forward ran;
Sword clash'd with sword together, as man confronted man.

XXXV

Howe'er renown'd was Dietrich, and train'd in combat well,
Yet Gunther fought against him so furious and so fell,
And bore him hate so deadly, now friendless left and lone,
It seem'd past all conceiving, how Dietrich held his own.

XXXVI

Both were of mighty puissance, and neither yielded ground;
Palace and airy turret rung with their strokes around,
As their swift swords descending their temper'd helmets hew'd.
Well there the proud King Gunther display'd his manly mood.

XXXVII

" Yet him subdued the Berner, as Hagan erst befell;
Seen was the blood of the warrior forth through his mail to well
Beneath the fatal weapon that Dietrich bore in fight.
Tir'd as he was, still Gunther had kept him like a knight.

XXXVIII

So now at length the champion was bound by Dietrich there,
How ill soe'er it fitteth a king such bonds to bear.
Gunther and his fierce liegeman if he had left unbound,
He ween'd they'd deal destruction on all, whome'er they found.

XXXIX

Then by the hand Sir Dietrich took the champion good,
And in his bonds thence led him to where fair Kriemhild stood.
She cried, " Thou'rt welcome, Gunther, hero of Burgundy."
" Now God requite you, Kriemhild, if you speak lovingly."

XL

Said he, " I much should thank you, and justly, sister dear,
If true affection prompted the greeting which I hear;
But, knowing your fierce temper, proud queen, too well I see,
Such greeting is a mocking of Hagan and of me."

XLI

Then said the noble Berner, " High-descended dame,
Ne'er have been brought to bondage knights of such peerless
    fame,
As those, whom you, fair lady, now from your servant take.
Grant these forlorn and friendless fair treatment for my sake."

XLII

She said, she fain would do so; then from the captive pair
With weeping eyes Sir Dietrich retir'd and left them there.
Straight a bloody vengeance wreak'd Etzel's furious wife
On those redoubted champions, and both bereft of life.

XLIII

In dark and dismal durance them kept apart the queen,
So that from that hour neither was by the other seen,
Till that at last to Hagan her brother's head she bore.
On both she took with vengeance as tongue ne'er told before.

XLIV

To the cell of Hagan eagerly she went;
Thus the knight bespake she, ah! with what fell intent!
" Wilt thou but return me what thou from me hast ta'en,
Back thou may'st go living to Burgundy again."

XLV

Then spake grim-visag'd Hagan, " You throw away your
    prayer,
High-descended lady; I took an oath whilere,
That, while my lords were living, or of them only one,
I'd ne'er point out the treasure; thus 'twill be given to none."

XLVI

Well knew the subtle Hagan, she ne'er let him 'scape.
Ah! when did ever falsehood assume so foul a shape?
He fear'd, that, soon as ever the queen his life had ta'en,
She then would send her brother to Rhineland back again.

XLVII

" I'll make an end, and quickly," Kriemhild fiercely spake.
Her brother's life straight bade she in his dungeon take.
Off his head was smitten; she bore it by the hair
To the Lord of Trony; such sight he well could spare.

XLVIII

Awhile in gloomy sorrow he view'd his master's head;
Then to remorseless Kriemhild thus the warrior said;
" E'en to thy wish this business thou to an end hast brought,
To such an end, moreover, as Hagan ever thought.

XLIX

" Now the brave King Gunther of Burgundy is dead;
Young Giselher and eke Gernot alike with him are sped;
So now, where lies the treasure, none knows save God and me,
And told shall it be never, be sure, she-fiend! to thee."

L

Said she, " Ill hast thou quitted a debt so deadly scored;
At least in my possession I'll keep my Siegfried's sword.
My lord and lover bore it, when last I saw him go.
For him woe wrung my bosom, that pass'd all other woe."

LI

Forth from the sheath she drew it; that could not he prevent;
At once to slay the champion was Kriemhild's stern intent.
High with both hands she heav'd it, and off his head did smite
That was seen of King Etzel; he shudder'd at the sight.

LII

" Ah! " cried the prince impassion'd, " Harrow and wellaway!
That the hand of a woman the noblest knight should slay,
That e'er struck stroke in battle, or ever buckler bore!
Albeit I was his foeman, needs must I sorrow sore."

LIII

Then said the aged Hildebrand, " Let not her boast of gain,
In that by her contrivance this noble chief was slain.
Though to sore strait he brought me, let ruin on me light,
But I will take full vengeance for Trony's murdered knight."

LIV

Hildebrand, the aged, fierce on Kriemhild sprung;
To the death he smote her as his sword he swung.
Sudden and remorseless he his wrath did wreak.
What could then avail her, her fearful thrilling shriek?

LV

There now the dreary corpses stretch'd all around were seen:
There lay, hewn in pieces, the fair and noble queen.
Sir Dietrich and King Etzel, their tears began to start;
For kinsmen and for vassals each sorrow'd in his heart.

LVI

The mighty and the noble there lay together dead;
For this had all the people dole and drearihead.
The feast of royal Etzel was thus shut up in woe.
Pain in the steps of Pleasure treads ever here below.

LVII

'Tis more than I can tell you what afterward befell,
Save that there was weeping for friends belov'd so well;
Knights and squires, dames and damsels, were seen lamenting
all.
So here I end my story. This is THE NIBELUNGERS' FALL.

NOTES

According to Professor Lachmann, this poem has no title in most of the manuscripts. In the two that have a superscription, it is styled the Book of Kriemhild. Its ordinary name, The Nibelungenlied, is derived from the Lassberg manuscript which ends with the words, *der Nibelunge liet,* the lay of the Nibelungs, while the better manuscripts for *liet* read *nôt,* calamity. The word Nibelung is a patronymic from *nebel,* mist or darkness, and means, child of mist or darkness. Who these Nibelungs were is involved in appropriate obscurity. In the first part of the poem, they are Siegfried's Norwegian dependents, formerly subjects of King Nibelung; in the second, they are the Burgundians, possibly as being then the possessors of the wondrous treasure. In F. H. von der Hagen's Remarks on the poem, there is a long rambling note on this word, a note, however, which is worth reading. The commentator travels from the Nephilim, or giants of scripture, down to Neville, the great Earl of Warwick, and his coal-black head of hair. I have followed Mr. Birch in using the form *Nibelunger,* as more convenient for the verse, and more suitable to our language, and also to mark the difference between the name of an individual, and that of a tribe. For the same reasons I have ventured to employ the form *Amelunger.*

FIRST ADVENTURE

(St VI.) The famous city of Worms derived its name, according to one tradition, from the *Lindwurm,* or dragon slain by Siegfried under the linden tree; according to another, from the multitude of dragons that infested the neighborhood. The Rose-garden of Kriemhild (which, though celebrated in other poems, is not noticed in this) was in the vicinity. The progress of civilization, elegance, cleanliness and classic refinement has converted the Rose-garden into a tobacco ground.

(St. XIII.) Lachmann's First Lay begins here, and ends with St. LXXXVIII, Second Adventure.

(St. XVII.) *Liebe,* here, is not *Love,* but *Joy, Pleasure.* See Lachmann's Treatise on the Original Form of the Poem, p. 91.

SECOND ADVENTURE

(St. XIII.) *Swertdegne* are young noble squires destined for knighthood. The *manic rîcher kneht* of St. XXXIV are also squires, the same as the *edeln knehte* at the end of the poem. The mere *knehte* were an inferior class, like our yeomen. Nine thousand of these last accompanied Gunther to Etzel's court, and were entertained apart.

THIRD ADVENTURE

(St. V.)   *Make,* an old form for *mate.*   Spenser has among other
passages

> And of fair Britomart ensample take,
> That was as true in love as turtle to her make.
>   " Faerie Queene," III, ii. 2.

It is common in German romances of a certain period for brides to
be carried off by force, and maidens to be wooed by suitors who have
never set eyes on them.   See Gervinus's Abridgment of his History of
German poetry.   See also the Gudrun.

(St. XXVII.)   Lachmann observes on the third verse: " This verse
cannot be explained from our Lays (*i.e.,* from anything in the poem) ;
the Netherlanders lost no friend but Siegfried.   Is there an allusion
to other legends, or is the departure adorned with the usual coloring?"   It really almost seems as if the writer of this particular stanza
had confounded Nibelungers, Netherlanders and Burgundians all
together.

(St. LI.)   Most of the marvels of modern romantic poetry may be
traced back to much older tales reported by Greek authorities.   The
Scythian griffins, who watched the treasures coveted by their neighbors
the Arimaspians, the dragon Ladon, who guarded the golden apples of
the Hesperides, the more celebrated bullionist, who kept an eye on the
golden fleece, are the undoubted ancestors of the more modern specimens of the serpent tribe, who inherited the like miserly passion, and
allured such champions as Siegfried and Orlando to tread in the steps
of Hercules and Jason.   The volatile disposition of Wayland the Smith
reminds us of Dædalus; his skill in his art exhibits him as a rival of
Vulcan; his grandfather Wiking, like Ulysses, " *æquoreas torsit amore
Deas.*"   The Alcinas and Armidas of the modern Italians are only
heightened copies of Calypso and Circe; Siegfried, Orlando and Ferraù,
with their invulnerable hides and superfluous armor, are each of them
a modernized Achilles.   This list might be easily lengthened.   I am
not, however, aware that the fancy of giving names to swords can be
traced to the classics.   Durindana, the sword of Orlando, Fusberta, that
of Rinaldo, Excalibur, of King Arthur, Joyeuse, of Charlemagne, and
others, may be paralleled by the following list from Northern fable,
Gram and Balmung belonging to Siegfried, Mimung to Wayland and
Wittich, Nagelring to Dietrich, Brinnig to Hildebrand, Sachs to Eck,
Blutang to Heime, Schrit to Biterolf, Welsung to Sintram the Greek
and Dietlieb, Waske to Iring, etc.   This list is anything but perfect.

(St. LV.)   The *tarnkappe,* from an old word *tarnen* to conceal, and
kappe, a mantle or cloak, otherwise called *nebelkappe,* from *nebel,* mist,
obscurity, was a long and broad mantle, which made the wearer invisible,
and gave him the strength of twelve men.   For want of a better word
I have translated it " cloud-cloak."

FOURTH ADVENTURE

(St. I.)   Lachmann's Second Lay begins here, and ends with St.
CXXII, Fourth Adventure.

(St. XLIV.)   A Skottysshe knight hoved upon te bent,
> A wache I dare well saye ;
> So was he ware on the noble Percy
> In the dawnynge of the daye.
>   English " Battle of Otterbourne."

(St. LXVII.) In this poem " *the Rhine* " is used to express the do-
minion of Gunther, though, strictly speaking, Siegfried was himself from
the Rhine, being a native of Xanten. It is remarkable that at St. I,
Second Adventure, this last circumstance is stated, and yet at St. XIII
and St. XV, Third Adventure, in the conversation between Siegfried and
his father, both of whom were then at Xanten, the phrase *ze Rine* is
used with reference to Gunther's country.

(St. LXIX.) " slew him many a slain." This phrase is borrowed
from Samson Agonistes.

FIFTH ADVENTURE

(St. I.) Lachmann's Third Lay begins here, and ends with St. LX
of this Adventure.

(St. XX.)   Ne she was derke ne browne, but bright,
              And clear as the Moone light,
              Againe whom all the starres semen
              But small candles, as we demen.

Chaucer's " Romaunt of the Rose " in the description of Beauty.

              For all afore, that seemed fayre and bright,
              Now base and contemptible did appeare,
              Compar'd to her that shone as Phebes light
              Among the lesser starres in evening clear.
                                  " Faerie Queene," IV, v. 14.

(St. XXIII.) So Chaucer says of Mirth in the " Romaunt of the
Rose " :

              He seemed like a portreiture,
              So noble was he of his stature.

(St. XXVIII.) In the last verse of this stanza Lachmann thinks
magetlichen, not *minnelichen,* was the original word; " We have," says
he rather austerely, " love enough and to spare in St. XXX, Fifth Adventure; " and certainly, if he be justified in rejecting St. CCXCVIII,
and consequently in putting St. CCXCIX next to St. CCXCVII, there
is rather a superabundance of the tender passion with *minnelichen,*
in two successive lines, and *minne* in a third. On the other hand, it
may be said that this very superabundance is produced by Lachmann's
own rejection of St. CCXCVIII, and that to alter the text of the preceding stanza in consequence of that rejection, is something like what
lawyers call taking advantage of one's own wrong. But however that
may be, it cannot be denied, that *magetlichen* is in St. CCXCVII far
more appropriate than *minnelichen,* and its suits my convenience as a
translator infinitely better. I have therefore gladly adopted it.

(St. XL.) In fame's eternal beadroll worthy to be fil'd.
                                  " Faerie Queene."

SIXTH ADVENTURE

(St. II.) Lachmann's Fourth Lay begins here, and ends with St.
LXXXVIII. The poem, which we now possess under the name of the
Nibelungenlied, throws into the shade the early history of Sjegfried
and Brunhild, and retains only a few obscure allusions to the fact that
they were old acquaintances. See the Preface.

Issland, the Kingdom of Brunhild, which I have thus written to distinguish it from our English word *island,* is identified by von der Hagen
with Iceland; Wackernagel, in the Glossary to his " Alt-deutsches Lese-
buch " prefers to derive it from *Itisland* (*itis,* woman in old German),
the land of women or Amazons. It is however against this derivation,

that, though Brunhild was a " Martial Maid " herself, her kingdom was not a kingdom of Amazons, like that of Radigund in the " Faerie Queene." Her female attendants were like other women, and her knights and the officers of her court were of the other sex.

(St. XVI.) In this stanza and those that follow we may clearly discern that several versions of the same tale have been huddled together. The same thing may be observed in other parts of the poem, but nowhere so clearly as here. For the *tarnkappe* see the note to St. CI.

(St. XXXVIII.)   tuus, O Regina, quid optes
    Explorare labor, mihi jussa capessere fas est.

(St. XLV.) Zazamanc, according to von der Hagen, is a city in Asia Minor; Lachmann seems to place it in the Land of Romance.

(St. XLVI.) The hides here meant, according to von der Hagen, are the hairy ones of warm-blooded marine animals rather than the skins of fishes properly so called.

(St. LII.) This stanza (not to mention some others) must have been interpolated by a poetical tailor.

(St. LXIII.) According to von der Hagen, the best Rhenish wine is produced about Worms. It is called " Our Lady's Milk," and is superior to Lacryma Christi.

SEVENTH ADVENTURE

(St. XII.) The Ballad of Lord Thomas and Fair Annet has something similar of the lady's horse:

> Four and twenty siller bells
> Wer a' tyed till his mane,
> And yae tift of the norland wind,
> They tinkled ane by ane.

(St. XVI.) This description of a castle (*burc*) does not materially differ from those which occur elsewhere in the poem. The castle was not one building, however large and complex, but included in the same ample circuit of its walls several extensive buildings, and afforded sufficient accommodation for a very great number of persons. The most conspicuous of the buildings within the castle seem to have been large detached erections, to which in this poem are applied the words *hûs* (house), *palas* (palace), *sal* (hall), and *gadem* (room). In the passage before us, *palas* and *sal* are distinguished from one another; the same is the case at St. LXXXIV, Twenty-fourth Adventure (*palas unde sal*), and at St. XXXVII, Ninth Adventure, where Etzel's and Gunther'ʼ dwellings are respectively spoken of. On the other hand, the hall where the Burgundians feast with Etzel, and where the repeated conflicts take place, is called *palas* at St. XIX, Thirty-sixth Adventure, *sal* at St. XX, same Adventure, *hûs* at St. IX, same Adventure, and *gadem* at St. XX, Thirty-ninth Adventure, not to mention other passages; and the large building in Etzel's castle, where Gunther and his knights sleep, is called *sal* at stanzas VII and XVI, *hûs* at stanzas XV and XVII, and *gadem* at St. XIX, of the Thirtieth Adventure. These terms therefore seem nearly synonymous, or at least equally applicable to the large detached buildings in question, which resembled our public halls, such as Westminster hall and Guildhall, and the halls of colleges and Inns of Court. Some of the halls in this poem seem to have been of truly poetical dimensions. Gunther (St. XXVI, of the Thirteenth Adventure) entertains in his hall twelve hundred knights of Siegfried's, besides his own Burgundians. Etzel's circle was still more numerous. The Burgundian knights were more than a thousand in number; Rudeger's five hundred or more: Dietrich had many a stately man, no doubt the six hundred mentioned at St. IV, of the Thirty-second Adventure, and we learn from stanza V, of the Thirty-fourth Adventure, that 7,000 Huns were massacred by the Burgundians; all these made up a dinner party of about 9,000 guests. The less aristocratic followers of Gunther, 9,000 in number, seem also to have been feasting in one immense room, when the Huns took advantage of their unarmed condition to massacre them. The term, indeed, applied to the building is *hûs*, but this, we have seen, is one of the words used to designate great public halls. The hall, where Gunther and his knights lay so splendidly (St. IX, Thirtieth Adventure), seems to have been an Eton Long Chamber on a gigantic scale. After allowing for the twelve knights with Dankwart and the yeomen, he must have had more than a thousand warriors in his train. Treachery and violence were so common in the Middle Ages, that a great man was not safe except with a multitude of dependents about him, and the peculiar circumstances of Gunther's case required peculiar precaution. Yet even Siegfried took a thousand warriors of his own, and a hundred of Siegmund's, when they went together to visit his brother-in-law. These large halls were used for feasting, dancing, conversation, and sleeping, but there were other smaller separate buildings (*kemenaten*) for the residence of people of consequence, which no doubt contained several rooms. These also formed the bowers, or private apartments, of high-born ladies. The *kamere* (chamber) seems to have been a room used for all sorts of purposes, among others for keeping stores and treasure as well as for living and sleeping. There seem to have been no private chapels within the walls of the castles described in this poem, none, for instance, such as St. George's Chapel in Windsor Castle, or the chapels in our Inns of Court and Colleges. Everybody went for his divinity to the minster. Kriemhild, who was in the habit of going to matins before daybreak, took her way to the minster, though it was so far from the castle at Worms that the ladies (St. XXXIV, Thirteenth Adventure) rode on horseback from one to the other. Gunther's castle was connected with the city of Worms, but seems to have communicated with the surrounding country, like the citadels of our present fortified towns. At stanzas XXXII, XXXIII, Thirteenth Adventure, the ladies view from the castle windows a tournament held in the country outside the walls. Etzel's castle, as far as I remember, is not represented as connected with any town.

(St. XXII.) All this description of the adventurers bears a resemblance to the passage in the Iliad where Helen points out the Greek chiefs to Priam; it reminds us also of the imitation of Homer in the "Jerusalem Delivered."

(St. XXXIV.) Siegfried here seems to apologize to Brunhild for presenting himself before her.

(St. XLIII.) Compare stanzas LXXXIV, Seventh Adventure—LXXXV, Tenth Adventure—XXXI, Nineteenth Adventure, and the observations.

(St. XLVI.) I cannot understand how the skin could be seen under a silken surcoat, which was so strong as never to have been cut by weapon, and which was moreover worn over a breastplate. Lachmann has reason to say "*die Brunne ist vergessen.*"

(St. LXX.) So did Sir Artegal upon her lay,
As if she had an iron anvil been,
That flakes of fire, bright as the sunny ray,
Out of her steely arms were flashing seen,
That all on fire you would her surely ween.
"Faerie Queene," V, v. 8.

(St. LXX.)   For *der helt,* the hero, Lachmann conjectures *der helde,* the concealed one.

(St. LXXXVIII.)   According to Lachmann the Fourth Lay concludes with this stanza (L. St. XLII).   What follows between this stanza and St. XLI, Tenth Adventure (L. St. XXVII, Ninth Adventure) he considers to consist of two continuations by different authors. Among other matters, they contain the two marriages of Brunhild and Kriemhild, events which I can scarcely imagine to have been passed over without notice, though I admit that they are not related in the clearest manner.

EIGHTH ADVENTURE

(St. I.)   Lachmann observes that this stanza is inconsistent with St. LXXXIV, Seventh Adventure, where Siegfried is said to have taken the cloak back to the ship.

(St. XVIII.)   Siegfried, I suppose, was not recognized from being in complete armor, but his shield might have identified him, as in the battle with the Saxons.   Nothing is said here of what he had done with his *tarnkappe.*

(St. XXIII.)   The *lûtertranc* (clear drink) was wine passed through spices, and afterward strained.

(St. XLV.)   Our common participle *bound* (bound for such and such a place) seems in this sense to be derived from the old northern verb *bown,* to make ready, and not from *bind.*

> And Jedburgh heard the Regent's order,
> That each should bown him for the border.
> > "Lay of the Last Minstrel."

NINTH ADVENTURE

(St. I.)   According to Lachmann (L. St. XCV, Seventh Adventure) another continuation begins here.   He thinks this addition is by another author than the composer of the first, and that it resembles in several respects the Third Lay of his edition, which answers to the Fifth Adventure ("How Siegfried first saw Kriemhild") of other editions.

(St. III.)   Hagan here speaks ironically, but with good nature, as to a friend.   He exhibits the same turn, but with the bitterness that suits the change of circumstances and the person whom he addresses, in his dialogues with his enemy Kriemhild, when he meets her in Hungary.

(St. XXVII, Ninth Adventure.)   The lady supplies the place of the modern pocket handkerchief *mit snêblanken gêren* in the original.   The German *gêre* is evidently the English *gore,* a word which puzzled no less a person than Tyrwhitt, and which Johnson, who writes it *goar,* has confounded with the *gusset.*   The latter is the piece under the arm of a shirt; the gore, as Tyrwhitt was afterward accurately informed by "a learned person," is a common name for a slip, which is inserted to widen a garment in any particular part.   It is a wedge-shaped piece, as the German commentators say of their *gêre.*   Shirts at present, however it may have been in Chaucer's or in Tyrwhitt's time, are not made with gores; the opening on each side renders gores unnecessary; but in the female of the shirt and in the smockfrock, gores are, I believe, still used.   The passage in Chaucer illustrates the passage before us. The poet says of the Carpenter's Wife (Canterbury Tales, 3235)—

> A seint (girdle) she wered, barred all of silk,
> A barme-cloth (apron) eke white as morwe (morning) milk
> Upon hire lendes (loins) full of many a gore.

In the last line the expression "full of many a gore" means, probably, full made, spread out by means of many a gore; otherwise "full of gores" would have been sufficient, and the addition of "many" an inelegant piece of surplusage. However that may be, it is clear that the apron stuck out and extended round the person of the wearer in consequence of the number of these gores, or wedge-shaped pieces, which made the bottom much wider than the top. An apron, thus made up of a multitude of gores, might not unaptly be itself called in the plural a woman's gores, and this seems to have been formerly the case in Germany. Kriemhild is here said to wipe her eyes with snow-white gores, and, in the Gudrun, the heroine of that name is rated by the tyrannical Gerlind for wrapping up her hands indolently in her gores. It is of course impossible for a translator to render these two passages literally, at least if he wishes to be intelligible.

(St. XLVIII.) The commentators are not particularly clear as to what these garments, called in the original " noble Ferrans robes," really were. Von der Hagan says there must have been a city of that name in the East, from which these robes came, while Lachmann says there is a stuff composed of silk and wool, which still goes by the name of *ferrandine*. The Dictionary of the French Academy mentions a silk stuff as *formerly* going by that name.

TENTH ADVENTURE

(St. XLI.) Lachmann's Fifth Lay begins here, and concludes with St. DCCV.

(St. LXIX.) The cord or girdle, thus worn by ladies, seems to have been tolerably strong, not merely from the use to which Brunhild put hers here, but also from the manner in which Florimel's is applied by Sir Satyrane.—" Faerie Queene," III, vii., 36.

> The golden ribband, which that virgin wore
> About her slender waste, he took in hand,
> And with it bownd the beast, that lowd did rore
> For great despight of that unwonted band.

(St. LXXII.) Ἰλίῳ αἰπεινᾷ Πάρις οὐ γάμον, ἀλλά τιν' ἄταν
ἀγάγετ' εὐναίαν ἐς Θαλάμους Ἑλέναν.

Eurip. Androm. 103.

(St. LXXXI.) If this and the following stanza are, as Lachmann thinks, an addition, they no doubt were added to supply a palpable defect in the narrative. If it were not for them, the company would be spoken of as rising from table (St. LXXXIV) when it is nowhere mentioned that they had sat down.

I must venture to remark that Lachmann's note to the next stanza is not very satisfactory. Though the knights and ladies may usually have eaten apart, it seems to have been allowable for the mistress of the house at least to be present when the knights were feasting (St. XXVI, this Adventure, to St. XXIII, Twenty-seventh Adventure), and there is nothing unreasonable in supposing that the married sister of the host might have accompanied her husband. This seems more natural than to assume that the queens left their apartments and went to the hall (probably a detached building) just to show themselves before they retired to bed. I must own I do not see the difficulty about *coming* and *going* noticed by Lachmann. Everybody, who goes to a place, comes to it when he gets there. As the poem stands, everything is consistent. The queens cross the palace court and go to the hall for the good substantial reason of getting their suppers. They come back to their private apartments, or bowers, where they remain awhile with their immediate attendants, and during the short interval, that elapses before dismissing the latter and going to bed, Siegfried slips through his wife's fingers, and goes to Gunther's private apartments.

I should add that, at St. XXIV, Twenty-seventh Adventure, the young margravine and her damsels are brought back into the eating hall after the men have finished their repast, but that depends on the correctness of the reading *die schœnen* (see note to St. XXXI, Twenty-seventh Adventure) and on the consequent expulsion of the latter stanza. If we retain the latter stanza, the young margravine is sent for *ze hove,* like Kriemhild at St. XXXI, Tenth Adventure. But we can scarcely apply to young married women and their near female connections, also married, passages like these, that relate to young spinsters. In the passages quoted in the note to St. XXIV, Twenty-seventh Adventure, men and women are mentioned as eating apart, but it is stated to be an old custom, and is noted as an ancient peculiarity.

(St. LXXXV, Tenth Adventure.) It appears from this description that the wearer of the cloak must have had the power of being visible or invisible as he chose. He might have on the mantle, and yet be visible. Siegfried does not here leave his wife in the ordinary way, and then put on the cloak. He seems to disappear miraculously. This differs from the account given in stanzas XLIII, Seventh Adventure, and LXXXIV, of the same, where Siegfried puts on the cloak before he becomes invisible, and remains so till he puts it off, but agrees with St. XXI, Nineteenth Adventure, where it is distinctly stated that Siegfried wore the cloak at all times. I should however add that, in the original, there is what appears to my ignorance a difficulty, though, as the commentators take no notice of it, I suppose there is really none. The original stands thus:—

> Si trûte sine hende mit ir vil wizen hant,
> Unz er vor ir augen, sine wesse wenne, verswant,

literally, "She fondled his hands with her very white hand, till he before her eyes, she knew not when, vanished." As to the interpreters, Braunfels simply modernizes the old dialect, rendering *wenne* by *wann;* Simrock and Marbach are equally literal, except that they put *wie,* how, where Braunfels has *wann;* Beta, who here as elsewhere is less rigorously literal than his comrades, merely says, "then it happened that he suddenly vanished before her sight." I must confess I cannot understand how Kriemhild could not know *when* a thing happened that passed before her eyes, though she might well be puzzled how to account for it. It is remarkable that the Lassberg manuscript, which is said by Lachmann and other competent judges to contain a revised and remodelled text, omits altogether St. LXXXVI, Tenth Adventure, and alters the stanza before it, and that after it in such a way, that the supernatural seems to disappear, and Siegfried is merely represented as stealing away from the women, and coming secretly and mysteriously (*vil tougen*) to Gunther's chamber. This manuscript however mentions the tarnkappe at St. LXXVII, same Adventure. Did the reviser of this manuscript wish it to be inferred, that Siegfried, after leaving his wife, went and put on the tarnkappe?

(St. CX.) In the Volsunga Saga Brunhild is a Valkyrie, or Chooser of the Slain, a sort of Northern Bellona, endowed with supernatural strength. This superhuman prowess is connected with her virgin state, and by becoming a wife she is reduced to the ordinary weakness of woman. In the Nibelungenlied this circumstance comes upon us by surprise, for we are nowhere told that the strength of Brunhild differed from that of other women, except in degree, and no reason is given why matrimony should produce any greater change in Brunhild than in the rest of her sex. The passage is in fact derived from the Scandinavian form of the legend, and seems scarcely in harmony with the spirit of the German poem.

ELEVENTH ADVENTURE

(St. XIV.) Worms beyond the Rhine, *Wormez über Rin.* The writer here as elsewhere speaks of Worms with reference to his own situation to the east of the Rhine, whereas Xanten, like Worms, is on the west side of that river.

(St. XVI.) Newsman's bread, *botenbrôt,* was the term for the present given to a messenger.

(St. XXXI.) Lachmann's Sixth Lay begins here and ends with St. XLIX, Fourteenth Adventure.

TWELFTH ADVENTURE

(St. XLVIII.) Gary, like a shrewd courtier, avoids praising Kriemhild's good looks to a rival beauty.

(St. LIV.) A difference of opinion exists in united Germany as to the interpretation of this passage, Lachmann, Simrock, Marbach, and Beta being on one side, and von der Hagen and Braunfels on the other. I readily vote with the majority. Rumolt's understrappers, as I conceive, are not the pots and pans, but the subaltern cooks, the scullions and other drudges of the royal kitchen.

THIRTEENTH ADVENTURE

(St. II.) I follow Lachmann's conjecture of *het* for *heten* in the third line of this stanza.

(St. XXII.) Chaucer in like manner says of the carpenter's wife, "Canterbury Tales," v. 3255—

> Full brighter was the shining of hire hewe,
> Than in the tower the noble yforged newe.

For the brilliant addition to the simile he is perhaps indebted to Dante's

Fresco smeraldo in l'ora che si fiacca.

The comparison of the brilliant color of a blooming northern beauty to gold, "red gold," as it is constantly called in old German and old English poetry, forms a curious contrast with the phrases of Catullus, "*inaurata pallidior statua,*" "*magis fulgore expalluit, auri,*" and that of Statius, "*pallidus fossor redit erutoque concolor auro,*" not to mention the saying of Diogenes, that gold was pale through fear of those who had a design upon it.

(St. XXIII.) Lachmann interprets the *gesinde* or followers to be Gunther's, and rejects the stanza as spurious, and manufactured for the purpose of introducing Dankwart, who is represented as seeking out new quarters, without necessity, for people who were already quartered in the city. But are not the followers of Siegfried meant?

(St. XXVII.) A curious instance of awkwardness in the service of the highest tables.

(St. XXXII.) The original has in the first verse *in dem lande,* in the country, *i.e.,* just outside the city walls, close under the castle, from the windows of which the ladies might see the tournament. The minster was in a separate part of the city, just as in London St. Paul's is at a certain distance from the Tower. Here the horses are sent for, which seems to show that the castle and the minster could not have been contiguous, yet they could not have been very far apart, as Kriemhild was in the habit of going to the minster before daybreak. (St. III, Seventh Adventure.)

FOURTEENTH ADVENTURE

(St. IV.) The same simile is applied to Kriemhild herself at St. XX, Fifth Adventure.

(St. XXX.) In the dialogues that follow the queens are not particularly complimentary, but they at least use no weapons but their tongues. I do not know what authority the writer of " Murray's Handbook for Northern Germany " has for the following statement. " The combat between Chrimhelda and Brunhelda is supposed to have been fought on the south side of the Dom."

(St. XXIII.) Wind, a mere nothing; this phrase is not uncommon in the poem.

The prophets shall become wind.—Jer. v. 13.

(St. XL.) Brunhild had been asserting that Siegfried was Gunther's vassal, or, in feudal language, his man. Kriemhild sarcastically alludes to this with more bitterness than delicacy.

(St. XLI.) Brunhild seems as much annoyed by this usurpation of her trinkets as by the scandalous imputation mentioned in the preceding stanza.

(St. L.) I have followed Professor Lachmann's explanation of the first line of this stanza. He makes the Seventh Lay open here, and end with St. XXXI, Fifteenth Adventure, but whatever we may think of his general theory of the poem, his prefatory remarks here are well worth an attentive perusal. It is clear that some stanzas, probably a good many, have been lost. As the work stands at present, even if we interpret the first line of this stanza to mean that many a fair woman departed, Siegfried is left behind to hear his brother-in-law and his friends discuss the expediency of knocking him on the head. In the part that is lost there was probably an account of the breaking up of the assemblage at the church door, and of the immediate summoning of a council in some more convenient place. It was no doubt explained how Siegfried's denial, which at first seemed so satisfactory, was afterward made of no account, and possibly a good deal, of which we have now only a fragment in stanzas L—LI, passed between Brunhild and Hagan, her husband's principal adviser. Probably, too, as Lachmann has observed, the invulnerability of Siegfreid was considered.

FIFTEENTH ADVENTURE

(St. XVIII.) The stanza, which contains this example of ancient discipline, is rejected by Lachmann on account of the *innere reim,* which, however, he thinks, suits perfectly with the " somewhat overcharged coloring " which the author has adopted. Pictures of domestic happiness in the same style of coloring are, I suppose, rarely to be met with in Germany in the present liberal and enlightened age.

(St. XXIV.) See note to St. V, Third Adventure.

(St. XXXVI.) The Wask forest is the mountainous range called in French the Vosges, which, as well as Worms, is to the west of the Rhine; this stanza is therefore at variance with St. I, Seventeenth Adventure, where the hunters cross the Rhine to return to Worms. Lachmann gets over the difficulty by his theory of separate lays. Ac-

cording to his arrangement St. XXXVI, this Adventure, is in the
Seventh Lay, and St. I, Seventeenth Adventure, in the Eighth, and
these two Lays are the work of different poets. Two points are certain; the first, that there were two traditions as to the place of Siegfried's death, one fixing it in the Waskenwald, the other in the Odenwald; the second, that Gunther and Hagan were generally believed
to have attacked Walter of Spain in the Waskenwald. Now there
appears to me nothing improbable in supposing, either that a minstrel
with his head full of Walter's history and the connection of Gunther
and Hagan with the Waskenwald, might have recited *Waskenwalde*
for *Otenwalde,* or, on the other hand, that one, who was familiar with
the tradition that Siegfried was killed in the Odenwald, might have
found *an den Rîn* at St. XXXVII, Sixteenth Adventure, and altered
it to *über Rîn.* At any rate I cannot help thinking that either of these
suppositions is less improbable than that a poet should first tell us how
Gunther and Hagan plotted against Siegfried, how the latter accepted
their treacherous invitation to the hunt, and how he went to take leave
of his wife, and that then the provoking rogue should immediately
close his poem without informing us what passed between Siegfried
and his wife, whether the hunt took place, or whether the plot succeeded.

SIXTEENTH ADVENTURE

(St. I.) Lachmann's Eighth Lay begins here and ends with St. I,
Seventeenth Adventure.

(St. XXII.) The *schelch* or shelk seems by the description in Braunfels's Glossary to have been a kind of tragelaphus, with hair down the
breast.

(St. XXIII.) *Des gejeides meister,* I presume, means Siegfried
himself, who at St. XXXIX is called *jegermeister.*

St. XXVII.) Tryst. Ye shall be set at such a tryst
That hart and hind shall come to your fist.
Squire of Low Degree.—Ellis's " Specimens," v. 1, p. 341.

Tryst is a post or station in hunting, according to Cowell as quoted in
Tyrwhitt's Glossary to Chaucer, but Walter Scott uses it for a place
of appointment generally.

(St. XXXVIII.) For the sweetness of " the panther's breath or
rather body " I refer the reader to Gifford's note in his edition of Ben
Jonson, v. 3, p. 257. It is worth while however to quote the following
passage on panthers from Pliny's Natural History, l. 8, c. 17, as it is
not noticed by Gifford. " *Ferunt odore earum mire sollicitari quadru-
pedes cunctas, sed capitis torvitate terreri; quamobrem, occultato eo,
reliqua dulcedine invitatas corripiunt.*"

(St. XXXIX.) I scarcely know whether I have translated this stanza
properly. The variegated work (expressed by *gestrout* in the original)
seems to have been produced by different sorts of fur. The *grâ unde
bunt* of St. XVI, Third Adventure, seems to mean the same thing.
Gold thread or wire, and something like gold lace appear to have
been fashionable ornaments in the dress of both sexes. Precious stones,
too, were in great request. But I own I have been much puzzled by
the milliners' and tailors' work in the poem, and I dare say have made
mistakes. I may observe that the women were both tailors and milliners. Kriemhild herself was an accomplished cutter (see St. XLIV,
Sixth Adventure), and, if it had not been for her assistance, her
brother and his companions would not have been fit to be seen at the
splendid court of Brunhild. The men were expert cutters in their line,
but their instrument was the broadsword.

(St. XL.) In this poem the edges of a sword are constantly spoken of in the plural. The warriors seem to have had only two-edged swords.

(St. LIV.) The fourth line of this stanza, which is admitted as genuine by Professor Lachmann, is one of those passages which are at variance not merely with his theory, but with that which attributes the two parts of the poem to two different authors. It refers to the slaughter toward the close of the second part, and would be impertinent and out of place in a poem that concluded with the death of one hero only.

(St. LVIII.) The poet says *the* broad linden, according to Lachmann, assuming that the story of Siegfried's death under a linden tree was generally known.

(St. LXII.) *Intelletto veloce più che pardo.*—" Petrarch, Sonn." 286.

(St. LXIV.) Johnson quotes from Ecclesiasticus, " I have no thank for all my good deed." So in St. Luke vi. 33—" If ye do good to them that do good to you, what thank have ye? "

SEVENTEENTH ADVENTURE

(St. II.) Lachmann's Ninth Lay begins here and ends with St. LXXI, Seventeenth Adventure. The Professor has no objection to considering this and the preceding Lay as works of the same author.

(St. IX.) The two last lines of this stanza and the two first of the next are rejected by Professor Lachmann, because, as he thinks, they contradict the last line of St. XI, where Kriemhild professes her ignorance of the murderer. But Kriemhild is not a witness on oath, but a woman in a frenzy of grief, who does not weigh her words, but one moment utters an obvious suspicion, as if it were an ascertained fact, and the next confesses that she has no positive proof, and cannot act upon what she feels to be true. There is no very great inconsistency in saying, " A. and B. are at the bottom of this: if I could only bring it home to them, I'd make them smart for it." But the neuter pronoun in the third line, referring to *houbet* in the second, proves that the second line is not interpolated. Professor Lachmann, indeed, gets over the difficulty by altering the gender of the pronoun to the masculine.

(St. XI.) The last verse of this stanza seems a preparation for the display of Kriemhild's character in a new point of view. The softer parts of her character have been exhibited thus far; her revengeful and unforgiving spirit will gradually swallow up every other feeling, and at last close the poem with a general massacre. See, too, stanzas XXIII—XXXII—XLV.

(St. XXI.) I have translated the second line of this stanza according to Simrock's version, but it is impossible to make any satisfactory sense of it. Professor Lachmann has justly printed the stanza in italics.

(St. XLIII.) On this curious superstition, which is as much English and Scotch as German, see Nare's Glossary under the word " Wounds," and the notes to " Earl Richard " in the second volume of the " Minstrelsy of the Scottish Border." The whole passage is condemned as spurious by Lachmann, principally on account of the discrepancy in the mention of wounds in the plural, while only one wound was given by Hagan. There are, however, two similar discrepancies in the poem. Kriemhild is killed by Hildebrand apparently with a single blow, and immediately after is spoken of as hewn in pieces; and Rudeger is killed by a single blow at St. XXXVII, Thirty-seventh Adventure, while at St. L, same Adventure, he is described as *verhouwen*, and at St. XXXII, Thirty-eighth Adventure, as lying with severe death-wounds fallen in blood.

EIGHTEENTH ADVENTURE

(St. I.) Lachmann's Tenth Lay begins here and ends with St. XI.V, Nineteenth Adventure.

(St. XXI.) *They* in the last line of this stanza seems to mean the Burgundians.

(St. XXVI.) Here they go home to Netherland; before, in this Adventure, the Nibelungers' land is spoken of as the country of Siegmund. This has not escaped the hawk's eye of Lachmann.

NINETEENTH ADVENTURE

(St. XVIII.) The *morning gift* was a present bestowed by the husband on the wife the morning after the wedding. It was often promised before marriage.

(St. XXI.) This passage, which states that Siegfried wore the cloud-cloak at all times, agrees with the description of its mode of operation at St. LXXXV, Tenth Adventure, but is inconsistent with stanzas XLIII—LXXXIV, Seventh Adventure, from which last it would seem to have been necessary for Siegfried to put on the cloak in order to become invisible, and to put it off when he wished to become visible again. The inconsistent passages probably arose from varying traditions as to the operation of this miraculous garment. There is another difficulty here. From Alberic's words it would seem that the possession of the treasure depended on the possession of the cloud-cloak. If he and his fellows had not lost the cloak *together with Siegfried* (by which last words he seems to refer not to the original loss of the cloak, when Siegfried first won it, but to its loss in consequence of that hero's death), the Burgundians should not have had the treasure, but we are nowhere told what became of the cloak after Siegfried's death, and Kriemhild claims the treasure as a gift from Siegfried, not as depending on the possession of the cloak.

TWENTIETH ADVENTURE

(St. I.) Lachmann's Eleventh Lay begins here, and ends with St. III, Twenty-first Adventure. "The historical relation of Etzel to Attila," says Professor W. Grimm ("Deutsche Heldensage," p. 67), "is quite clear." It is here strengthened by the "mention of his brother Blœdelin, who answers to the Bleda of Priscus and Jornandes, and is found in the Klage, in Biterolf, in the Vilkina Saga, and other later poems. Helche, otherwise Erka, Herche, Herriche, and Hariche, reminds us of the Kerka of Priscus." Priscus was secretary to Maximin, the ambassador of Theodosius the Younger at the court of Attila, and wrote a history, of which extracts are still extant. The following is his account of an interview with Kerka, the "*frou Helche*" of our poem. Ἐνταῦθα τῆς Ἀττήλα ἐνδιαίτουμενης γαμετῆς, διὰ τῶν πρὸς τῇ θύρᾳ βαρβάρων ἔτυχον εἰσόδου, καὶ αὐτὴν ἐπὶ στρώματος μαλακοῦ κειμενην κατέλαβον, τοῖς ἐκ τῆς ἐρέας πιλωτοῖς τοῦ ἐδάφους σκεπομένου, ὥστε ἐπ' αὐτῶν βαδίζειν. περιεῖπε δὲ αὐτὴν θεραπόντων πλῆθος κύκλῳ καὶ θεράπαιναι ἐπὶ τοῦ ἐδάφους ἀντικρὺ αὐτῆς καθημεναι ὀθόνας χρώμασι διεποίκιλλον, ἐπιβληθησομένας πρὸς κόσμον ἐσθημάτων βαρβαρικῶν· προσελθὼν τοίνυν καὶ τὰ δῶρα μετὰ τὸν ἀσπασμὸν δοὺς ὑπεξήειν. Gibbon in the 34th chapter of his History has given almost a translation of Priscus. "The wife of Attila received their visit sitting, or rather lying, on a soft couch; the floor was covered with a carpet; the domestics formed a circle round the queen, and her damsels, seated on the ground, were employed in working the variegated embroidery which adorned the dress of the barbaric warriors." There is a full account of Attila and the Huns with much relating to the Nibelungenlied in the late Hon. and Rev. William Herbert's Historical Treatise subjoined to his Poem on Attila.

(St. V.) The Margrave Rudeger is perhaps the most interesting character in the poem, but there is no one, with regard to whom the historical, the legendary, and the mythical are more unintelligibly jumbled. Whether he was an historical Austrian Margrave of the tenth century, a mere legendary hero, or " a divine being," as Lachmann is disposed to think him, is more than any plain Englishman can venture to decide. It seems that his native country was Arabia, but whether by that name is meant the region commonly so called, or a district in the centre of Spain, is as yet anything but a settled point. Wherever it was, he was driven from it by a king of Toledo, and took refuge with Etzel.

(St. XX.) I am uncertain whether I have given the true meaning of this stanza, which is rejected by Lachmann, and, indeed, can scarcely be reconciled with the rest. I have used *Hun* and *Hungarian* indifferently. The Hungarians were of a different race from the Huns, but Mr. Hallam says of them, " The memory of Attila was renewed in the devastations of these savages, who, if they were not his compatriots, resembled them both in their countenances and customs."

(St. XXXI.) See Lachmann (St. 1113, L.) who conjectures *ersiwet* for *erfüllet* or *ir sulet*.

(St. XLVII.) This refers to something not related in this poem.

(St. LIX.) Here again is an allusion to something not mentioned in the poem, namely, to some service rendered by Rudeger to Hagan.

(St. LXIV.) The poet, who put this speech into the mouth of Gunther, could have had no notion of the real history and extensive power of Attila.

(St. CXX.) King Etzel appears to have been a truly liberal and enlightened monarch.

(St. CXLV.) In the last line of this stanza, the plural of the verb is authorized by three manuscripts, and, though they may be none of the best, their readings deserve attention, when they are commanded by necessity and common sense. The plural (*in* for *ihnen*) in the preceding line requires the plural in this. The young ladies cried at leaving home, but were soon reconciled to their lot by the gayeties of King Etzel's court. If the reader is not satisfied with this, he can replace *they* by *she*. Kriemhild will then be meant.

TWENTY-FIRST ADVENTURE

(St. III.) Vergen. Veringen in Suabia, on the Lauchart, three leagues from the junction of that river with the Danube.—Lachmann, St. 1231, L.

(St. VII.) This good bishop Pilgrin, who is an historical personage, died in the tenth century, and therefore could scarcely have been Attila's wife's uncle, if chronology is to pass for anything with popular poets. All that relates to him is rejected as spurious by Lachmann and W. Grimm. See the latter's " Deutsche Heldensage," p. 71.

(St. XIV.) Efferding. A town of Austria beyond the Ems near the Danube (von der Hagen, v. 5221).

(St. XXVI.) Botlung was the father of Etzel according to the poets. His real name was Munduic.

(St. XL.) Medilik, now Mölk. An abbey still renowned for the abundance and excellence of its wine stores. It supplied Buonaparte's army in 1809.

TWENTY-SECOND ADVENTURE

(St. XIII.) Lachmann rejects stanzas XIII, XVI, XVII (1288, 1291, 1292 of his edition). He thinks that, even if one were determined to defend the first, nobody could tolerate the frigidity and abject style of the two last. For my own part, I am more struck by the absurdity of Rudeger's caution to Kriemhild not to kiss all Etzel's men. I suppose he was afraid she would have no lips left after such reiterated osculation.

(St. XIX.) These German strangers or guests (*Tiuschen gesten*) are the Burgundians according to von der Hagen, but Thüringians according to Lachmann. The latter says, the expression does not occur elsewhere in the Lays of the Nibelungers. This restricted use of a term, which was afterward extended to a whole nation, resembles the restricted use of the word Hellen in Homer.

(St. XXIII.) The good margrave seems here to discharge the duties of a male duenna.

(St. XL.) Von der Hagen here notices the custom of tilting by the way in festal processions. Similar descriptions occur elsewhere in this poem, as for instance at the landing of Gunther and Brunhild (St. VII, Tenth Adventure). In this respect the Nibelungenlied differs from the " Orlando Innamorato " and " Furioso," as well as from the " Faerie Queene," in all of which poems tournaments are exhibited with far more pomp and ceremony, and as matters of long previous preparation.

(St. XLI.) Haimburg, a town of Hungary on the borders of Austria, was fortified, according to von der Hagen, by Duke Leopold, of Austria, out of the ransom of Richard Cœur de Lion.

(St. XLIV.) Etzel's castle, now Buda, so called from Attila's brother, Buda or Bleda.

TWENTY-THIRD ADVENTURE

(St. III.) Lachmann's Thirteenth Lay begins here and ends with St. LXXXIV, Twenty-fourth Adventure.

TWENTY-FOURTH ADVENTURE

(St. I.) See the note to St. XLV, Eighth Adventure.

(St. LXIII.) This stanza seems out of its place here. It should come somewhere before the council of the Burgundian chiefs, for it is necessary to know when an entertainment is to take place in order to determine whether one can attend it, and when one ought with propriety to set out. Hagan, besides, must be considered to have had a knowledge of this, before he arranged the plan of setting out only a week after the departure of the ambassadors.

TWENTY-FIFTH ADVENTURE

(St. II.) Lachmann's Fourteenth Lay begins here and ends with St. LVI, Twenty-sixth Adventure.

(St. XVIII.) This is the only stanza in the second part where the term Nibelunger is applied to Siegfried's subjects as in the first part. In all succeeding passages it means the Burgundians.

(St. XIX.) Ostervranken, according to von der Hagen, is Austrasia, or the Eastern portion of the Empire of the Franks, afterward, though in a more restricted sense, the Circle of Franconia.

(St. XXIII.) Professor Lachmann observes that, if the fight with the Bavarians be not alluded to, the prediction contained in this stanza is not fulfilled, "quite against the prophetic style of this lay;" but I venture to submit that this is no prediction at all, but a mere expression of the very natural opinion that, if any army should attempt to swim a large river in a state of flood, many may be swept away and drowned. Gernot makes a similar remark on the want of a boatman at St. LXIV.

(St. XXIX.) The raiment of these mermaids, which is styled *wondrous* farther on, seems to have been the swan-raiment worn by the Valkyries or Choosers of the Slain, which enabled its wearers to assume the shape of swans, or at least to fly away. Hagan therefore had good ground to begin with laying hands on the wardrobe of these water-nymphs, though his reason for doing so is so obscurely alluded to in the poem that it may be doubted whether the poet was himself aware of the original force of the legend. In the traditions respecting Vælund, Wieland, or Wayland the Smith, that hero captures a wife by a similar stratagem. The swan-maiden in Wieland's case was one of the Valkyries, and indeed the two mermaids in the Nibelungenlied appear, from the part assigned to them in the poem, to be genuine Choosers of the Slain. These swan-maidens, as far as their volatile character is concerned, seem to have given a hint to the author of Peter Wilkins.

(St. XLVIII.) So in the old lay of Hildebrand (a fragment of which, written on the first and on the last leaf of a manuscript of the "Book of Wisdom" and other religious pieces, was discovered in the public library of Cassel by W. Grimm) that hero offers arm-rings to his son, who, not knowing him, had challenged him to fight. It was the custom to offer such rings on the point of a sword or spear, and to receive them in the same way. To prove this, W. Grimm quotes this passage among others. See Lachmann's treatise on the "Lay of Hildebrand" in the Transactions of the Berlin Academy of Sciences, 1833. The same word (*bouc*) is used both here and in the old lay.

(St. LXVII.) This stanza, which appears in only two manuscripts, seems incompatible with the rest of the narrative. It was probably introduced by a reciter from the description of a ferry-boat in some other poem.

TWENTY-SIXTH ADVENTURE

(St. V.) On the other side Adam, soon as he heard
The fatal trespass done by Eve, amaz'd,
Astonied stood, and blank.

"Paradise Lost," ix. 888.

Upright men shall be astonied at this.—Job, xvii. 8.

(St. LIV.) Rudeger is an Austrian Axylus.—" Iliad," vi. 14.

ἀφνειὸς βιότοιο, φίλος δ'ἦν ἀνθρώποισιν,
πάντας γὰρ φιλέεσκεν, ὁδῷ ἐπὶ οἰκία ναίων.

The German poem is here certainly not inferior to the Greek. Similes are as rare in the Nibelungenlied as they are abundant in the Iliad, but it would be difficult to find one more just and elegant than this.

(St. LVII.) Lachmann's Fifteenth Lay begins here; it concludes with St. XIV, Twenty-eighth Adventure.

TWENTY-SEVENTH ADVENTURE

(St. XXIV.) I quote some passages from Ellis's " Specimens " on the custom of the two sexes eating apart:

> The king was to his palace, tho the service was ydo,
> Ylad with all his menye, and the queen to hers also,
> For hii held the old usages, that men with men were
> By hem selve, and women by hem selve also here.
>> Robert of Gloucester.—" Specimens," vol. i. p. 100.

The above metre, though very rough and uncouth, resembles that of the Nibelungenlied. In the corresponding passage quoted by Ellis from Geoffry of Monmouth, the custom is said to have come from Troy. " *Antiquam consuetudinem Trojæ servantes Britones consueverant mares cum maribus, mulieres cum mulieribus, festivos dies separatim celebrare.*" Ellis gives a similar account of Arthur's coronation from Robert de Brunne's translation of Wace:

> Sometime was custom of Troy,
> When they made feast of joy,
> Men thogether should go to meat
> Ladies by themself should eat.

See the note to St. LXXXI, Tenth Adventure.

(St. XXXI.) There is a difficulty here from its being said that the young margravine was desired to go to court, *i.e.*, to the assembly in the hall, when at St. XXIV the ladies (*die schönen* in the original) had already returned thither. Lachmann removes the difficulty by condemning the stanzas XXXI, XXXII, XXXIV as spurious; he thinks it impossible that anyone can collect from the third line of St. XXII that the men went into a different hall from that which they had entered at St. XIX; but it is not the third but the second line of St. XXII that describes the separation of the men and women, and that too in the following words,

> " *Rittere unde vrouwen die giengen anderswâ;* "

now who can collect from this verse that the women went and the men stayed? If words mean anything, both went away. As to the return of the ladies at St. XXIV, that rests on a doubtful reading, *die schönen,* the fair ones, whereas the best manuscript, that on which Professor Lachmann's text is generally founded, reads *die künen,* the bold ones, meaning the knights. I should add that the preliminary conversation from St. XXV to St. XXXI is fitter to be held in the young lady's absence.

(St. XLIV.) These foreign champions are the Burgundians themselves according to von der Hagen. This is far from satisfactory, but I can offer nothing more so. Can it be possible that there was once a version (now lost) of the story, in which the Nibelungers, properly so called, accompanied the Burgundians into Hungary? This might account not merely for these foreign champions, but for the term *Nibelunge* being applied to the Burgundians. But, in fact, everything relating to the Nibelungers is obscure and confused to the last degree.

(St. L.) Nudung was the son, or, according to another account, the brother of Gotelind.

(St. LXVI.) Lachmann transposes this and the two following stanzas to after St. XVI, Twenty-eighth Adventure, where they form the beginning of his Sixteenth Lay, which ends with St. XLIV, Twenty-ninth Adventure. The speech which begins at the third line of this stanza is attributed to the messenger by von der Hagen, and perhaps justly, as appears from the last verse of the next stanza, from which it would seem that the king heard the news afterward. On the other hand, Kriemhild here is addressed in the singular, while in a similar passage (St. XCI, Fourth Adventure) she is addressed by a messenger in the plural. She, however, would scarcely have uttered before Etzel the words at the close of St. LXVIII, Twenty-seventh Adventure.

TWENTY-EIGHTH ADVENTURE

(St. I.) Bern is Verona according to von der Hagen and Wacker-nagel and the whole body of Commentators. Von der Hagen applies to Hildebrand the words in the third line, *ez was im harte liet;* so does Marbach. Braunfels and Beta apply them to Dietrich. But in that case would not the author have said *dem was ez?*

(St. IV.) The Amelungs, or Amelungers, were the reputed descendants of Amala, king of the Goths, the tenth ancestor of Theodoric king of Italy.

(St. V.) This famous hero, the redoubted Dietrich, is only a secondary character in the Nibelungenlied, though in old German traditions generally he bears the principal part. He was the son of a nocturnal spirit, and his fiery breath made him more than a match for Siegfried himself, as it melted the horny hide of his antagonist. He is identified, I believe, by universal consent, with Theodoric the Ostrogoth. I am afraid that it is too certain that he came to a bad end, but whether he disappeared on being summoned by a dwarf, or was carried off by the devil in the shape of a black horse, or, according to the monastic legend reported by Gibbon, was deposited by foul fiends in the volcano of Libari, is more than I can decide.

(St. XX.) Lachmann's Seventeenth Lay begins here and ends with St. XXXII, Thirtieth Adventure.

(St. XXI.) Hagan's suspicions are natural enough, for Kriemhild appears to have kissed nobody but Giselher, whereas, according to the etiquette of this poem, she should not only have kissed her other two brothers, but Hagan himself, not merely as her cousin, but as one of Gunther's principal retainers.

(St. XXVI.) This stanza is rejected by Lachmann on account of the interior rhyme *wœre* and *swœre* in the third and fourth lines, but surely the outbreak of Hagan in the next stanza is the beginning of a speech. It would have been more plausible, if St. VIII is to be rejected, to reject St. XXI, Thirtieth Adventure, as well, for the first line of St. XXVII would come in very well after the last of St. XXIV; but then, on the other hand, no answer would be given to Kriemhild's question, " Where have you that bestowed? "

(St. XXVII.) The two languages agree in taking the devil's name in vain by using it as a ludicrous but forcible negative. The phrase is authorized by Johnson.

(St. XXVIII.) Von der Hagen explains these two robberies by observing that Hagan had despoiled Kriemhild of her own inheritance as well as of the wondrous hoard. The poem itself, however, seems to explain the matter somewhat differently. Hagan committed the first robbery when he took the hoard (St. XXXV, Nineteenth Adventure); the second, when he seized Siegfried's other treasures (St. CXXXII, Twentieth Adventure).

(St. XXXIV.) Lachmann places this and the following stanzas after St. XIX, as part of his Sixteenth Lay.

TWENTY-NINTH ADVENTURE

(St. I.) Von der Hagen discovers here (v. 7055 of his Remarks) a trace of the tradition (which, however, is not noticed in this poem) that Hagan had lost an eye. This appears visionary to me. At St. XVII, Thirty-second Adventure, the same words are applied to Dankwart, who certainly had two eyes in his head. Twice in this poem a personal description of Hagan occurs (St. XXV, Seventh Adventure, and XVII, Twenty-eighth Adventure) and in neither case is a hint given that he was a *dux luscus*. The author or authors of the Nibelungenlied, therefore, must have followed a different tradition.

(St. XXVIII.) It is Folker's long broadsword that the poet, with a grim kind of merriment, calls his fiddlestick. We shall soon see the minstrel κῶμον ἀναυλότατον προχορεύειν.

(St. XL.) Walter of Spain, *Waltharius manu fortis*, is the hero here alluded to. See note to St. XXI, Thirty-ninth Adventure.

(St. XLVII.) This stanza, and those that follow, come, according to Lachmann's arrangement, after St. XXXIII, Twenty-eighth Adventure, and form part of his Seventeenth Lay.

(St. XLVIII.) This allusion to the future is of such a nature as to be irreconcilable with the notion of separate lays. The like may be said of many other passages.

(St. LV.) *Morat* or *morass*, as far as I can make out from a rather confused note of von der Hagen's, was a sort of caudle, flavored with mulberry or cherry juice. Ziemann's recipe is to take old and good wine, and to mix it with mulberry syrup, rose julep, cinnamon water, and an *ad libitum* infusion of simples. All this together composes the sweet drink in question.

THIRTIETH ADVENTURE

(St. XVIII.) So in the Ballad of the Lochmaben Harper in the "Minstrelsy of the Scottish Border,"

> And aye he harped, and aye he carped,
> Till à the nobles were fast asleep.

(St. XIX.) "As now," says von der Hagen, "at the entrance of many old buildings, particularly churches, a tower stands, containing the stairs which lead directly to the upper story."

(St. XXI.) This stanza, which is only found in the Lassberg and two other manuscripts, seems to have been inserted, like several others, in order to soften the ferocious character attributed to Kriemhild in the latter part of the poem.

THIRTY-FIRST ADVENTURE

(St. I.) The whole of this Thirty-first Adventure is supposed by Lachmann to be an addition to the foregoing. His reasons are anything but conclusive.

(St. X.) According to von der Hagen the shields were high enough for the bearer to lean upon them, and pointed below, so that they might be firmly fixed in the ground. They thus, I presume, in some degree protected the owners, even while the latter were resting.

(St. XII.) The dust was raised by the horses, as the Huns seem to have ridden from the palace.

(St. XXIII.) "The kings" here, as mostly elsewhere, are the three Burgundian brothers.

(St. LXIII.) Kriemhild here deals with Blœdel as Juno does in the Iliad with Sleep, and in the Æneid with Œolus.

(St. LXXII.) Something seems defective here, for it is not explained what bad object Kriemhild had in view in sending for her son, though it so happened that mischief came of it. Von der Hagen and Vollmer mention the account in the Vilkina Saga, according to which Kriemhild, in order to set the Huns and Burgundians by the ears, told her son to strike Hagan in the face, and Hagan returned the compliment by cutting off the lad's head and throwing it into his mother's lap, but this is incompatible with the manner in which the fighting begins in our poem, though this particular stanza seems to refer to something of that sort. The reviser of the Lassberg manuscript seems to have observed the difficulty; at least the last line of the stanza is different in that manuscript. Possibly this stanza may have crept in from a now lost recension, which more nearly resembled the Vilkina Saga. The like may be said of St. IV, Thirty-second Adventure, which contains the celebrated contradiction about the age of Dankwart.

THIRTY-SECOND ADVENTURE

(St. IV.) This stanza is completely at variance with the earlier parts of the poem, in which Dankwart is represented as Siegfried's companion in arms. It is therefore a most efficient ally of those critics who attribute the poem to two or twenty different bards, and this has perhaps rather blinded them to its defects. It is quite inconsistent with the heroic character displayed by Dankwart in this very portion of the poem, and, as an answer to Blœdel's speech, is a consummate piece of stupidity. Blœdel had not accused Dankwart of having murdered Siegfried or offended Kriemhild, but of being the brother of Hagan, who had done both. Dankwart should either have attempted to show that Hagan, not himself, was innocent, or that they were not brothers, or he should have urged the hardship of making one brother suffer for the crimes of another. Any of these answers would have been to the purpose; not so the speech which is put into his mouth here. Blœdel, with equal absurdity, after having already told him that he must die because his brother Hagan had murdered Siegfried, now replies that he must die because his *kinsmen* Gunther and Hagan had done the deed. It appears probable that here, as elsewhere, a passage has crept in from another version of the legend, which agreed, more nearly than our poem, with the Vilkina Saga. I quote the following passage from the summary of that work in Vollmer's Preface to the " Nibelunge Nôt." " Hogni begged Attila to give peace to young Giselher, as he was guiltless of Sigurd's death. Giselher himself said that he was then only five winters old, and slept in his mother's bed; still he did not wish to live alone after the death of his brothers." In the Vilkina Saga Hogni, who answers to the Hagan of our poem, is represented as the *brother* of the other three kings. It may appear visionary to speculate on the contents of a poem which may never have existed, but certainly in any version of the legend, which represented Hagan as the brother of Gunther and Giselher, Giselher might naturally have made the speech here put into the mouth of Dankwart, and have been told in reply that he must die for the crime that his *brothers* Gunther and Hagan had committed. The idea of a recension more nearly allied to the Vilkina Saga than that which we possess is no notion of mine. It was started years ago by no less a person than Professor W. Grimm, though not with reference to this passage of the poem. See his " Deutsche Heldensage," p. 182.

(St. VII.) This mention of Nudung's bride, together with what follows in the next stanza, is quite unintelligible, if we suppose an independent lay to begin at St. I.

THIRTY-THIRD ADVENTURE

(St. XXII.) Lachmann seems here with reason to read *Volkern* for *Giselheren*, but have not the two stanzas, XXII and XXIII, changed places?

(St. XXX.) With this stanza (St. 1916, L.) ends Lachmann's Eighteenth Lay. I must own that it appears to me quite impossible that any writer could end a separate poem in this manner. Similar objections may be made to the conclusion of most of these *Lieder*.

(St. XXXI.)　　　　with huge two-handed sway
Brandish'd aloft the horrid edge came down
Wide wasting.　　　　　　　" Paradise Lost," b. 6.

(St. XLV.) There certainly seems some confusion here. The only people who had injured Gunther in Hungary were the Huns who had massacred the yeomen, and these were not present in the hall. If, on the other hand, he suspected that the Huns in the hall were privy to it, why allow Etzel and Kriemhild to depart without so much as an observation? Why, as Lachmann has observed, does not Dietrich think it necessary even to make a request in their behalf? It is easy to remove these objections by declaring everything spurious between St. XXX and St. XII, Thirty-fourth Adventure, but unfortunately, though St. XXIV, Twenty-eighth Adventure, which brings Etzel and Kriemhild into the hall, is not admitted into Lachmann's Lays, it is clear from stanzas XII–XIV, Thirty-third Adventure (1898–1900 L.), which form part of his Eighteenth Lay, that both Etzel and Kriemhild were present in the hall when the fighting began, and indeed Lachmann admits that the plan of his Eighteenth Lay requires that they should quit it. The composer however of the lay, who surely ought to know his own plan best, seems to have been of a different opinion, for, after having set the Huns and Burgundians by the ears in the hall, and put Dankwart and Volker to keep the door, he has left us to guess the final result of these serious preliminary arrangements. The 7,000 Huns massacred here are no doubt the same as the 7,000 who accompanied Kriemhild to church at St. XX, Thirty-first Adventure, and the same perhaps as the men of Kriemhild mentioned at St. XX, Thirtieth Adventure. These last had *attempted* mischief, and Gunther may here take the will for the deed.

(St. LVIII.) The meaning of this stanza is anything but clear. From the original, and the two readings *von* and *vor*, it would seem doubtful whether Hagan laments that he sat at a distance from Folker or that he took precedence of him.

THIRTY-FOURTH ADVENTURE

(St. XI.) I must confess I cannot see any inconsistency between the first line of this stanza and the third of the preceding one; but there is certainly a discrepancy between the second line, in which both Hagan and Folker are mentioned as scoffing at Etzel, and the two stanzas immediately following, which confine the invectives to Hagan.

(St. XII.) Lachmann's Nineteenth Lay begins here and ends with St. V, Thirty-sixth Adventure. Scarcely any of the whole twenty begin and end so unappropriately as this.

(St. XIX, XX, XXI.) I have arranged these stanzas as Simrock and Beta have done. Braunfels places them XX, XIX, XXI.

THIRTY-FIFTH ADVENTURE

(St. XX.) I have here, without intending it, stumbled on an in. terior ryhme, *sounded confounded*. Still I can assure Professor Lachmann that the stanza is genuine.

THIRTY-SIXTH ADVENTURE

(St. VI.) Here begins Lachmann's Twentieth Lay.

(St. IX.) Here they are described as coming *ûz dem hûse,* which seems to contradict Kriemhild's exhortation at St. XX, not to let the Burgundians come *für den sal.* Perhaps they here merely come out of the hall into a vestibule at the top of the staircase, so as to speak with Etzel and Kriemhild, but not into the open air. So at St. V, Thirty-ninth Adventure, Gunther and Hagan are said to be outside the house, but at St. XXV, same Adventure, Hagan rushes down from the staircase to attack Dietrich. From St. XXVI, Thirty-sixth Adventure, the staircase seems to have been of no great length.

THIRTY-SEVENTH ADVENTURE

(St. XVII.) Compare stanzas CXV, CXVI, Twentieth Adventure.

(St. LIX.) It is odd, that the hall, which must have been the principal eating-hall in the castle, is here called Kriemhild's. Von der Hagen thinks Kriemhild had appropriated it by having attempted to set it on fire, but arson is an odd kind of title. He supposes, too, it may be the hall mentioned at St. IV, Twenty-ninth Adventure; yet it seems strange that Etzel should have received his guests anywhere but in his own hall.

(St. XCI.) This stanza, as Professor Lachmann justly observes, cannot belong to Hagan, but is appropriate to Giselher, who is mentioned immediately after. Still there is an awkwardness here.

THIRTY-EIGHTH ADVENTURE

(St. II.) The king himself has come to the feast, has made one of the party, that is, has been slaughtered with the rest. See Lachmann's note (St. 2173 L.).

(St. XLIII.) I have with Simrock and Beta followed the reading of the Lassberg manuscript, *struchen* for *stieben.* The latter is explained by Braunfels and von der Hagen with reference to the flying out of sparks from armor, but this effect follows in the next line. To an Englishman the reading *stieben* appears to bear a comical resemblance to our vulgar phrase, " dusting a man's jacket."

(St. LXXXIX.) The Amelungers' land was Bern, that is Verona, the hereditary possession of Dietrich: who was driven from it by his uncle Ermanrich, Emperor of Rome. He took refuge with Etzel, and remained in exile 30 or 32 years. For what further relates to him and the Amelungers see the notes to Sts. IV and V, Twenty-eighth Adventure.

THIRTY-NINTH ADVENTURE

(St. V.) The phrase, outside the house, *ûzen un dem hûse,* appears to mean merely outside the hall. They seem to have stood in a sort of vestibule at the top of the stairs that led down into the courtyard. Compare St. IX, Thirty-sixth Adventure, and the note.

(St. IX.) I have ventured, in conformity with the original, to talk of "joys lying slain," though certainly the phrase seems harsh in English. One manuscript reads *freunde* friends, instead of *freuden* joys.

(St. XXI.) Walter of Spain ran away with Hildegund from the court of Etzel, as that monarch himself informs us in an earlier part of this poem. As the young hero was passing with her through the Vosges or Wask mountains, he was attacked by Gunther with twelve knights, among whom was Hagan. The latter however, "for old acquaintance' sake," refused to fight against Walter, and persevered in his refusal, till the Spaniard had killed eleven knights, and Gunther himself was in danger. At last, after all three were wounded, they made up matters. According to the Vilkina Saga, Walter, after slaying the eleven knights, put Hagan to flight, and then, having lighted a fire, sat down with Hildegund to dine on the chine of a wild boar. As he was thus agreeably employed, Hagan fell upon him by surprise but was pelted so severely by Walter with the bones of the wild boar, that he escaped with difficulty, and, even as it was, lost an eye.—See W. Grimm's "Deutsche Heldensage," p. 91.

The Latin poem "Waltharius," which is translated from a lost German one, gives a more dignified account of the matter. There also Hagano refuses to fight at first, and says

> "Eventum videam, nec consors sim spoliorum,"
> Dixerat, et collem petiit mox ipse propinquum,
> Descendensque ab equo consedit, et aspicit illo.

Eleven knights are killed, but next day, after Walter has left a stronghold, where he could be attacked by only one at a time, he is assailed on his march by Gunther and Hagan, and the fight continues till Gunther has lost a foot, Walter his right hand, and Hagan his right eye and twice three grinders. The combatants are then reconciled. For the situation of this field of battle, see "*Lateinische Gedichte des* 10. *und* 11. *Jahrhunderts*" by J. Grimm and Schmeller, p. 123.

(St. XLVI.) This stanza, which is in the Lassberg manuscript only, has been added apparently, like others, to soften the character of Kriemhild.

(St. LII.) Harrow and welaway. Old exclamations of distress or anger.

> Harrow and welaway!
> After so wicked deed, why liv'st thou lenger day?
> "Faerie Queene," II, viii. 46.

(St. LVII.) The *edeln knehte* here, and the *vil manic riche kneht* of St. XXXIV, in both passages associated with knights, were no doubt of a far superior station to that of the mere *knehte,* 9,000 of whom followed Gunther into Hungary. These last we may call yeomen, the other, squires. The *edeln burgære* (St. XXXV, Seventeenth Adventure), seem to have been not the mere townsfolk, but the chiefs of the corporation the lord mayor, aldermen, and common council of Worms.

2471